Welcome to the first How It Works Annual

Inside, you will find the answers to a multitude of fascinating questions about the world around you… the kinds of compelling questions that you often ask yourself but never quite find the time to look up. Well, Volume One of the **How It Works Annual** has instantly saved you a lot of time and hassle by laying out the answers in uncomplicated language together with inspiring full-colour visuals, such as dynamic cutaways that reveal the internal workings of your favourite gadgets, and beautiful illustrations to help you learn about the planet's incredible geographical systems.

Whether it's a far-reaching topic such as the mysterious bodies in the outer reaches of space that excites you, or even just the science involved in giving your pint a refreshingly effervescent fizz, you'll find the solution to many of life's mysteries right here. With breathtaking photography and a great range of subjects to interest and entertain anyone with a natural inquisitiveness, the **How It Works Annual** is the perfect way to feed your mind. So if you love learning about science, technology and the world around you, sit back, relax and start soaking up some nutritious 'edutainment'.

HOW IT WORKS
Annual

Imagine Publishing Ltd
Richmond House
33 Richmond Hill
Bournemouth
Dorset BH2 6EZ
☎ +44 (0) 1202 586200
Website: www.imagine-publishing.co.uk

Compiled by
Helen Laidlaw

Designed by
Danielle Dixon, Stephen Williams

Editor in Chief
Dave Harfield

Head of Design
Ross Andrews

Photo Studio
Studio equipment courtesy of Lastolite (www.lastolite.co.uk)

Printed by
William Gibbons, 26 Planetary Road, Willenhall, West Midlands, WV13 3XT

Distributed in the UK & Eire by
Imagine Publishing Ltd, www.imagineshop.co.uk. Tel 01202 586200

Distributed in Australia by
Gordon & Gotch, Equinox Centre, 18 Rodborough Road, Frenchs Forest, NSW 2086. Tel + 61 2 9972 8800

Distributed in the Rest of the World by
Marketforce, Blue Fin Building, 110 Southwark Street, London, SE1 0SU.

ip
IMAGINE
PUBLISHING

D1534436

HOW IT WORKS CONTENTS

VOLUME 1

The magazine that feeds minds!

Sections

54
Megastructures

58
Olympic swimsuit tech

15
How golden eagles hunt

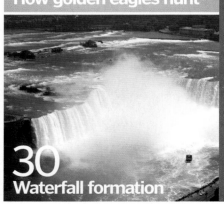

30
Waterfall formation

128
How fireworks go off

40
Dolphin anatomy

Science

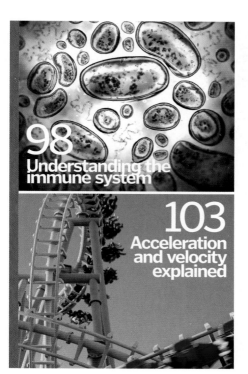

98
Understanding the
immune system

103
Acceleration
and velocity
explained

HOW IT WORKS
CONTENTS
VOLUME 1

The magazine that feeds minds!

131
Under your skin

136
Your complete guide to electricity

142
An in-depth journey around our solar system

186
Inside the Eurofighter Typhoon

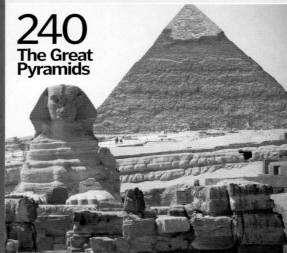

240
The Great Pyramids

224
Hydrogen-powered cars

198
Oasis of the Seas luxury liner

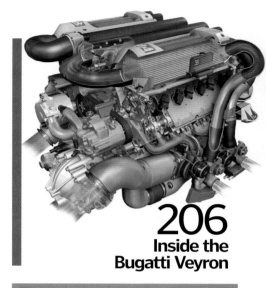

206
Inside the Bugatti Veyron

HOW IT WORKS

ENVIRONMENT

Marvel at the natural world around you

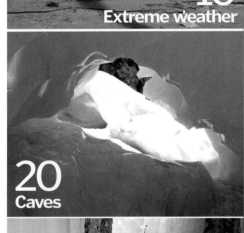

10 Extreme weather

20 Caves

30 Waterfall formation

34 How sharks survive

48
World's
fastest animals

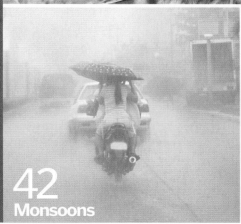

42
Monsoons

44
The Earth's structure

Extreme

The making of a tsunami
How a deep-sea rumble forges a killer wave

On 26 December 2004, a 9.0 magnitude earthquake off the coast of Sumatra, Indonesia triggered a series of tsunamis – giant seismic sea waves – that claimed 300,000 lives around the Indian Ocean basin. It was deadliest natural disaster in recorded history.

Tsunamis are not 'tidal' waves. They are created when a violent geological event – like a submarine earthquake, landslide or underwater volcanic eruption – displaces a huge amount of water.

The Indian Ocean earthquake occurred along a subduction zone, a place where one tectonic plate wedges under another. During the record-setting quake – which released more energy than 23,000 Hiroshima-era atomic bombs – a section of sea floor 1,000 kilometres long was pushed ten metres horizontally and several meters vertically.

The violent displacement generated a massive deep-ocean wave only a few meters high, but hundreds of kilometres long. The almost imperceptible swell travelled across the open water as fast as a jet aeroplane. As the deep-ocean seismic wave neared the shore, it was slowed down by the quickly rising sea floor. But as the wave compressed horizontally, it rose vertically, reaching heights of 30 metres in some cases.

weather

Marvel at the raw power of nature at its nastiest

A gust of air rattles the windows. The sky darkens ominously as coal-black clouds creep across the horizon. Thunder rumbles thickly in the distance accompanied by the first flickers of lightning, like paparazzi.

Suddenly, the rain comes down in sheets, blown sideways by howling winds. With a crackling explosion, a tree across the street is torn in half by a stroke of lightning. But as suddenly as it started, the rain stops. The clouds remain low and terribly dark, almost green. You look out the back window in search of a reprieve. Instead, you see the twister.

Mother Nature deserves respect. Before you complain about the light drizzle that spoiled your picnic, thank your lucky stars you've never experienced a true weather disaster: a six-story tsunami wave, 150 kmph hurricane winds, or tornadoes that can toss an 18-wheeler like a Matchbox car.

We'll help you make sense of the Weather Channel chatter and learn what causes the world's most extreme weather phenomena. ✿

Tornadoes explained
Why twisters descend from the sky and drill a path of destruction

Tornadoes are born in beefed-up storm clouds called supercells. While normal storm clouds form and dissipate in 30 minutes, supercells can last for hours and spread severe weather across hundreds of kilometres. But the most unique characteristic of a supercell is its powerful counter-clockwise rotation.

Supercells start like normal thunderstorms. Moist, warm air near the surface is pushed aloft by a physical force like a cold front. The warm air condenses into water droplets as it reaches higher altitudes, forming towering clouds. Supercells grow large because of an abundance of warm, wet air below and cool, dry air above.

But why do they rotate? It's down to a phenomenon called wind shear, a sudden change of wind speed and direction. Typically, winds blow faster the higher you climb. This creates a paddle wheel effect in the atmosphere, generating columns of air that spin on horizontal axes.

With supercells, the warm, low-lying air is sucked up into the storm with such force that it grabs one of these horizontally rotating columns of air and twists it vertically. The result is a mesocyclone, an intensely rotating column at the heart of the supercell. Meanwhile, rain and hail falling from the supercell are caught in these rotating winds. Much of the precipitation evaporates, releasing pockets of cool air that pull downward on the swirling vortex.

As intensely rotating winds reach the ground, friction slows the effects of centrifugal force, tightening the funnel. There is incredibly low air pressure inside the funnel, which acts like a vacuum. As more and more air is sucked into the vortex, the speed of rotation increases, like a figure skater pulling in her arms for the final head-spinning twirl.

The resulting tornado can generate winds over 480 kmph, tear through reinforced structures like a buzz saw, lift large vehicles, and flatten homes.

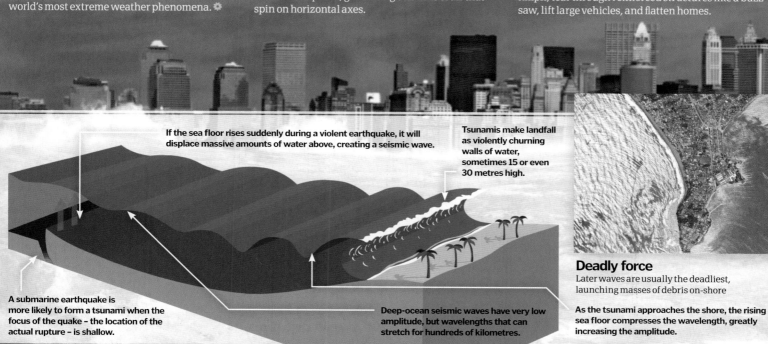

If the sea floor rises suddenly during a violent earthquake, it will displace massive amounts of water above, creating a seismic wave.

Tsunamis make landfall as violently churning walls of water, sometimes 15 or even 30 metres high.

A submarine earthquake is more likely to form a tsunami when the focus of the quake – the location of the actual rupture – is shallow.

Deep-ocean seismic waves have very low amplitude, but wavelengths that can stretch for hundreds of kilometres.

Deadly force
Later waves are usually the deadliest, launching masses of debris on-shore

As the tsunami approaches the shore, the rising sea floor compresses the wavelength, greatly increasing the amplitude.

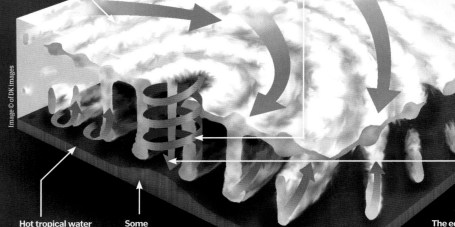

A combination of the Coriolis force and pressure gradient (the rush of air from high to low pressure), give hurricanes their dizzying spin.

The eye wall – a solid ring of clouds where rain bands converge and compress – contains the hurricane's most powerful winds.

Image © of DK Images

There's a storm coming...

The origins of hurricanes, a deadly force of nature

Hurricanes are massive heat engines. They form over tropical waters with a minimum temperature of 27°C. Hot water evaporates very quickly, rising up through the atmosphere until it condenses into clouds and water droplets. The incredible thing is that condensation itself creates even more heat. The recharged air soars even higher, building a cluster of towering, fat thunderstorms called a tropical disturbance.

Once the heat engine has been jump-started, rapid condensation within the storm continues to force air upward while more hot air rushes in from below to fill the void. This suction of hot air from the ocean surface creates lower and lower air pressure. When air rushes from high pressure to low pressure, it creates powerful winds. When wind velocity reaches 61 kmph, the storm is called a tropical depression.

Satellite images of hurricanes show a swirling vortex of storm clouds. The spin is caused by two main forces: the Coriolis force and the pressure gradient. In the northern hemisphere, the Earth's rotation pulls winds to the right (Coriolis force), but the extreme low pressure at the storm's centre pulls them back to the left, creating a net counter-clockwise spin. The opposite is true south of the equator. As the heat engine chugs on, more water condenses, more heat rises, the pressure drops further and spin increases until winds reach 60 to 120 kmph, enough to qualify as a tropical storm. Seven out of ten tropical storms spin even faster than 120 kmph, officially becoming a hurricane. ✿

Hot tropical water evaporates, rises as vapour and condenses into rings of towering storm clouds called rain bands.

Some meteorologists believe storm surges are caused by mounds of water drawn upwards by the low surface pressure in the eye of the hurricane.

The eerily calm and cloudless eye of the hurricane is the point of lowest pressure, causing air to sink straight down towards the ocean surface.

The hurricane seasons...

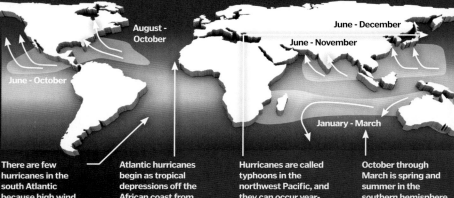

August - October

June - December

June - November

June - October

January - March

There are few hurricanes in the south Atlantic because high wind shear near the ocean surface shreds tropical storms.

Atlantic hurricanes begin as tropical depressions off the African coast from June to November, when the tropical waters are steamiest.

Hurricanes are called typhoons in the northwest Pacific, and they can occur year-round due to high average water temperature.

October through March is spring and summer in the southern hemisphere, meaning more cyclones (India) and willy-willys (Australia).

Extreme heat
Hundreds of lightning bolts strike the earth every second, each generating temperatures exceeding 27,000° C

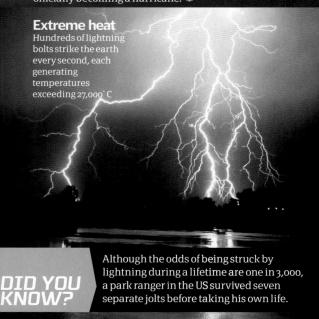

DID YOU KNOW? Although the odds of being struck by lightning during a lifetime are one in 3,000, a park ranger in the US survived seven separate jolts before taking his own life.

Thunder and lightning
Beauty has never been so powerful...

Inside the chaos of a storm cloud, falling bits of ice collide with updrafting water droplets, shearing off electrons to create newly charged particles. The negative particles sink to the bottom of the cloud, while positive particles rise to the top, just like a colossal battery. As a storm cloud swells in size, the force of its negatively charged underside repels negative ions away from the surface of the Earth, creating a net positive charge on the ground. Something needs to correct the imbalance between theses huge oppositely charged masses.

Lightning is a violent electrical discharge between clouds and surface objects, clouds and other clouds or points within the same storm cloud. In fact, only ten per cent of lightning strikes hit the earth. Cloud-to-ground lightning begins when a negative charge from the cloud begins to carve a path of least resistance through ionised air, zigging and zagging every 25 metres. When it nears the ground, a positive charge called a 'streamer' reaches up from surface objects, completing the circuit. The resulting strike is instantaneous, travelling at 300 million m/s with the power of 100 billion volts.

A clap of thunder is caused by shock waves created by the expanding and contracting air around the superheated lightning.

5 TOP FACTS

HURRICANES

The world's most powerful generator
1 If you calculate the total heat generated by condensation inside a hurricane, it equals 200 times our daily worldwide energy-generating capacity.

No-holds-barred Nancy
2 Typhoon Nancy, which tore across Japan in the September of 1961, clocked sustained winds of 185 kmph, the fastest on record.

A four-ce to be reckoned with
3 Only twice in modern history – 1893 and 1998 – did four hurricanes power their way simultaneously through the Atlantic basin.

Another myth down the drain
4 It is untrue that the Coriolis force causes toilets to flush in different directions in the northern and southern hemispheres.

A name to be remembered
5 Since the Fifties, all tropical storms and hurricanes in the Atlantic basin receive a name. If the storm's particularly deadly, the name is retired.

How are blizzards created?

These deadly winter storms can strike without warning

In January 1996, 100 million tons of snow fell on the streets of New York City and nearby Philadelphia was buried under a record 78 centimetres. Ice storms and sub-zero temperatures stretched as far south as sunny Florida, trapping people in their homes, often without electricity. In 1891, easterly winds dumped 3.6 metres of snow in London. Trains were completely buried under tremendous drifts and 65 ships sank under the heavy ice and snow.

Blizzards form exactly like thunderstorms. A cold front pushes warmer, moist air into the atmosphere, condensing into clouds. If temperatures stay below freezing, snow falls instead of rain. If huge amounts of snow are accompanied by gale-force winds, it's possible to achieve a complete whiteout, when earth and sky merge in a disorienting canvas of white.

DID YOU KNOW? For a winter storm to qualify as a blizzard, there must be sustained winds of at least 58 kmph and less than 0.4 km visibility for three hours or more.

Blanket covering!
You're going to need more than an ice scraper to get out of this one mate...

Waterspout

While it's never truly rained 'cats and dogs', it has rained frogs and fish. In the past century, towns in the United States, Greece and Serbia have been inundated with falling amphibians (some of them frozen solid) that pile up in the streets. While a Biblical plague isn't out of the question, the more likely culprit is a waterspout, a tornado-like vortex that forms over water.

There are two kinds of waterspouts: tornadic and fair weather. Tornadic waterspouts form under the exact same conditions as tornadoes and can generate winds over 300 kmph with powerful internal updrafts. The low-pressure core of the waterspout can dip several metres under water, sucking up anything in its path, including fish, frogs and lizards. Fair weather waterspouts grow from the ocean up, created by the sudden convergence of smooth and choppy seas. Swirling water is pulled upward by rising air currents, without the help of a major storm system.

While fair weather waterspouts are weak and rarely cause damage, tornadic waterspouts have torn apart ships at sea. Famed waterspout researcher Joseph Golden believes many so-called 'Bermuda Triangle' disappearances are caused by killer waterspouts.

The walls of a waterspout are semi-transparent, since they are made of windswept water, not dirt and debris

Water world
You know you're in trouble when your street looks more like a river than a road

Floods After the rains, the deluge

When you think of killer weather, you picture tsunami-battered coasts or twisting black tornadoes. But one of the deadliest weather phenomena worldwide is flooding. Flash floods – where small rivers and creeks swell without warning to raging torrents – are the number one weather-related killer in the United States. Flash floods can happen almost anywhere. In cities, there often isn't enough green space to absorb the runoff from a severe storm. This can overwhelm drainage systems, causing flash floods in low-lying areas.

In the mountains, a sudden torrential downpour can feed hundreds of small streams that merge in a single river valley. The result can be dramatic and deadly, creating a wall of churning water – five to ten metres of mud, rocks and debris – that wipes out everything in its path. Violent hurricane winds – gusting over 135 kmph in some cases – can push a mound of water in front of the hurricane called a storm surge. During Hurricane Katrina, powerful surges breached the levee system, causing widespread destruction by flooding.

The 2007 floods in the UK were an example of river flooding caused by sustained, powerful rains. Over the course of 12 hours, parts of northeast England received a sixth of their annual rainfall, swallowing whole towns in swollen rivers.

The rat-eating plant

Explorers discover a rare pitcher plant with a big appetite

In 2000, two Christian missionaries on the remote Palawan Islands of the Philippines become hopelessly lost while trying to install a radio tower on an uncharted jungle mountain. When they were rescued after 13 days without food, they told stories of a giant carnivorous plant, large enough to swallow a rat.

When explorers returned to the mountain seven years later, they discovered that the starved missionaries weren't hallucinating. The mountain was home to a brand-new species of carnivorous pitcher plant – also known as a pitfall trap or monkey cup – that the researchers named Nepenthes attenboroughii after the beloved British naturalist and TV host Sir David Attenborough.

Pitcher plants are evolutionary freaks. They're exclusively found in sodden, low-nutrient soils like bogs or fens. Desperate for sustenance, the plants have developed an 'unnatural' taste for flesh and blood.

The trap itself is formed from a modified leaf that balloons with water and air until its top snaps open, revealing a pool of lethal liquid surrounded by ultra-slick walls. The plant lures its prey with swollen red lips and a fragrant nectar that smells irresistibly corpse-like.

Anything that lands or stands on the curved lip of the trap – from tiny insects to fat rodents – will instantly slip inside thanks to a waxy coating that flakes away on contact. When the creature hits the water, the plant excretes powerful digestive enzymes that immediately start eating through flesh and bone, even while the victim struggles to escape. ✿

"Pitcher plants are evolutionary freaks"

Image © Stewart McPherson

5 TOP FACTS
PITCHER PLANTS

1 Opportunity for opportunists
Some animals poach corpses from the pools of pitcher plants, even small, freshwater crabs.

2 Where to find pitfall traps
There are 91 species of Nepenthes in the world, over 30 found exclusively on the island of Borneo.

3 Poison ponds
Large pitcher plants can carry two or three pints of liquid.

4 Open for business
The lid of a pitcher plant does not snap closed like the Venus Flytrap.

5 Popular namesake
Other species have been named after Attenborough, including an anteater, a tree and a Jurassic marine reptile.

Learn more

For more information about pitcher plants visit **www.redfernnaturalhistory.com** where you can uncover more details and learn about the different species found across the globe.

BIGGEST

1. Martial eagle
The title for the largest eagle is hotly contested, but the martial eagle of Namibia has a wingspan that can reach 2.6 metres.

HEAVIEST

2. Steller's sea eagle
This fish-eating eagle lives on the Kamchatka Peninsula in northeast Asia and can weigh up to nine kilograms.

LONGEST

3. Philippine eagle
With a body length of up to 1.12 m, the Philippine eagle isn't just the longest, it also has the longest life expectancy. Some are estimated to live for as long as 60 years.

DID YOU KNOW? Golden eagles have learnt to kill tortoises by scooping them up and dropping them to crack open their shell

How golden eagles hunt

Telescopic vision and terrifying talons: be glad you're not a Scottish rabbit

Golden eagles are apex predators, adapted to hunt in very harsh landscapes. With a wingspan of more than two metres, they are huge birds, capable of lifting prey weighing as much as five kilograms. There are documented cases of golden eagles attacking adult deer and even bear cubs but their usual targets are hares, foxes, grouse and, on the coast, seabirds.

Golden eagles nest in trees and on remote mountain crags. They can't hunt in thick forest so they have specialised to scour moors and uplands. Food is much scarcer here and the eagles have to patrol huge territories; sometimes as much as 160km². To do this they operate like stealth bombers, flying very high above the ground to scan a wide area without alerting their prey. They need to be able to soar for hours at a time and strong enough to kill whatever animal presents an opportunity. ✿

Anatomy of a hunter

Flexible neck
Because the eyes are so large, they can barely move in their sockets. Instead the neck twists 270 degrees.

Large eyes
Facing forward to provide excellent binocular vision. They can spot a mountain hare from two miles away.

Primary feathers
The gaps between the 'fingers' of the primary feathers help to fine-tune the airflow over the wings.

Powerful wing muscles
Golden eagles can weigh up to 7kg but must be able to take off from the ground in a single bound.

Feathered legs
Unlike the long, bony legs of a swan, these are short and well muscled, with feathers to keep them warm.

Tail
The tail can act as a rudder, to compensate for crosswinds or be spread wide to increase lift.

Deadly talons
The curved claws restrain prey and kill it. Smaller animals are simply carried aloft, back to the nest.

Eagle-eyed hunters

Eagle eyes are very large relative to their body size: if our eyes were similarly proportioned, they would be the size of oranges. They also have 600,000 cone receptors per mm² on their retinas – four times the density in human eyes. These factors combine to give golden eagles two and a half times better resolving power in their vision.

Golden eagles have a translucent second eyelid, called a nictitating membrane, which blinks sideways. In the last moment before the eagle strikes, this membrane closes to protect the precious eyes.

ON THE MAP

Golden eagles need wide open spaces with access to cliffs or trees for nesting but without dense woodland. In more northerly latitudes, this terrain can extend all the way down to sea level. Further south, golden eagles stick to the mountains.

■ **Nesting area** ■ **Wintering area** ■ **Resident all year**

Death from the sky

The golden eagle rarely attacks prey directly from altitude with a dive bomb or 'stoop'. Instead, it wheels out of the sky, some distance away and swoops in from downwind, close to the ground. The eagle relies on a sudden overwhelming attack. If it misjudges the initial strike, it's unlikely to prevail in a chase.

Golden eagles use the primary feathers on their wingtips to control the turbulent vortices of air along the trailing edge of the wings and increase lift. The eagle can spread its tail wide to merge with the wings into a single 'delta wing', or folded for maximum speed.

"The calf drinks more than 400 litres of milk a day"

Blue whales

What's as long as three London buses and as heavy as 112 giraffes?

The blue whale isn't just the largest animal alive, it is the largest animal ever to have lived. Even the largest dinosaurs are topped by this leviathan. Everything about the blue whale is huge. It has a heart the size of a small car, a tongue that weighs 2.7 tons and lungs that can hold 5,000 litres of air.

Blue whales spend most of their lives swimming alone or in pairs, unlike other baleen whales such as the humpback. The female gives birth every two or three years to a single calf that weighs as much as an adult hippopotamus. For the first seven months, the calf drinks more than 400 litres of milk a day to enable it to put on 90kg of weight every 24 hours.

Blue whales aren't really very blue. The top half of their body is a bluish grey and the underside is a lighter colour to make them harder to see when viewed from below, against the sky.

Blue whales are also extremely fast swimmers. They cruise at 20kmph and can sprint at 50kmph. This makes it virtually impossible for barnacles and other parasites to attach themselves. In spring, however, a thin film of diatom algae growing on the skin can sometimes give them a yellow-orange hue and 19th Century whalers referred to them as 'sulphur bottoms'.

Despite their size, blue whales are preyed upon by orcas (killer whales) and 25 per cent of adult blue whales show orca bite scars. ✿

One in four blue whales show scars caused by orcas

© Morningdew 05

Baleen plates
The blue whale doesn't have teeth. Instead the baleen plates hang down to create a colander made of keratin.

Rostrum bulge
This oil and wax-filled chamber focuses sonar pulses, used for echolocation.

Ventral pleats
60 to 90 folded grooves expand the mouth to six times its size after a huge gulp of water and krill.

Pectoral fin
Three metres long and used like the diving planes in a submarine to adjust depth and for steering.

Huge size...

Human
Average length: 1.6m

Blue whale
Average length: 30m

| 5 | 10 | 15 | 20 | 25 | 30 |
LENGTH IN METRES

A blue whale swimming with her calf

© Andreas Tille

African elephant

1 Size: 5,400kg
The largest land animal currently living. Elephants are large enough to be safe from all predators but must spend 16 hours a day eating.

Polar bear

2 Size: 600kg
The largest bear and the largest land carnivore, although it spends much of its time in the sea. Its bite can crush a seal skull.

Mountain gorilla

3 Size: 200kg
The largest primate. Although they have powerful canine teeth, they are herbivores with a diet that includes celery, bamboo and stinging nettles.

Whale shark

4 Size: 36,000kg
The largest fish, whale sharks are filter feeders like the blue whale, but their food is even smaller than krill – microscopic plankton.

Blue whale

5 Size: 180,000kg
The largest animal that has ever lived. Its upper lip bone is the largest bone in the animal kingdom ever discovered.

DID YOU KNOW? A blue whale's heart beats five times a minute. It pushes ten tons of blood through 1.6 million km of vessels

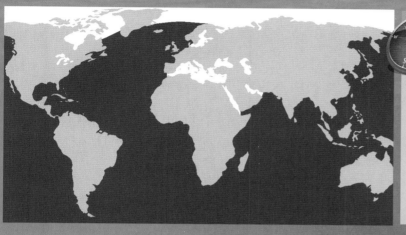

ON THE MAP

Where to find blue whales
Shown in blue, these behemoths roam virtually the whole ocean, following the seasonal abundance of the various species of krill. They avoid shallow seas such as the North Sea however, because their main defence against orca attacks is their ability to dive deeper.

Tail flukes
Like all whales, the tail flukes are horizontal, unlike a fish's vertical tail. Capable of propelling the whale at 50kph.

Blue whale anatomy
The body of a giant

Dorsal fin
Tiny, compared to sharks and many other whales. In some blue whales, it is barely more than a slight bulge.

© DK Images

Blow holes
Blue whales have twin blow holes, like nostrils. They are protected by a splash guard to the front.

The Statistics
Blue whale

Type: Mammal
Diet: Carnivore
Average life span: 80 years
Weight: 180 tons
Size: 30m

Blubber
Up to half a metre thick in places. It conserves body heat and keeps a rigid shape to reduce drag.

How does the largest animal feed on one of the smallest?

Blue whales don't eat plankton. Instead they eat krill, which are one step up from plankton in the food chain. Krill resemble small shrimp, except that they swim in open water in huge swarms. Most krill are only a couple of centimetres long and since a blue whale needs around 1.5 million calories every day, that means it needs to eat a lot of krill – up to 40 million a day, in fact.

To catch them, a blue whale swims at speed towards a swarm and opens its mouth to gulp in 90 tons of water at a time. It then uses its massive tongue to force the water back through the baleen plates. These are 300 feathery bars, each one a metre long, that are attached to the upper jaw. They are made of keratin, like your fingernails. The krill get sieved out by the baleen and then swallowed.

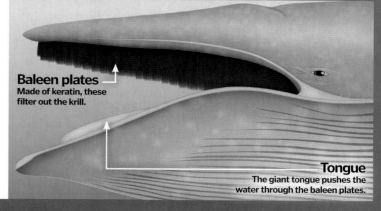

Baleen plates
Made of keratin, these filter out the krill.

Tongue
The giant tongue pushes the water through the baleen plates.

"Some species of salamander have no lungs or gills"

Starfish anatomy

Discover the inner workings of these carnivorous creatures called echinoderms, which means 'spiny skin'

Skin
A starfish has no head and no brain; instead it uses sensitive skin cells to detect smells and chemicals from food, special eye spots at the end of each arm can also detect light. These remarkable sense cells send signals through a system of nerves.

Tube feet
An internal system of tiny flexible pipes extends outside the body. At the tip of each tube is a sticky sucker called a tube foot, which the starfish uses to crawl over rocks and right itself if it gets flipped over. Because there are so many of them, they can be very powerful and can even be used to open shells.

Arms
Most starfish have at least five arms, but some species have up to 40. Starfish can grow a new arm if one is damaged or amputated – regeneration can take up to a year.

Madreporite
A hole on the back of the starfish that lets water enter the body.

Anus
Most undigested food is regurgitated, but any waste is ejected through the anus.

Oesophagus

Ring canal
Filtered seawater taken into the body via the madreporite is filtered and branches from the ring canal to the radial canal before passing into the tube feet.

Radial canal

Gonad/Gonopore
Sex cells (spermatozoids and ovules) are produced in the gonad. The gonopore is an opening on a starfish's back where these gametes are released into the water for fertilisation.

Mouth

Ampulla
Starfish have no blood; instead filtered seawater flows around their arms. When the bulb-like ampulla contracts, water flows into the tube feet, allowing them to extend. When the ampulla dilates, the feet retract, enabling the starfish to move and anchor itself.

Stomach
Some starfish have suction discs, which they use to prize open the shells of clams and other invertebrates. The starfish then pushes its supple stomach membranes out through its mouth and inside the shell of the prey. The starfish then secretes digestive enzymes, which allow food to be absorbed. Those without suction discs swallow prey whole and spit out anything they can't digest.

Pyloric duct/cecum
Here digestive juices are produced and digested food is stored.

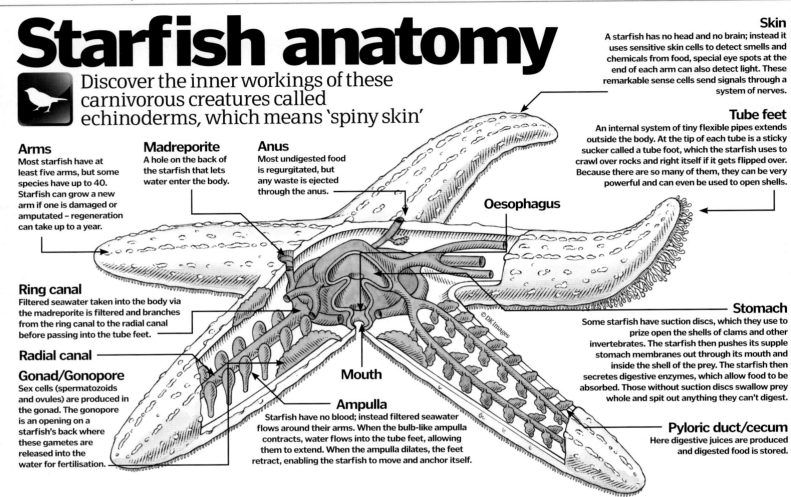

© DK Images

Amphibian skin

Skin is the body's main protective barrier against the outside world, and although an amphibian's skin is only very thin it has many qualities vital to keeping amphibians alive

Amphibians can breathe in and out through their skin – on land and under water – and they take in water not through their mouths but through absorbent skin on their underside called a seat patch. Most adult amphibians have lungs, but additional oxygen is taken in through the skin. Some species of salamander have no lungs or gills and breathe exclusively through their skin.

The reason amphibians feel slippery is that their skin is full of glands that produce mucus, which spreads across the surface of the skin. This mucus moistens the skin,

making it softer and therefore more oxygen absorbent. Although amphibians have few defences against predators, they do have additional poison glands on their skin that secrete irritating toxins for repelling would-be diners. Most are only mildly poisonous, but some species, such as the poison dart frog, are deadly to the touch.

Amphibian skin must stay moist to prevent the body from becoming too hot or cold, and also to avoid desiccation (drying up), which spells the end for Mr Toad. This constant need for moisture means that, as well as producing mucus, amphibians should live close to a water source.

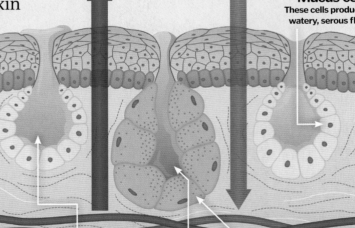

Breathe out
Carbon dioxide leaves the body through the skin.

Breathe in
Oxygen passes into blood vessels via the skin.

Mucus cells
These cells produce a watery, serous fluid.

Mucus gland
Mucus cells group together to form a sac-like gland.

Poison gland
Groups of poison glands are located in areas most likely to be attacked by predators.

Poison cells
The toxicity of the poison secreted is reliant on the amphibian's diet.

5 TOP FACTS
AVALANCHES

The thick of it
1 A large avalanche might release up to 300,000 cubic yards of snow, which is equivalent to something like 20 football pitches covered with ten feet of snow.

The white killer
2 Each year, avalanches kill around 150 people – the victims are usually males in their twenties who are experienced mountaineers or skiers more likely to take risks.

Fresh snow = bad news
3 A snow-faring adventurer is most likely to witness an impressive avalanche during or just after a storm that has deposited around 30cm of fresh snow.

Breath of life
4 If caught under an avalanche, wait for the slide to stop and then use your hands to clear an area in which to breathe, then punch a fist upwards and outwards.

Intentional avalanches
5 When a lot of snow builds on a slope where an avalanche is likely, small avalanches are intentionally triggered using explosives to prevent one potentially deadly slide.

DID YOU KNOW? *A noise cannot trigger an avalanche; it's a myth – a plot device fabricated for films*

Avalanche!
What causes these often deadly snow slides?

Although the potential for an avalanche is present wherever you find a mass of snow on a slope, there are three main types of avalanche each dependent on several conditions: the type of snow in the snowpack, the temperature, wind, the steepness and orientation of the slope, and vegetation (or anchors). ⚙

1. Trigger
This disturbance is where the avalanche begins to fracture and it tends to be high up the slope but can still occur anywhere on a mountain. 90 per cent of fatal avalanches are triggered by the victims.

The avalanche path
This consists of the starting zone, the track and the run-out zone.

2. Starting zone
The starting zone is the section of the avalanche path at which the avalanche is released sending unsecured snow downhill. It normally occurs on a steep slope of between 30 and 50 per cent.

3. Track
The track is the main path down which an avalanche flows. The snow will either slide down as a sheet or concentrated in gullies. Towards the bottom of a track you may well see large piles of snow, boulders and tree remains.

4. Run-out (debris toe)
As the slope flattens out or meets another slope, the avalanche will come to rest. This area is the run-out and consists of a pile of snow and debris picked up along the run. Any unfortunate victims would likely be found in this area of deposition. The very end of the deposited snow is referred to as the avalanche toe.

Main types of avalanches

Dry (80mph)
Occurring below freezing, dry avalanches are usually triggered by loading from new snow or blowing snow. These high-speed slides consist of air and powdery snow, beginning at a single point and gathering speed and mass. As it moves downhill, pressure builds ahead of the mass of snow, creating a powerful blast of air capable of destroying most things in its path.

Slab (60-80mph)
The most common – not to mention deadly – type of avalanche occurs when a layer of compacted snow overlies softer snow. When the weaker snow can no longer support the snow above – or if a passing skier adds to the weight – the hard layer (usually 30-80cm) will fracture like a pane of glass and slide away. If a victim is in the middle of the slab, they are unlikely to survive.

Wet (10-30mph)
Wet avalanches move slower than their drier relatives and occur as a result of rain or warmer weather melting the snow. Rain or humidity softens the snowpack, breaking the bonds between water molecules. Although wet avalanches are slower and don't feature a dust cloud, they are still highly destructive, capable of dragging boulders and even trees down the mountainside.

Interview

We spoke to **Cam Campbell**, public avalanche forecaster for the Canadian Avalanche Centre, to find out more

How It Works: What are the most common avalanche triggers?
Cam Campbell: The most common triggers for all types of avalanches are natural; [including] loading from new snow, rain or blowing snow, rapid warming of the snowpack from an increase in air temperature or intense solar radiation, falling cornices, or other natural snowpack stressors. [...] Most fatal avalanches are human-triggered by the victim or someone in their party.

HIW: How and why are avalanches sometimes triggered intentionally?
CC: [Avalanches are triggered intentionally] to reduce the threat of future uncontrolled avalanches. Any time an avalanche is intentionally triggered, strict procedures, such as access closures and spotters are in place to ensure nobody will be adversely affected. Ski resorts or commercial backcountry operations often stabilise slopes by triggering avalanches before opening to the public. Intentional triggering can be achieved safely through remote-controlled explosives well away from the avalanche path, or hand- or helicopter-deployed explosives above the path.

Survival tips
The top ten survival tips for mountaineers and skiers

- ☑ Take avalanche safety course
- ☑ Read avalanche bulletin
- ☑ Choose route or terrain appropriate for conditions
- ☑ Carry and practise using safety gear (transceiver, shovel and probe)
- ☑ Never travel alone
- ☑ Avoid common trigger points such as convexities, thin areas, or below protruding rocks or trees
- ☑ Travel on avalanche prone slopes one person at a time and spot from safe locations
- ☑ If caught do everything in your power to escape the flowing mass
- ☑ If burial is imminent, create an air pocket in front of your face with hands and arms
- ☑ If buried, remain calm and await rescue

"Seemingly endless gutters running down and down into the Earth"

A cave explorer lowers himself over 182 metres into a sinkhole

© Dave Bunnell

A cave laced with stalactites, stalagmites and tube straws

© Semu

Soluble rock
This, a good cross-section diagram of a formation of solutional-formed caves, demonstrates how soft soluble rock is eroded over time by acidic groundwater. Water becomes acidic through a combination of climate effects (pollution) and by being absorbed by/passed over organic hydrocarbons.

Caves

Formed over millions of years, caves are wondrous and diverse natural phenomena, which have held humans in both awe and dread for thousands of years

Solutional caves, as found across the Yucatan peninsula, are the most commonly occurring Earth cavities found across the globe. They are formed when a soluble rock such as limestone or marble is dissolved slowly by natural acid in the resident groundwater that seeps through the planes, faults and joints which, over epochs, slowly become cracks, then gulleys and finally caves. This dissolving process produces a distinctive landform known as 'karst', which is characterised by subterranean drainage, sinkholes and extensive interlinked cave networks.

The other most notable feature of solutional caves are the striking calcium carbonate formations that are produced by the slow precipitation of acid-laced groundwater. These formations include: stalactites – from the Greek "that which drips", a type of secondary mineral that hangs from the ceiling of caves; stalagmites – from the Greek "drop", a secondary mineral material which drops from the ceiling to the floor where it forms a calcium carbonate deposit; and soda straws, which are thin mineral tubes that grow out of cracks and carry water in their interior.

While solutional caves are by far the most common caves found world wide, other varieties also exist and can be formed in numerous different ways. Primary caves for example are formed at the same time as the surrounding rock, instead of afterwards like the solutional varieties that we've mentioned before. These caves are mostly formed by lava flowing downward and cooling and solidifying on top, while continuing to progress at the base, creating a lava tube once dissipated.

Another variety of cave formed in a similar manner to primary caves are glacial caves. Here, caves and tunnels are formed when embedded ice melts under glaciers and – as with the lava – flow downwards before eventually freezing again on top and solidifying once more. Finally, littoral caves (commonly referred to as sea caves) are formed when coastal rock is eroded away by the tidal action of the ocean waves, eating away at soluble rock along weakened points such as fault lines. ✿

Cave mouths give little clue to the depths a cave can reach

5 TOP FACTS
CAVES

Down
1 The deepest cave in the world is the Krubera (Voronya) Cave in Abkhazia, Georgia, at over 2,200 metres in depth. That is the equivalent of a vertical drop of 2.2km.

Eye
2 Polyphemus, the son of Poseidon and Thoosa, is said in Homer's Odyssey to trap Odysseus and his men in a large cave. Odysseus escapes by blinding Polyphemus.

Troglo
3 Cave-dwelling animals fit into three categories: troglobites (cave-limited), troglophiles (live in and out of caves), and trogloxenes (need caves to complete their life cycle).

Lair
4 The only superhero to have their base of operations in a cave is Batman, who utilises an extensive cave network underneath and adjacent to Wayne Manor.

Potty
5 The traditional British term that is used to describe recreational cave exploration is 'potholing', while the American term to describe said activity is 'spelunking'.

DID YOU KNOW? The longest cave system in the world is the Mammoth Cave System in Kentucky, USA

New Mexico's Lechuguilla cave is an other worldly example of an extremely deep cavern.

© Dave Bunnell

Calcium carbonate
After the acidic groundwater penetrates the rock's planes, faults and joints, it can drip down from the ceiling of a preformed cave leaving mineral deposits either at its base, or on its roof, which then hardens into calcium carbonate formations such as stalactites and stalagmites.

Ice caves form when melted ice flows downwards before resolidifying, leaving long tube-like formations underground

Karst formation
As the soluble rock is eroded, a series of extensive tunnels, channels and holes is formed underground, culminating with many cave mouths often leading into valleys or rivers. In addition, if the erosion is severe then sinkholes may be formed (as can be seen here) when the roof of hollowed-out areas collapse in on itself. These are the characteristic features of karst topography.

© Science Photo Library

Subterranean drainage
Once formed, any drainage channels will continue to erode if the area is subjected to heavy rainfall, with the gulleys being carved out by underground streams and rivers.

© Dave Bunnell

The mouth of a littoral or sea cave, which has developed along a fault line in the cliff

Volcanoes explained

Around the world, sleeping giants lie in wait for their 15 megatons of fame

Imagine the Earth as a giant ripe orange. Beneath the thin, dimpled peel is a thick layer of pulp and juice, 90 per cent of it liquid. The Earth's peel is called the lithosphere, a fragile crust of rock – 75-150km thick – that floats on a massive sea of impossibly hot, semi-fluid magma that extends 5,000km below the surface.

When German meteorologist Alfred Wegener first proposed his theory of "continental drift" back in 1912, people thought he was crazy. How could a colossal hunk of solid rock such as Asia or Africa possibly drift? As we now know, the continents are indeed solid, but they are fragmented into seven major plates and seven minor plates that eternally jostle for position like buoys on troubled water.

The engines that power this perpetual tectonic dance are giant convection currents in the Earth's molten mantle that slowly push magma upwards and outwards. Wherever rising magma manages to break through the thin lithosphere, it's called volcanism, but the vast majority of volcanoes aren't the explosive, violent variety. Instead, they are slow-bubbling cauldrons along a 60,000km underwater seam called the mid-ocean ridge.

The mid-ocean ridge is like an open, oozing wound in the crust where two oceanic plates diverge. The plates are pulled away from each other by the slow and steady convection currents and the gap between them is constantly refilled by thousands of unknown, unnamed underwater volcanoes. As this underwater lava cools, it creates new ocean floor covering 60 per cent of the Earth's surface.

Forget the orange analogy and think of the Earth's crust like a giant moving walkway in an airport. The walkway emerges from below the floor, travels a set distance and then rolls back underground. The divergent plate boundaries along the mid-ocean ridge are where the Earth's "moving walkway" begins. The diverging plates are carried along this magma conveyor belt – travelling only three to four centimetres per year – until they meet a plate moving in the other direction.

When two plates converge, something has to give. An incredible 90 per cent of earthquakes occur along convergent plate boundaries and so do the world's biggest and deadliest volcanoes. The prime example is the Ring of Fire, the unbroken string of seismic and volcanic activity that encircles the Pacific Ocean. The Ring of Fire is a giant subduction zone, where oceanic plates "dive" below

continental plates and are melted back into magma in the blazing hot forge of the mantle.

Ocean sediment holds tons of water, carbon dioxide, sodium and potassium. When oceanic crust enters the blast furnace of the mantle, these sea-borne elements lower the melting point of surrounding rock, forming a gaseous, yet viscous magma that rises quickly towards the surface. If the rising magma reaches an obstacle – an impenetrable thick layer of solid rock – it pools below the surface, building increased pressure as more gaseous, volatile molten materials push up from below.

And then one day – boom! All it takes is a weak point in the cap of rock holding back the magma. On Mount St Helens, a landslide cleared a swathe of rock from the north flank of the mountain, lowering the downward pressure on the boiling pot of magma below. The result was an explosion that produced a monstrous pyroclastic surge – a wall of searing hot fluidised gas, debris and ash – that vaporised everything within a 500-square-kilometre area.

Some of the most famous and infamous eruptions came from subduction zone volcanoes ▶

"90 per cent of earthquakes occur along convergent plate boundaries and so, too, do the world's biggest and deadliest volcanoes"

5 TOP FACTS
VOLCANIC ERUPTONS

How many active?
1 There is some disagreement on what makes a volcano "active" but 1,510 volcanoes have erupted in the last 10,000 years. There are many more volcanoes on the sea bed.

Biggest in the world?
2 The biggest volcano in the world is Mauna Loa in Hawaii. Its whole volume is about 80,000 cubic kilometres. Its most recent eruption occurred on 24 March 1984.

Can they do good?
3 Volcanic slopes left after an eruption are very steep, so rare and delicate plants and animals can set up home there and be protected. Volcanic ash is very good for soil.

Eyjafjallajökull
4 The Icelandic volcano Eyjafjallajökull caused massive disruption to European flights in 2010. The volcano's crater measures three to four kilometres across.

Largest in the solar system
5 In the wider solar system, Mars is believed to hold the honour of housing the largest volcano – the 30 km tall Olympus Mons, which you learn more about on page 147.

DID YOU KNOW? The loudest noise in history was the eruption of Krakatoo in 1883, a 180dB explosion heard 3,500km away

Why volcanic eruptions can spark lightning

The mesmerising lightning storms that danced among the ash clouds of Iceland's Eyjafjallajökull volcano in 2010 were caused by the same conditions that trigger regular thunderstorms. High in the black clouds of a rainstorm, hail and water droplets whirl and collide, freeing large numbers of electrons. Newly charged positive ions congregate in the upper portion of the clouds while the negative particles drift down. When the charge separation becomes too great, a spark of lightning releases the pent-up energy, bringing the system back to equilibrium.

In a volcanic lightning storm, the same principles are at work. In this case, the colliding particles include ash, water and even hail. Electrical fields form within the ash cloud and the frequent and eye-popping lightning strikes (often in vivid purple and orange colours) resolve the charge separations. Another ingredient of volcanic lightning is electrically charged silica particles that are blown airborne from deep in the Earth.

© Science Photo Library

© Science Photo Library

023

along the Ring of Fire: Tambora in Indonesia, Pinatubo in the Phillipines, Gagxanul in Guatemala, Mount Pelée in Martinique, the list of killer volcanoes goes on. In fact, 400 of the world's 500 known active volcanoes occur along subduction boundaries.

But not all famous volcanoes are of the subduction variety. The volcanoes of the Hawaiian Islands are an example of something called hot spot volcanism. Think back to those powerful convection currents in the mantle that push magma up towards the crust. In certain 'hot spots' around the entire planet, convection currents are able to ooze magma to the surface with very little resistance.

Picture the hot spot under the Hawaiian Islands as a giant tube of toothpaste. Squeeze the tube and the little dollop of paste becomes the first Hawaiian Island, Kauai. Now keep the tube in the same place while the ocean plate travels a few hundred kilometres northwest. Squeeze the tube again and you've created the second island, Oahu. Hawaii, the Big Island, is still sitting over that magma pump, fuelling magnificent, slow-boiling eruptions that are literally building the island.

The intensity and duration of a volcanic eruption depends mostly on the consistency of the magma rising to the surface and the obstacles preventing the magma from reaching the surface. Subduction volcanoes are so ear-poppingly explosive because the magma fuelling them is loaded with gas bubbles and silica from sea floor sediments. The high silica content makes the magma more viscous, preventing gas bubbles from easily escaping. The result is like shaking a bottle of soda. When that pressure is released – pop!

Egmont
The Space Shuttle Atlantis exposed this image of the Mount Egmont volcano, New Zealand.

Young
Egmont is a young stratovolcano that began to form 70,000 years ago.

© NASA

The hot spot volcanoes of Hawaii, on the other hand, feature highly fluid magma formed from basaltic rock with low silica content. The 'watery' quality of Hawaiian magma allows gas to escape easily. After an initial, relatively calm eruption, Hawaiian volcanoes spew fountains of lava forming large river-like flows that creep slowly to the sea.

The Hawaiian volcanoes Mauna Loa, Kilauea and Mauna Kea are the most closely studied volcanoes in the world, which is why different varieties of lava are classified with Hawaiian names. Pahoehoe is a highly fluid basaltic lava that cools with a smooth, ropy surface. A'a is a thicker lava carrying large chunks of pyroclastic debris like lava blocks and bombs. The result is a slow, jagged flow that cools with a very rough-looking texture.

Lava flow crossing a road during volcanic activity on Reunion, an island in the Indian Ocean

Types of volcanic eruption

Oozing, bubbling, spraying, fountaining, splattering, exploding! When magma reaches the surface, it's sure to be a memorable event. Check out the many different kinds of volcanic eruptions.

Eruption type: Magmatic

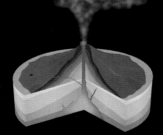

Strombolian
Huge gas bubbles rise and explode at the surface, shooting fast-cooling projectiles like lava bombs, glassy spatter and ash.

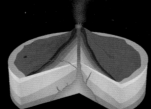

Vulcanian
Caused by the sudden release of a lava plug, these violent bursts of lava can send molten material several kilometres in the air.

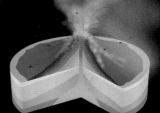

Pelean
Incredibly deadly, a towering wall of rock, debris and lava pour down the slope of a volcano at speeds upwards of 150km/h.

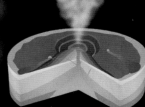

Hawaiian
The classic Kilauea-style eruption is where highly fluid lava 'fountains' spurt upwards from long, narrow fissures or vents.

Head to Head
DEADLY ERUPTIONS

INSTANT KILLER

1. Mount Pelée
On 8 May 1902, a pyroclastic flow travelling at a rate of 160km/h incinerated the town of Saint-Pierre, Martinique, killing all but two of its 28,000 residents.

WORLD CHANGER

2. Tambora
The largest eruption in recorded history, this Indonesian volcano's 1815 eruption took at least 71,000 lives, approximately 11,000 of those directly from the eruption.

SUPERVOLCANO

3. Yellowstone caldera
Over 500,000 years ago, an eruption 1,000 times as powerful as Mt St Helens blew the lid off of the western US, creating the Yellowstone caldera.

DID YOU KNOW? The ash from the 1815 eruption of Tambora created a "year without summer" as far away as New York

Mount Redoubt
Mount Redoubt, Alaska. The glacier that filled the crater is collapsing because of the increase in ground temperature underneath.

© MattiPaavola

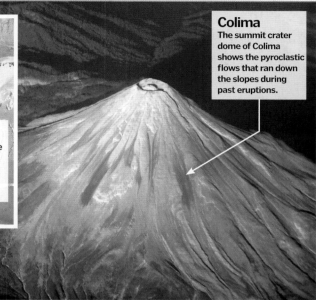

Colima
The summit crater dome of Colima shows the pyroclastic flows that ran down the slopes during past eruptions.

A colourful stromboli eruption

© Wolfgang Meyer

When a lava flow meets water, you get some lovely rounded formations called pillow lava, but if freshly emerging magma meets water, the results are far more explosive. A phreatic or 'steam blast' eruption discharges large rock fragments and ash, but little lava. The monstrous ash cloud that grounded flights across Europe for several weeks in 2010 was the product of magma meeting glacial ice. The ash from such an eruption isn't the soft, fluffy stuff that gets in your eyes when you have a campfire. Volcanic ash particles are hard, jagged fragments of rock, minerals and glass that can measure up to around 2mm in diameter.

The effect of a large-scale volcanic eruption is both local and global, immediate and long-term. Pyroclastic surges travelling 150km/h can obliterate an entire city in a matter of seconds, while a massive ash storm can block the Sun's rays so thoroughly that the Earth's surface temperature lowers for months if not years. The 1815 eruption of Tambora in Indonesia spewed so much ash into the global atmosphere that it created a "year without a summer", complete with June snow storms in New York. ✿

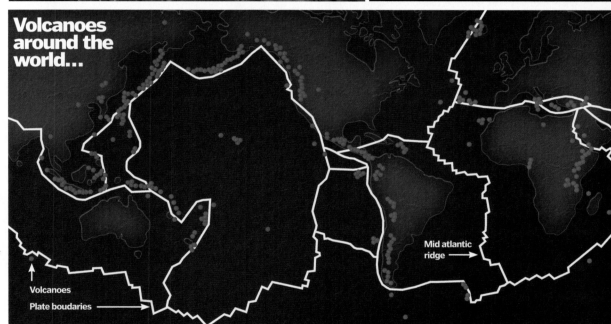

Volcanoes around the world...

Mid atlantic ridge →

→ Volcanoes

Plate boudaries →

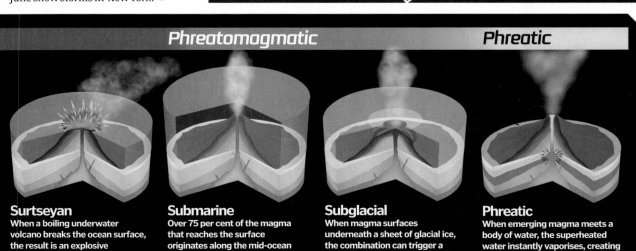

Phreatomagmatic

Surtseyan
When a boiling underwater volcano breaks the ocean surface, the result is an explosive hydromagmatic reaction.

Submarine
Over 75 per cent of the magma that reaches the surface originates along the mid-ocean ridges that circle the planet.

Subglacial
When magma surfaces underneath a sheet of glacial ice, the combination can trigger a lahar, a mud and debris flow.

Phreatic

Phreatic
When emerging magma meets a body of water, the superheated water instantly vaporises, creating a monumental 'steam blast'.

🔴 Learn more

In the Discovery Channel's online video archives, you can watch 20 informative video clips from TV documentaries such as *Ultimate Guide To Volcanoes*, including rare footage of a pyroclastic flow http:// dsc.discovery.com/videos/ volcano-video.

For a video featuring intrepid adventurer Professor Iain Stewart, check out www.howitworksdaily. com for a clip from NatGeo, which reveals how volcanoes brought Earth out of the Ice Age.

"The strongest bite of any known creature, producing a force of around 5,000 pounds per square inch"

Earthworms

Worms are well known to us, often spotted in back gardens across the country but, more importantly, can they actually survive if they are cut in two?

Earthworms need moisture to survive and consequently commonly live underground in damp soil. They are cylindrical in shape, and their body structure is surprisingly simple with a muscular outside body that lines their digestive tract and circulatory system.

This circulatory system is very simple. Only two blood vessels (the dorsal and the ventral) which run between the anterior and posterior of the creature, with blood being pumped by aoertic arches in the case of the ventral vessel, or moved back to the anterior by the dorsal vessel contracting. However, although simple, earthworms do display distinct segments, which are more specialised towards the anterior (head). Consequently, segments situated further back in the body can be regenerated in many cases, but it is dependent on the type of species and the actual extent of damage.

Earthworms are also hermaphrodites, holding both male and female sexual organs. However, they commonly mate and then store the other individual's sperm for reproduction. ✿

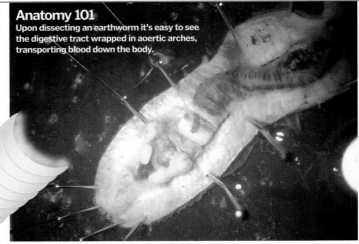

Anatomy 101
Upon dissecting an earthworm it's easy to see the digestive tract wrapped in aoertic arches, transporting blood down the body.

Muscular body
This allows movement by stretching out, pushing the anterior segments forward, and then pulling the rest of the body after.

Digestive tract
This stretches throughout the individual, and is where food taken in through the mouth is processed.

Ventral nerve

Mouth

Clitellum

Dorsal vessel
This brings blood which has been pumped down the body back to the front to be oxygenated and then pumped back down the ventral vessel.

Ventral vessel
Blood gets pumped by the aoertic arches down the body to supply oxygen where needed.

Aoertic arches
These work like a human heart, pumping the blood around the earthworm's body. The number of these present varies between species.

Crocodile jaws

Why do crocodiles have the strongest bite of any creature known, yet are not able to open their jaw if we place an elastic band around it?

A crocodile has the strongest bite of any known creature, producing a force of around 5,000 pounds per square inch. The muscles that control this bite down have evolved and developed to be extraordinarily strong, and alongside relative speed over short distances on land and the immensely sharp teeth that crocodiles prominently display, this forms an immense weapon for the crocodiles to successfully hunt within a competitive environment.

However, although the jaw muscles used to snap the jaw shut are well developed, the muscles used to open the jaw are considerably weaker, so much so that if the jaw is taped shut or a large rubber band is put around it, the muscles are not strong enough to push up against the force created by these. ✿

Jaw-dropping strength
A crocodile's bite is immensely powerful, but when it comes to opening its jaw the muscles are very weak.

High strength:
5,000
lbs inch^2

Low strength

He hasn't lost a game of snap yet!

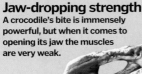

© Science Photo Library

Head to Head
MASSIVE SINKHOLES

GIANT SINKHOLE

1. Xiaozhai Tiankeng, southern China
At over 600m deep and wide, this gigantic sinkhole may be the world's largest. Tiankeng means 'sky hole'.

DEEPEST LAKE

2. El Zacatón Cenote, Mexico
A 319m deep lake, this is the world's deepest water-filled vertical shaft – popular with divers and NASA explorers hoping to use research gained to search for life in space.

LARGEST UNDERWATER

3. Great Blue Hole, Belize
The world's largest blue hole – otherwise known as an underwater sinkhole – lies off the Belize coast. It's almost perfectly round and 300m across.

DID YOU KNOW? The ancient Mayan civilisation threw live victims into sinkholes to appease their rain god

A near miss for these house owners in Kentucky, USA

© Science Photo Library

How do sinkholes form?

Discover why limestone landscapes are riddled with hollows and holes

Sinkholes, dolines, swallow or shake holes, or cenotes are bowl-shaped hollows created when limestone is eaten away by acidic groundwater. Limestone chemically reacts with acidic water because it's mostly calcium carbonate – the alkali used in some indigestion tablets to neutralise stomach acid.

Sinkholes form in two main ways. First, due to acidic water seeping through and widening cracks in the limestone. If the cracks are close together, a small hollow forms and grows bigger as rainwater flows into it.

Second, sinkholes also form when caves collapse. Rivers in limestone areas often run through underground tunnels that they widen into caves. If the cave reaches the surface and the roof falls in, it can create a sinkhole.

Holes in the ground in other rock types are sometimes called sinkholes. An enormous sinkhole that swallowed a Guatemala City clothing factory in May 2010, for example, is in an area of volcanic rock and ash. ✿

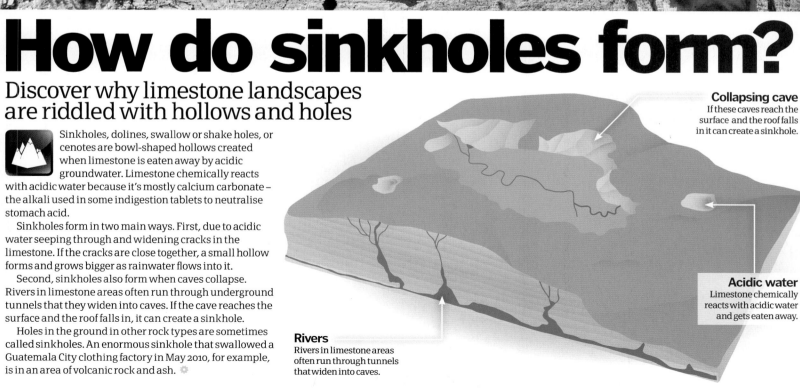

Collapsing cave
If these caves reach the surface and the roof falls in it can create a sinkhole.

Acidic water
Limestone chemically reacts with acidic water and gets eaten away.

Rivers
Rivers in limestone areas often run through tunnels that widen into caves.

"If a deadly venomous spider does bite you, your chance of dying as a result of it is less than ten per cent"

Anatomy of a spider

Inside the animal behind the most common phobia in Britain

Part of the arachnid class of animals – which actually includes scorpions, ticks and mites – spiders are eight-legged arthropods with two body sections. With its ability to inject venom into its prey, immobilising them for ease of eating, the spider has become both feared and revered. ✿

Fancy a bite?

The poison gland connected to a venomous spider's fangs contains dangerous chemicals that are released into a victim by digging the fangs into the victim's body. Unless the spider feels threatened, these fangs will remain tucked away. Some spider poisons have horrible side effects, including tissue degeneration, cell death, and sickness, and yet even if a deadly venomous spider does bite you, your chance of dying as a result of it is less than ten per cent. Male funnel-web venom contains robustoxin, which affects the nervous systems of humans and monkeys, but not of other mammals.

While most species have trachea and book lung respiratory systems, some just have one or the other

Forward-facing eyes
Despite having numerous eyes, the spider is not known for its good eyesight. Forward-facing eyes enable the spider to better judge distances. Most spiders have four pairs of eyes – a main pair and three small pairs – but some species have fewer.

Pedipalps
This pair of small feelers are ideal for controlling and tearing up food.

Chelicerae
These fangs are small but deadly projections that inject poison into the spider's prey.

Mouthparts
The mouthparts enable the spider to inject victims with digestive enzymes and then use their fangs to liquefy the body, which can then be sucked up as food.

© Lukas Jonaitis

Cephalothorax
The cephalothorax is the fusion of head and thorax that distinguishes spiders from insects, which have three separate head, thorax and abdomen sections. This large section of the spider's body carries four pairs of legs and two pairs of mouthparts.

Brain

Leg joints
The spider's jointed legs have seven individual sections, helping them to move quickly. The hairs on a spider's legs can detect vibrations in the air, helping them to anticipate predators.

Poison gland

Coxa

Trochanter

Femur

Patella

Tibia

Metatarsus

Tarsus

Tarsal claw

Feet
A spider's foot is covered in hairs, each of which is covered in microscopic feet. These mini feet allow the spider to grip on to any surface.

5 TOP FACTS
SPIDERS

Good vibrations
1 Spiders do have eyes but they aren't very effective. Instead, spiders use vibrations. The tiny bristles all over a spider's body surface are sensitive to touch, vibration and airflow.

Spiders' digest
2 Spiders digest food outside their bodies. They cover the insects in digestive enzymes, which break down the body and allows the spider to suck up the liquid prey.

Arthropods
3 Spiders are arthropods, so the skeletal system of their body is the outermost layer. The hard exoskeleton helps the spider maintain moisture and not dry out.

Special silk
4 Spider silk has uses other than spinning webs. Black widow silk was at one time used in military gun sights because of its strength and uniform thickness.

Flying spiders
5 Young spiders, or spiderlings, can travel great distances by doing something called 'ballooning' – the process of floating on the breeze using a strand of silk.

DID YOU KNOW? *If a train was to hit a sheet of spider's silk the thickness of a pencil it would stop the vehicle in its tracks*

Pedicel
This thin section of the body connects the cephalothorax and the abdomen.

Abdomen
The abdomen, which is covered in hairs that stand on end to deter enemies, is where you will find the heart, lungs, liver and silk-producing spinnerets.

Stomach

Heart

Ovary

Sperm receptacle
(not visible on diagram)

Oviduct
(not visible on diagram)

Silk gland

Book lung
Some but not all spiders breathe using lung books – so-called because they look like the pages of an open book – in the abdomen.

Intestine

Digestive gland

Anus

Spinnerets

©DK Images

How do spiders breathe?

There are two kinds of respiratory system inherent to the spider – trachea and book lungs. The trachea system consists of tubes running the length of the body. The natural movements of the spider forces air into the body, where it diffuses into the blood. Carbon dioxide is then diffused back into the air and forced out of the body again by the spider's movements. The book lungs, meanwhile, consist of very thin leaf-like structures filled with blood that also exchange oxygen and carbon dioxide through diffusion.

Nature's strongest fibre

Weight for weight, spider silk is stronger than steel. Produced in the silk gland in the abdomen, the silk is made from proteins called fibroin. It's exuded as a liquid that hardens on contact with the air when the molecular structure is aligned by the spider pulling it with its legs. The spider squeezes the silk from the tail end of its body using structures called spinnerets. It then uses its legs to stretch the material into long threads for weaving into webs to catch prey.

MOST WANTED

Some of the most notorious spiders on the planet

1 Brown recluse
The brown recluse can be distinguished by the dark violin-shaped marking on its back. It uses stealth – not a web – to catch its prey by sneaking up and sinking its venomous fangs into the victim. Most bites to humans are accidental and painless, until three to eight hours later when the site becomes red and painful. In bad cases the wound becomes necrotic causing the cells and tissue to die, which can leave severe scarring.

2 Black widow
Identified by their vivid red-on-black markings, black widows are found in the more temperate regions of the globe. Though the venom can bring about nasty symptoms in adults, a bite from the black widow doesn't actually sound the death knell for its victims. Children and the elderly, however, are more at risk.

3 Mexican redknee tarantula
The Mexican redknee is most wanted not because it's a deadly creature but because it makes for a popular pet. Found in the mountains of Mexico and often employed for its impressive appearance as a Hollywood prop in the likes of the *Indiana Jones* and *James Bond* films, this spider is actually very docile and moves very slowly.

4 Wolf spider
Mottled brown in colour – and therefore often confused with the brown recluse (top) – the wolf spider is so-named because it was once thought to have hunted in packs. Though wolf spiders are hairy, they are not closely related to the tarantula. Wolf spiders are not poisonous unless you're allergic, and they can be found throughout Europe and in Britain.

5 Funnel-web spider
A native to the coastal and mountain regions of eastern Australia, the funnel-web is a small but deadly part of the family. Its glossy, almost hairless body gives it a menacing appearance and some species can serve a highly toxic, fast-acting venom. The female funnel-web will spend most of her life inside her burrow, which is lined with white silk.

> "A WATERFALL FORMS AS RIVER WATER FLOWS OVER A BAND OF HARD ROCK LYING NEXT TO A BAND OF SOFT ROCK"

The often-breathtaking natural product of vertical erosion, a waterfall occurs in a river's steep upper course high above sea level. A waterfall forms over many thousands of years as river water flows over a band of hard rock lying next to a band of soft rock downstream. The erosive effects of hydraulic action (water pushing air into tiny cracks in the riverbed) and abrasion (rocks scraping over each other) cause the soft rock to erode quicker than the hard. So while the hard rock remains solid for longer, the soft rock below is worn away, lowering the riverbed from that point and forming a step drop.

At the foot of the step, a deep plunge pool forms where water and rocks collect and swirl about, abrading more of the riverbed and less-resistant rock in the process. The harder, overhanging 'cap' rock is gradually undercut and eventually collapses due to its own weight, breaking off into the plunge pool.

Further collapse of the hard rock sees the waterfall itself recede back upstream, creating steep-sided gorges either side of the waterfall. ✿

Waterfall fo

How are these dramatic geological river features formed?

Niagara: the most famous waterfall in the world

Frozen waterfalls make for a great climbing obstacle

A waterfall formed by volcano

On the border between Argentina and Brazil, surrounded by subtropical rainforest, Iguazu Falls is among the most impressive waterfall systems on Earth. Part of a World Natural Heritage Site, Iguazu is distinctive because it formed as a result of a huge volcanic eruption that left a big crack in the earth. Though there are many taller and more powerful falls, at 2.68 km Iguazu is one of the widest, making it an awesome spectacle. The whole area consists of 275 individual waterfalls spread out across the Iguazu River. A mammoth semicircular waterfall lies at the heart of a series of cascading falls, and the main plunge waterfall, known as Garganta del Diablo, or the Devil's Throat, is 82 metres tall.

Iguazu Falls is a major draw for tourists in South America

TALL

1. Niagara Falls
Height: 51 metres
Situated on the America/ Canada border, Niagara is undoubtedly the most famous fall in the world, and yet it stands at just 51 metres.

TALLER

2. Victoria Falls
Height: 107 metres
Named after Queen Victoria who reigned during its discovery, this fall on the Zambia/Zimbabwe border has a total height of 107 metres.

TALLEST

3. Angel Falls
Height: 979 metres
Found in Venezuela, Angel Falls' total height is a whopping 979 metres, making it the tallest waterfall on Earth, and the world's longest drop.

DID YOU KNOW? Waterfalls can freeze mid-flow due to freezing temperatures slowing the water molecules down

rmation

That's some water feature for a garden that size

TYPES OF... WATERFALLS

There are ten different ways to classify waterfalls

1 Block
Occurring over a wide stream where the waterfall is wider than it is tall. It spills over like a wide sheet of water.

2 Cascade
Flows either over a series of small steps in the rock in quick succession, or over a rugged sloping surface.

3 Curtain
Found on a wide section of stream where the fall is taller than it is wide. These falls tend to narrow during periods of low discharge.

4 Fan
Occurring when the width of the water spilling over increases as it descends, making the base appear much wider than the top.

5 Horsetail
Found on vertical waterfalls, the falling water is in constant or semi-constant contact with the bedrock.

6 Plunge
Water spills over vertically, usually losing contact with the bedrock altogether. Often known as a cataract waterfall.

7 Punchbowl
The flow of water is squeezed through a narrow opening and is then blasted out and down into a pool.

8 Segmented
If the stream is broken into multiple channels this will inevitably cause several falls to occur side by side.

9 Slide
Slide waterfalls flow down over a smooth, sloping bedrock surface while maintaining contact with the bedrock.

10 Tiered
Tiered waterfalls form when several distinct drops occur one after the other, in close succession.

Learn more

For additional information about the many different waterfalls around the world, head on over to **www.world-waterfalls.com/** where you can read about waterfalls from every corner of the Globe, and even choose your favourite.

Waterfall creation
The processes involved in waterfall formation

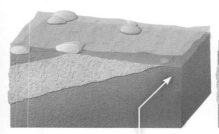

1. Undercutting/ overhanging
A layer of resistant hard rock is undercut by the erosion of the softer rock beneath. This forms a step over which the water flows.

2. Plunging
The force of the falling water hitting the soft rock below creates a plunge pool, which is deepened by the abrasion of fallen angular rocks.

3. Collapsing
Further erosion, worsened by splashback from the falling water in the plunge pool, causes overhanging hard rock to eventually collapse under its own weight.

4. Receding
As this cycle of erosion and collapsing continues, the waterfall steepens and recedes back upstream, creating a steep-sided gorge and an increasingly tall waterfall.

A lie-in that we could only dream of...

Secrets of spider silk

A spider's silk is a versatile and often deadly tool

 The thousands of spider species we have today build and use webs in a multitude of ways. Spiders are able to build their webs thanks to in-built spinnerets, of which they can have up to eight that move independently yet work in perfect unison. These spinnerets are the spider's silk-spinning organ and can produce a variety of silk types to fulfil varying purposes. Silk types can range from a smooth safety line, to a sticky silk line ideal for trapping prey, through to an incredibly fine silk line perfect for embalming. Over its lifetime a spider is capable of producing up to eight different types of silk and web use can include net creation, egg protection, victim preservation and body armour. ✿

A spider weaving the more traditional orb web

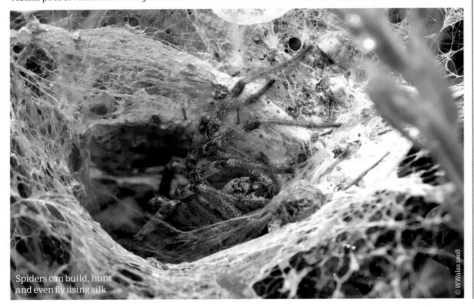
Spiders can build, hunt and even fly using silk

© W Walas 2008

Hibernation explained

Why can mammals go to sleep for months on end?

 While birds and winged creatures can fly to warmer climes to escape cold and fruitless winters, many mammals enter a deep sleep to survive. This state is called hibernation and, depending on the animal, it can last between a few days, weeks, or even months.

In preparation for true hibernation, the animal must make a cosy burrow in which to sleep, and eat lots of food to store up as fat. Some animals can survive the whole winter on little or no food as the animal's heart rate and body temperature decrease, which means they use very little energy during hibernation.

Hibernating mammals also have two types of fat: regular white fat, which is used for storing energy and insulating the body, and a special brown fat that isn't burned for energy. This brown fat is most important to hibernation because it forms around the organs that need it most – the brain, heart and lungs – and generates heat to keep the animal alive. ✿

DID YOU KNOW? Some desert-dwelling animals also enter a state of hibernation in order to survive droughts or hot weather. This is called aestivation.

Image © DK Images

The world's most venomous fish

Almost invisible among the coral reefs, the stonefish is a real-life killer

 The stonefish is the world's most venomous fish thanks to its ability to inject deadly neurotoxins from the spines on its dorsal fin into its target. The stonefish's neurotoxins work by attacking the nerve cells of whatever it is injected into, causing severe pain, sickness, nausea, paralysis and, depending on the depth of spine penetration into skin, death within three hours.

Unlike most other poisonous fish who dwell in the dark depths of the ocean – leaving little chance of human contact – stonefish live in shallow waters and are likely to be found anywhere between just beneath the surface down to a depth of three metres. ✿

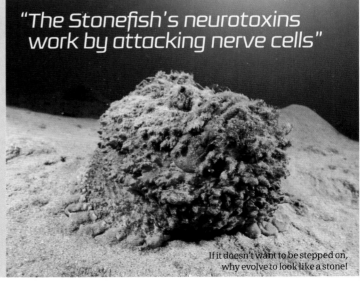
"The Stonefish's neurotoxins work by attacking nerve cells"

If it doesn't want to be stepped on, why evolve to look like a stone!

CARNIVOROUS

1. Pitcher plant
After trapping its prey, this deadly species known as Nepenthes then digests them with powerful enzymes. For more info on this plant, turn to page 14.

NIGHT BLOOMER

2. Lady of the Night
The Lady of the Night is a plant with flowers that are closed during the day but open up at night, releasing its scent.
© Cary Bass, 2006

SENSITIVE

3. Makahiya
The Makahiya's leaves react to touch, light or heat due to a drop of pressure in its cells. The plant looks like a creature as its leaflets furl up and the stalk droops.
© Frank Vincentz, 08

DID YOU KNOW? The largest species of plant and the tallest living organism in the world is the California Redwood tree

2. Compound leaf
Compound leaves are divided into smaller leaflets. There is a single bud at the base of the petiole stalk.

3. Terminal buds
A bud found at the tip of the stem is called a terminal bud and will allow the stem to grow in length.

Inside a leaf

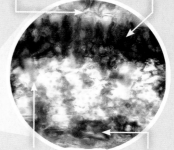

UPPER EPIDERMIS   PALISADE CHLOROPHYLL

Lamina (leaf blade)

SPONGY MESOPHYLL   LOWER EPIDERMIS

Leaves
These green fleshy parts are vital to the plant's ability to create its own food. The process of photosynthesis enables a plant to produce carbohydrates from the Sun's energy. The leaves therefore expose as much surface area as possible in order to absorb the most sunlight, they will even turn towards the Sun for maximum absorption.

1. Simple leaf
Consisting of a flat and solid blade, a simple leaf is supported by and attached to the stem by a small petiole stalk.

4. Lateral buds
Axillary buds are those located on the area between the upper side of the leafstalk and the stem.

Leaf veins

Plant anatomy

Explaining the parts of a plant and their functions

Plants feature two main systems: the roots and the shoots. Above ground, the shoot system comprises the food-making leaves, buds, stem, and any flowers or fruit the plant may have. Below ground, the food-storing root system, which anchors the plant in the soil and prevents it from blowing away, features nutrient-absorbing roots, tubers, and rhizomes. Let's start from the top and work down. ✿

Node, point of attachment of branch or leaf

Vascular tissue   Epidermis layer

Ground tissue

Stem
The plant's strong stem offers support for the leaves and other above-ground parts. It is made up of nodes and internodes, with the nodes representing the site where the leaves are attached and the internodes, predictably, indicating the area of the stem between nodes. Green stems are photosynthetic, they just don't produce as much carbohydrate as the leaves. The stem is a vascular system, which means they transport water and minerals to the leaves and the roots.

6. Stem cross section
Stems consist of a thin transparent epidermis layer that produces a juicy substance that can attract insects, a vascular tissue layer made up of xylem and phloem (the transport tissues that move water and sugars through the plant), and providing the bulk of the stem's mass is the ground tissue, in which starch can be stored.

9. Root cap
Right at the end of the root is a thimble-shaped cap that protects and lubricates the root as it grows through the soil.

8. Root tip
This is the area of the root where cell division takes place.

Shoot system

Primary root

Roots
The roots permeate the soil, anchoring the plant. The part of the plant embryo that sprouts into a root (the radicle) immediately gets to work securing the plant by growing downwards and branching off to grow secondary roots.

Many plants develop structures that are not roots but specialised stems. Rhizomes, for example, are horizontal plant stems that grow underground and can develop new roots and shoots. Below the surface you may also find tubers, which are thickened swollen plant stems (such as potatoes).

Secondary root

Root system

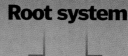

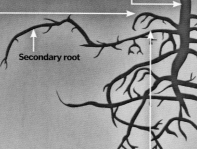

5. Adventitious buds
These unruly buds will develop anywhere but where they're meant to, such as on the root.

7. Root hairs
The hairs on a root have a huge surface area, enabling it to more efficiently soak up water and minerals – especially nitrogen and sulphur – by way of either osmosis, diffusion or active transport.

"Because sharks continually shed and replace their teeth, they can get through more than 30,000 in their lifetime"

How sharks survive

There's more to these fascinating and endangered creatures than their one-dimensional portrayal as mindless movie predators

Sharks belong to the group of fish known as elasmobranchii. This means that their skeleton is made of cartilage instead of bone. The earliest sharks appeared in the fossil record around 420 million years ago but the first modern sharks did not appear until 100 million years ago, around the time of the dinosaurs. The cartilage skeleton of sharks is not a primitive trait; sharks evolved from fish that did have bones. It is possible that the lighter, more flexible cartilage skeleton may have evolved to make sharks faster and more agile but it may also have been a way to conserve the amount of phosphorus needed by the shark metabolism. Sharks need phosphorus for their teeth and because sharks continually shed and replace teeth, they can get through more than 30,000 in their life. The availability of mineral phosphorus to make new teeth is one of the primary constraints for the spread of shark species around the world.

In the 19th Century, sharks were generally regarded as entirely benign to humans. Though reports of shipwrecked sailors being attacked had been around since 1580, they were dismissed as exaggerated or mistaken. In 1891, millionaire Hermann Oelrichs offered a $500 reward for an authenticated case of a shark attack on a human off America's east coast. This went unclaimed.

Then in 1916, a spate of widely publicised shark attacks marked the start of a complete reversal in the image of the shark. After almost a century of bad press, sharks are only just starting to be properly understood. ✿

5 TOP FACTS
SHARKS

Huge liver
1 The liver of a shark can comprise up to 30 per cent of its body mass and performs an incredible number of tasks, including keeping it afloat.

No reverse gear
2 Sharks can't use their fins to paddle, like most other fish. This means that they are unable to swim directly backwards.

Familiar eyes
3 Sharks have eyelids – although they never blink – but they can contract and dilate their pupils, like humans, something no bony fish can do.

Power napping
4 The spiny dogfish uses its spinal cord to co-ordinate swimming, rather than its brain, meaning it can swim while sleeping.

Fishy barometer
5 It is possible sharks may be able to use their lateral line to detect approaching frontal pressure systems and swim deeper to avoid hurricanes.

DID YOU KNOW? There are more than 440 species of shark that live in the world's seas and oceans

Physical characteristics

The hammerhead certainly won't win

Sharks range in size from 30cm to over 12 metres long and can weigh up to 20 tons. Their skeleton doesn't include ribs so without the water to support them, the weight of their own bodies would crush their internal organs. Sharks don't have a swim bladder either so they generate buoyancy using squalene oil stored in the liver. Because they can't quickly change the amount of squalene in their body, sharks can't maintain neutral buoyancy at rest. Instead they tune their buoyancy so they are slightly denser than the surrounding water. Many species of shark have capitalised on this to become bottom dwellers and the pelagic (open sea) species make up the difference in buoyancy with dynamic lift generated by the flow of water over their fins as they swim. Most sharks live in waters no deeper than 2,000 metres.

Although sharks don't have true bones, areas of the body subject to the largest mechanical stress are reinforced with a hexagonal grid of crystalline calcium salts. Large sharks such as the great white may have several layers of this reinforcement. Shark skin is much tougher than that of other fish. The base layers are a helical mesh of collagen fibres, like the sheath on

a rope and this is covered with a layer of tiny scales, called dermal denticles. Each denticle is made from dentine, which is another calcium-impregnated tissue. Dentine is a major component of teeth and in fact, it is likely that the teeth of vertebrates evolved from these denticles, so a shark is actually covered from nose to tail in a coat of teeth! As well as providing protection, the denticles act in a similar way to the dimples on a golf ball. By generating tiny vortices at their trailing edges, they reduce drag and allow sharks to swim more efficiently.

Sharks have only average eyesight but extremely acute hearing and smell. Like most other fish, they also have a strip of vibration-sensitive hair cells, running the length of their body. This is called the lateral line and is used to detect the movement of prey. In sharks these cells also run in a complex pattern around the head, which makes their vibration sense much more directional. And sharks have yet another sense: electroreception. The Ampullae of Lorenzini are modified lateral line cells that can sense the weak electric fields produced by all living things. A few other fish have an electroreceptive sense but the sharks are by far the most sensitive. As well as finding prey at night, sharks can use the electric field generated by ocean currents moving within the Earth's magnetic field as an internal compass.

Shark teeth

Gummy
Shark teeth are not anchored in the jaw but instead are embedded in the gums.

Knife edge
Narrow, dagger-shaped teeth like these are used to grip slippery fish. Serrated teeth are for slicing through large mammals.

Reinforcements
Hexagonal crystalline blocks of calcium are embedded for reinforcement of the jaw cartilage.

Top: tooth from a great white and (below) a jaw from a mako shark

Snout
The snout, or rostrum, is made of much spongier cartilage than the rest of the body, to cushion any impacts.

Mouth
Prehistoric sharks had the mouth at the front but it now sits slung well back, behind the sensory equipment.

Spine
Unlike bony fish, the spinal cord extends into the top fin of the tail. The notch breaks up turbulence.

Muscles
Without a rigid skeleton, the swimming muscles are anchored to the helical collagen fibres of the inner skin layers.

Intestines
Sharks have very short intestines but food is slowed by a corkscrew valve arrangement to allow time for digestion.

Fins
The pectoral fins act as hydroplanes, generating lift in the water.

© DK Images

Anatomy of a shark
They might look like other fish but sharks are startlingly different

035

This poor little fella is a few pounds lighter after a shark encounter

Shark attacks

Two tons and up to 3,000 teeth? That's going to hurt...

Shark attacks are recorded worldwide by the International Shark Attack File, which was set up in 1958 by the US Office of Naval Research. It has data on over 4,000 incidents, going back to the 16th Century. Shark attacks on humans peaked in 2000 with 79 attacks worldwide, of which just 11 were fatal. Since then attacks have been steadily dropping and the number of fatalities is now less than five per year worldwide. Most of these occur in the USA, probably because of the high overlap of surfing beaches with shark territories. This compares with over 3,300 Americans who drown each year.

Only four species of shark are responsible for fatal, unprovoked attacks on humans: the great white, tiger, bull and oceanic whitetip shark. The oceanic whitetip almost never comes close to the shore and all of its attacks on humans have been on shipwrecks and plane crash survivors.

Sharks do not generally attack humans to eat them. Bites are either exploratory, where the shark isn't sure what to make of a wetsuit-clad surfer, or they may be because the shark is defending a territory. Even when a shark is intending to kill, it will generally bite once and then retreat, while it waits for you to die from blood loss. This often gives swimmers time to reach shore or a boat and survive.

ON THE MAP

Where sharks attack

1. **1916, New Jersey, USA**
   Four killed and one person injured in a spate of attacks over 12 days in July, which inspired the Peter Benchley novel *Jaws*.
2. **1945, Phillippine Sea**
   USS Indianapolis is torpedoed by a Japanese submarine and 60-80 crew are killed by oceanic whitetip sharks.
3. **1964, Lady Julia Percy Island, Australia**
   Diver Henri Bource manages to film part of the attack in which a shark bit his leg off.
4. **2008, New Smyrna Beach, Florida**
   28 attacks that year make this the shark bite capital of the world.

How to survive a shark attack

When you hear that ominous cello music, here's what to do

A reassuring 80 per cent of shark attack victims survive. Mostly this is because the shark loses interest but there are cases of people successfully fighting off a shark. Some studies have shown that just touching a shark on the snout can cause it to halt in mid strike, but the International Shark Attack File advises hitting the nose as hard as you can. Don't use your fists or feet unless you have no other weapons to hand – it's too easy to get them bitten off.

Grabbing for the eyes is unlikely to work. They are a very small target and great whites will roll their eyes back in their sockets for protection right before they strike anyway. The gill slits are a more promising target; the gills inside are both delicate and sensitive.

Don't play dead, sharks are more likely to bite you if you look defenceless. Equally though, too much splashing and noise will act to attract sharks. If you manage to drive the shark away, don't relax just yet. Sharks are very curious and this one will be back soon. Get out of the water straight away if possible. If you are diving in open water, come to the surface, swimming back-to-back with your diving buddy.

Respecting the shark's territory is essential

How sharks reproduce

Like many top carnivores, sharks take good care of their young

Rather than producing huge numbers of eggs, each with very little chance of survival, sharks produce between two and 100 young at a time. This is much lower than most fish. Fertilisation is internal with the male using a pair of organs called claspers in much the same way as a penis. Some of the smaller shark species, such as the horn shark and the cat shark, lay eggs, which are protected within a leathery egg case and often wedged into crevices. Most sharks retain the eggs in the female body though. This is called ovoviviparity and it is different from the live birth or viviparity found in mammals because all the nourishment for the embryo comes from the yolk of the egg. Only in a few species, including the hammerhead and tiger shark, are the embryos fed with a placenta connected to the mother.

In many species, the first shark to hatch will eat any remaining eggs in the oviduct as its first meal and newly hatched grey nurse shark will even eat the other developing embryos. Sharks have very long gestation periods – as long as 24 months for some species.

A newly hatched shark emerges from its egg

The whale shark is the largest living fish species

Sharks in danger

What are the threats to sharks worldwide?

A hundred million sharks a year are killed by humans for food. Because sharks reproduce slowly and take a long time to reach adulthood, most fishing stocks are in steep decline. Studies have shown population declines of 70-90 per cent for the commercially fished species in the last 30 years.

As well as for their meat, sharks are fished for their fins to meet the massive demand for shark's fin soup in Asia. Often these are removed using a hot knife and then the shark is thrown back but unable to move, or they quickly die anyway. Shark cartilage is also used to make alternative medicines due to the belief that it can cure or prevent cancer. There is no scientific evidence to support this idea.

Sharks are also threatened to some extent by coastal development, marine pollution and over fishing of their own prey, as well as sport fishing. But all of these are much less significant than the effect of commercial fishing. Only three species – basking, whale and great white sharks – are subject to international trade restrictions. One third of European shark species are currently classed as threatened.

A shark feeding frenzy, reminds us of scenes at an all-you-can-eat buffet

What do sharks eat?

It's not just surfers on the menu

Virtually all sharks are carnivorous but the 440 known species have diversified to almost every marine niche. Angel sharks lie in wait, camouflaged on the seabed and suck small fish suddenly into their mouths. Hammerheads use their widely spaced electroreceptors to catch flatfish and crustaceans lurking under the sand. Port Jackson sharks have molar-like rear teeth for cracking open molluscs.

Some sharks are filter feeders, eating mainly plankton and tiny fish. To sieve through the vast volumes of water necessary to strain out enough food, they may either take huge gulps and suck the water in, like the whale shark, or just swim through patches of plankton with their mouths open, like the basking shark. The water is expelled through the gill slits at the side but any food is trapped in fibrous gill rakers and when enough has been collected, it is swallowed.

The tiger shark is an indiscriminate hunter and specimens have been found with seals, birds, dolphins, turtles and even old tyres and car licence plates in their stomach. But most species will hunt only one particular type of prey. The viper dogfish for example has teeth that point outwards from its mouth and it uses these to skewer small squid before swallowing them whole. Thresher sharks use their elongated tails to whip schools of fish, herding them into ever-tighter groups until they can take a bite out of the mass as if it were a single, huge, fish.

The stereotype of the shark as a solitary ambush predator of the open sea is really only accurate for a small number of species, inclding the bull shark, tiger shark and great white. These are also the species most likely to attack humans so they attract much more attention. These species are highly territorial and often patrol close to the surface. This is because their usual prey is below them and their white bellies make them hard to see against the sky. Bull sharks have specially adapted kidneys that allow them to cope with fresh water and they can swim for hundreds of miles up major rivers in search of prey.

Five myths about sharks   Don't believe everything you hear...

1. Sharks have to swim or suffocate
Only about half the shark species need to keep swimming in order to move water across their gills. The others will still sink if they stop but they can pump water with their mouths.

2. Sharks are drawn to blood
Although sharks can detect blood at concentrations of just one part per million, they are much more attracted to the smell of guts and often linger near sewage outfalls.

3. Sharks are mindless machines
Sharks have similar brain to body mass ratios to both mammals and birds. Many shark species show strong problem-solving skills and recognisable social traits.

4. Sharks are immune to cancer
This is mainly pushed by some medical 'experts' who are probably attempting to sell shark cartilage remedies. There is no scientific evidence to support this.

5. Sharks are 'living fossils'
Quite the opposite, sharks are in fact highly adapted to their current environment and show many advanced traits that their ancestors simply didn't have.

Acid rain

Understanding this largely man-made problem

The effects on natural and man-made objects are frighteningly obvious

The thought of acid rain is a stark one. Drops of highly concentrated acid falling from the sky, burning and eroding everything they touch, it is enough to scare anyone into never leaving the house again. So why do we? Well, for one because acid rain isn't pure acid but rather a diluted form of it created when clean rain reacts with sulphur dioxide or other nitrogen oxides. This oxidisation of the sulphur and nitrogen compounds lowers the natural pH level of rain, which is around 5.6, to a more acidic one and further from the neutral pH level of seven shared by distilled water.

Most notably the effects of acid rain have been closely associated with the dilapidation of forests worldwide and the destruction of entire ecosystems. However, the effects of acid rain can be seen around us every day, from the corroded statues in our town squares to the bare trees lining the busiest of roads.

Unfortunately, the problem of acid rain is very much a man-made one, despite there being natural causes for the release of both sulphur dioxide and nitrogen oxides, such as volcanic emissions. The vast majority of emissions though are derived from fossil fuel combustion. ✿

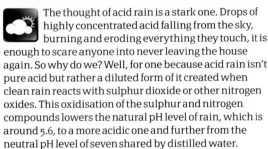

Anemometers measure wind speed

Weather vanes have been used for centuries to determine wind direction

Measuring wind

How strong is the wind? The Beaufort Scale will tell you

Before more sophisticated instruments were developed for measuring wind speed and strength, sailors and other seafarers had to use observable environmental changes on the surface of the water to judge whether conditions. However, in 1805 an Irishman called Francis Beaufort conceived a system for determining different winds using just the effects on the environment. Still relevant today, the Beaufort Scale is divided into a series of 13 values ranging from 0 to 12: 0 being calm and still, and anything over 12 being hurricane force.

Each individual number on the scale represents a classification of wind speed with a description of the effects over the land or sea. These days, wind speed can be measured more precisely, using either an anemometer or windsock for near-surface winds. And for gauging upper atmospheric winds, meteorologists can use radar to follow and chart weather balloon activity. However, Beaufort's system and its descriptions of wind conditions remain highly significant to meteorological disciplines today. ✿

Wind description	Sea conditions	Wind speed	Inland conditions
0. Calm	Calm (glassy)	0mph/<1kn	Smoke rises vertically
1. Light air	Calm (rippled)	1-3mph/1-3kn	Light air causes smoke to drift
2. Light breeze	Smooth (wavelets)	4-7mph/4-6kn	Wind felt on face, leaves rustle, vane moves
3. Gentle breeze	Slight	8-12mph/7-10kn	Leaves in constant motion, light flag extend
4. Moderate breeze	Slight to moderate	13-18mph/11-16kn	Small branches move
5. Fresh breeze	Moderate	19-24mph/17-21kn	Small trees sway, crested wavelets on inland water
6. Strong breeze	Rough	25-31mph/22-27kn	Large branches in motion
7. Near gale	Rough to very rough	32-38mph/28-33kn	Whole trees in motion
8. Gale	Very rough to high	39-46mph/34-40kn	Breaks twigs off trees, walking impeded
9. Severe gale	High	47-54mph/41-47kn	Slight structural damage to buildings
10. Storm	Very high	55-63mph/48-55kn	Large branches broken, some trees uprooted
11. Violent storm	Very high	64-72mph/56-63kn	Large trees uprooted and widespread damage
12. Hurricane	Phenomenal	73+mph/64+kn	Widespread devastation

How whales communicate

Whales produce a wide range of complex sounds through differing techniques

Whales communicate by creating sounds through methods that differ depending on their family type. Toothed whales – which include dolphins – produce high-pitched sounds by the manipulation of air stored in their head through their phonic lips, a structure loosely akin to the human nasal cavity. As air is passed through the phonic lips they contract causing vibrations in the surrounding tissue before being consciously streamed by the whale.

Baleen whales differ in their sound creation, as they do not possess a phonic lip structure, doing so through manipulation of air passing through their larynx instead. The larynx works through the vibrations of internal vocal cords when air is passed over them. However, mystery shrouds this method of communication as baleen whales lack vocal cords, so presently scientists are unsure as to the exact manner in which their low-pitched sounds emanate from their larynx. ✿

5 TOP FACTS
NORTHERN LIGHTS

Other aurorae
1 Other planets – including Jupiter, Saturn, Uranus, Neptune and many of their moons – have their very own aurorae.

Solar music makers
2 The massive electrical activity of the northern lights transmits eerie crackling and whistling noises over radio receivers.

Biggest display ever
3 A massive magnetic disturbance back in 1989 caused visible aurarae as far as Texas and even Northern Australia.

The 'stuff' of space
4 Amazingly, a phenomenal 99 per cent of visible matter in the universe is actually made up of plasma of one sort or another.

Pole dancing
5 The North and South Poles have switched places 400 times in the past 330 million years, the last occurrence being 780,000 years ago.

DID YOU KNOW? *The colours in the aurora borealis consist of red, blue, violet and green*

Northern lights

Stormy space weather produces the world's biggest neon sign

Space weather

The cold vacuum of space seems an unlikely place for a storm. But that's exactly what happens when a solar flare explodes into the Sun's upper atmosphere, instantly heating nearby gasses to millions of degrees.

The extreme heat causes gas atoms to split into positively charged ions and negatively charged free electrons. This supercharged soup of ionised gas is called plasma. The Sun emits a constant stream of plasma in all directions at a speed of 500 kilometres per hour. But when the flow of plasma becomes a flood, the Earth is in for some bad space weather.

Geomagnetic storms cause more than the majestic northern lights. They can warp the Earth's magnetic field so badly that satellites are knocked out of orbit and invading electrons overwhelm power grids. In 1989, 6 million people in Montreal, Quebec lost power for nine hours thanks to a particularly strong solar storm.

"Gentle solar winds turn into geomagnetic storms"

The aurora borealis, or northern lights, taken by astronaut Donald R Pettit, on board the International Space Station

All Images © NASA

What would the North Pole tourist bureau do without the northern lights? Ten-month winters don't make for good travel brochures. But only here, in this most inhospitable open-air theatre, can you witness the most hauntingly beautiful light show ever conceived. Curtains of shimmering, chameleon-hued light as unpredictable as an artist's temper.

The scientific explanation behind the aurora borealis ('northern dawn' in Latin) is almost as improbable and magical as the lights themselves. The Earth, it turns out, is constantly bombarded by highly charged particles blown around by solar winds. Few of these particles ever reach the atmosphere because they are deflected by the Earth's magnetic field.

But every so often, the gentle solar winds turn into geomagnetic storms. Solar flares and coronal mass ejections (CME) – explosions of solar material into interplanetary space – can send powerful waves of charged particles toward the Earth. As these cosmic electrons collide with the Earth's magnetic field, they generate millions of amps of electric current that arc along the magnetic field toward the poles.

If the force of a geomagnetic storm is severe enough, particles will breach the magnetic field at the poles, creating what is essentially the world's biggest neon sign. As the supercharged electrons pass through the atmosphere, they excite gas atoms like oxygen and nitrogen.

The excited gasses emit different coloured lights depending on their altitude and the power of the surge. Low-altitude oxygen is responsible for the fluorescent green hues and high-altitude oxygen produces those brilliant crimson reds. Nitrogen flares up as shades of blue and purple.

The celestial light show is visible at the South Pole as well (there, it's called the aurora australis), but the Antarctica tourist board is woefully understaffed. ❖

"Dolphins are considered to be the most intelligent of all marine mammals"

Head
A complex structure as it contains the brain, melon (the egg-shaped yellow ball), blow hole and jaw structure, the bottom part of which (yellow section) acting as a biological antenna for incoming signals

© DK Images

Anatomy of a dolphin
Under the skin of this intelligent mammal

Scapula
Connects the flipper bones with the spinal column

Lung
Its large lung capacity helps it remain underwater for extended periods

Blow hole
Allows the dolphin to breath and exhale communicative sounds

Melon
Aids the dolphin's echolocation abilities

Teeth
Dolphins can have up to 250 teeth

Eye
Dolphins have very acute eyesight

Larynx
Where many sounds and noises emanate from

Heart
Dolphins have a tough muscular heart

Liver

Flipper
The dolphin's dual flippers help propel its mass through the water and maintain equilibrium

Popular in human culture due to their intelligence and playfulness, dolphin species can be found all over the world, ranging in shape, size and character dramatically

Dolphins

There are many species of dolphin ranging from the modestly sized Maui dolphin, right up to the giant Orca killer whale. They are found all over the world, both in the ocean and also in rivers, and are considered to be the most intelligent of all marine mammals. All species are carnivorous, eating mostly foraged fish and squid, and numerous varieties hunt in packs, encircling schools of small fish to confuse them. Dolphins evolved from terrestrial mammals over 50 million years ago and are theorised by scientists to be descended from artiodactyls.

Dolphins have evolved to have a very streamlined fusiform (fat in the middle and tapered at both ends) body, ideally adapted for fast swimming and sudden, dynamic movements and changes in direction. This is aided by their tail fin (fluke) construction, which provides massive propulsion as well as acute directional control. Their prominent fin also aids mobility, providing stability at speed and through hairpin turns. At the front of their body lies their elongated head, jaw and beak structure, as well as a large area on the forehead called the melon. This is the part of the dolphin's body that deals with echolocation (biological sonar) and is a crucial tool for

MOST FAMOUS

1. Bottlenose
One of the most famous of species, Bottlenoses tend to live in packs of 10-20 and hunt collectively. They are highly playful, often being utilised in aquarium shows.

MOST STREAMLINED

2. Common
Characterised by their narrow nose and streamlined body, the Common dolphin is one of the fastest swimming cetaceans in the world.

MOST DECORATIVE

3. Spotted
Spotted dolphins are more exotic in their colouration than most other species. They are endemic to temperate and tropical oceans.

DID YOU KNOW? For the ancient Greeks, spotting a dolphin while at sea was considered a good omen

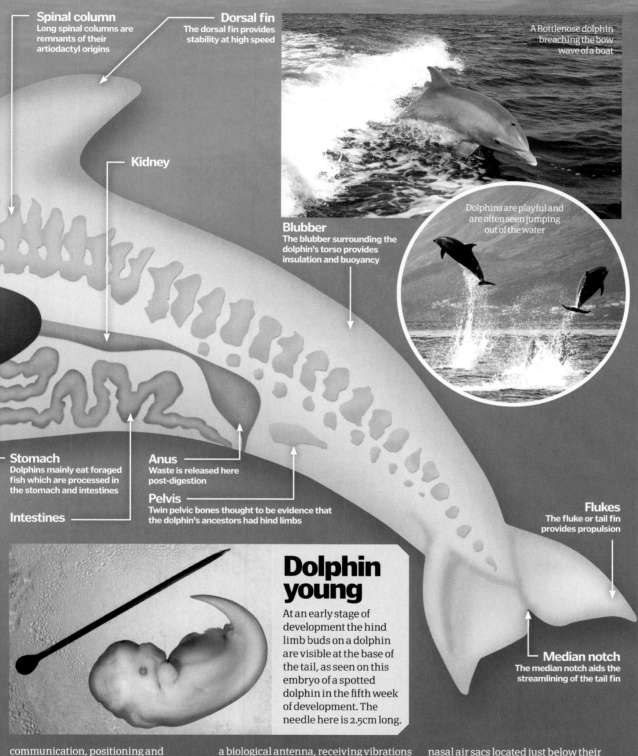

Spinal column
Long spinal columns are remnants of their artiodactyl origins

Dorsal fin
The dorsal fin provides stability at high speed

A Bottlenose dolphin breaching the bow wave of a boat

Kidney

Blubber
The blubber surrounding the dolphin's torso provides insulation and buoyancy

Dolphins are playful and are often seen jumping out of the water

Stomach
Dolphins mainly eat foraged fish which are processed in the stomach and intestines

Anus
Waste is released here post-digestion

Intestines

Pelvis
Twin pelvic bones thought to be evidence that the dolphin's ancestors had hind limbs

Flukes
The fluke or tail fin provides propulsion

Dolphin young

At an early stage of development the hind limb buds on a dolphin are visible at the base of the tail, as seen on this embryo of a spotted dolphin in the fifth week of development. The needle here is 2.5cm long.

Median notch
The median notch aids the streamlining of the tail fin

Whaling problem

Despite the wide variety of dolphin species, many are dwindling in number or have been completely eradicated by natural and man-made causes. Indeed, in a 2006 survey the Yangtze river dolphin was officially labelled as extinct as no examples were recorded. One of the biggest human-caused reasons that dolphins are becoming extinct is whaling, which in some parts of the world is legal and bound in local tradition.

In Taiji, Japan and over the entirety of the Faroe Islands, dolphins are traditionally considered as food and are often killed en masse in harpoon or drive hunts, practices protected by law. This comes despite dolphin meat being high in mercury, causing health issues for humans if excessive quantities are consumed. Other contributory factors leading to the declining populations of dolphins include pesticides, heavy metals and plastics contaminating their habitat, as well as accidental deaths caused by fishing nets and motorboat propellers.

Learn more

There's a great documentary from the BBC called *Dolphins: Deep Thinkers*, narrated by Sir David Attenborough. You can watch it on YouTube if you go to **http://tinyurl.com/yevm6ll** where it's available in three parts. It attempts to find out how intelligent dolphins are through observing their behaviour.

communication, positioning and environmental awareness.

Indeed, dolphins have a very complex sensory system, driven by their vivid eyesight and echolocation ability. Through their tiny ear structure they can discern and hear frequencies up to ten times the upper limit of adult human hearing and scientists postulate that their lengthy jaw with its numerous teeth (up to 250 in some species) acts like a biological antenna, receiving vibrations and sound waves and amplifying them within the skull. Processing this information is the dolphin's brain, which is not only one of the largest but also one of the most complex of all mammals, be they marine or terrestrial.

Despite having no sense of smell whatsoever, dolphins can make a series of noises to communicate or aid echolocation by manipulating a series of nasal air sacs located just below their blowhole. To communicate with each other they use a series of burst-pulse sounds and frequency modulated whistles, while to determine their positioning and the positioning of other animals or areas of interest (such as humans on boats), a series of clicks are adopted. These clicks tend to be continuous and increase in frequency the closer the dolphin is to the target. ✿

"In summer, monsoon winds bring heavy rainfall"

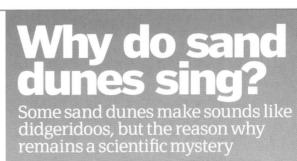

Carrying umbrellas on motorbikes can damage your health

Monsoons

The wind systems that reverse seasonally, bringing dramatically different weather to subtropical regions

 Monsoons are seasonal wind systems occurring in tropical and subtropical regions south, southeast and east of the large landmasses in the northern hemisphere. They see the prevailing wind direction and conditions in these areas reverse between summer and winter. ❁

Where?
The major monsoon systems of the world are the West African and Asia-Australian monsoons (marked in red).

Seasonal monsoon conditions across southern Asia

© Science Photo Library

Summer
In summer, monsoon winds bring heavy rainfall. The land is heated much quicker than the ocean, causing the warmer air to rise, creating a strong, large area of low pressure. The cool, wet air from the ocean is drawn in, bringing with it warm southwesterly winds. When the moist air reaches the Himalayas, clouds form and produce heavy rainfall that can lead to flooding.

Winter
South Asia's winter monsoon winds bring much dryer, cooler, clearer conditions. Because this time the sea is cooling much slower than the land, the low pressure and clouds instead form over the ocean, drawing the cool, dry air from the mountains into the area. These winter monsoon winds blow from a northeasterly direction.

Why do sand dunes sing?

Some sand dunes make sounds like didgeridoos, but the reason why remains a scientific mystery

 'Booming' dunes have invoked fear and curiosity for centuries, but scientists remain uncertain how they work. One reason is they're rare – found in around 30, usually isolated, places worldwide.

Booming dunes can sound like musical instruments because they produce a single, droning note – E, F or G – for up to 15 minutes. It's thought dunes boom if loose, smooth, similar-sized sand grains avalanche down over a harder, wetter underlying layer. The dune must be at least 45m high and at an angle of around 35 degrees to avalanche.

The layers act like a violin – the dry particles vibrate like the strings, while the harder layer magnifies the sound like the instrument's hollow body. The grain size and depth of the loose sand controls the 'note' that the dune 'plays'.

'Squeaking' sands are found on many beaches. The whistling lasts under a second and is caused by friction when sand grains rub together. ❁

Head to Head
NATURALLY OCCURRING NOISES

LOUDEST EVER

1. Volcanic eruption
The 1883 eruption of Krakatoa, Indonesia, may be the loudest sound ever recorded. It was heard in Australia and Bangkok.

VERY LOUD

2. Blue whales
Blue whales are among the noisiest animals alive with songs reaching more than 165 decibels.

SMALL BUT LOUD

3. Pistol shrimps
Their snapping claws can generate over 200 decibels of sound to stun their prey.

OLDEST

1. Bathyscaphe Trieste
Deepest dive: 10,900m
Date of dive: 23 Jan 1960
Fact: Deepest manned vehicle to explore Challenger Deep.

FIRST SAMPLES

2. Kaiko
Deepest dive: 10,898m
Date of dive: February 1996
Fact: First to collect sediment samples from Challenger Deep.

DEEPEST

3. Nereus
Deepest dive: 10,902
Date of dive: 31 May 2009
Fact: Fibre-optic tether allows Nereus to visit ice-covered oceans.

DID YOU KNOW? The depth of the Mariana Trench is about the same as the cruising altitude of a commercial aeroplane

The Mariana Trench
Exploring the deepest place on Earth

The Pacific Ring of Fire is a massive area around the edge of the Pacific Ocean where most of the world's volcanic and seismic activity occurs. Just south of Japan, at a maximum depth of 11,034m, lies the deepest point on the surface of the planet: the Challenger Deep. This depression in the seabed is located at the southern end of the Mariana Trench, the geological product of the convergence of two tectonic plates – the Pacific Plate and the Mariana Plate – and a process called subduction whereby the larger and denser of the two converging plates (that being the Pacific Plate) gets subducted under the Earth's mantle, creating a deep depression in the Earth's crust. These trenches make up the deepest parts of the world's oceans – and for this reason such areas remain practically uncharted.

Less than five per cent of the world's oceans have been explored due to the inaccessible nature of deep sea (the lowest layer in the ocean) and the massive pressure (some 16,000psi) exerted on objects at these depths. In 1960, however, intrepid oceanographers Jacques Piccard and Lt Don Walsh ventured to the bottom of the Mariana Trench in a bathyscaphe called the Trieste: the only manned submersible to reach the bottom and return in tact. Although the men could not collect photos, data, or samples from the seabed, their voyage provided a new vision of what could be achieved in deep-sea exploration.

More often these days, unmanned, remotely operated submarines and observation vessels are used for locating, mapping, collecting and photographing deep-sea geology and biology. In this pitch-black world it is extremely cold and the pressure of the seawater above makes for a very inhospitable environment for marine life let alone eager explorers. However, each new dive seems to uncover another species of aquatic life in this unique underwater ecosystem and with new developments in submersible vehicles we are drawing ever closer to uncovering more of this, the unfathomable deep. Right now, we've only scratched the surface. ✿

Sea level
Continental Shelf

Continental slope

Abyssal plain

Trench

How deep they go

475ft	Scuba divers
1,968ft	JIM diving suit
4,920ft	Giant squid
12,500ft	RMS Titanic shipwreck
18,500ft	Deep-sea sponges
27,460ft	Deepest recorded fish
35,802ft	Bathyscaphe Trieste

Forming the trench
How the Mariana Trench was created

1. Convergence
Due to the seismic activity where two oceanic plates meet, you will find an ocean trench and usually undersea volcanoes.

2. Trench
The deepest parts of the Earth's surface are created by the trench formed at the point of subduction.

3. Subduction
The larger, denser Pacific Plate is subducted under the Earth's crust beneath the Mariana Plate.

Mariana Plate

Pacific Plate

Manned mission

This is Lt Don Walsh (left) and Jacques Piccard (centre) in the pressure sphere on-board the Bathyscaphe Trieste. In 1960, these oceanographers embarked on the only successful manned expedition to the Challenger Deep.

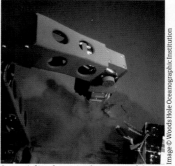

A specialised manipulator arm of the remotely operated vehicle Nereus samples sediment from the deep

Nereus – a new era of exploration

While Trieste is the only manned vessel to scour the depths of the Challenger Deep, Woods Hole Oceanographic Institution's unmanned robot Nereus is the only research submarine to do this and return with valuable findings.

Nereus is a cross between a tethered remotely operated vehicle (ROV), and a free-moving autonomous underwater vehicle (AUV). The issue of tethering was overcome with miles of fibre-optic cable, which relayed real-time video and data, and enabled the pilots on the surface to operate Nereus remotely. In AUV mode, it can hover to collect rock and deep-sea animal samples using a hydraulic arm. Meanwhile, it can also travel great distances along the ocean floor to map the terrain.

Nereus's lightweight yet durable quality is derived from the ceramic materials – instead of metals and glass – used to keep it buoyant and protect the electronics from intense pressure. This remarkable vehicle will enable explorers to venture to other inaccessible areas of the planet such as polar ice caps – a huge step in the exploration of Earth's greatest mystery.

On 31 May 2009 Nereus, which rhymes with serious, dove 10,902 metres

"Essentially, the internal structure of the Earth is made up of three core elements: the crust, the mantle and the core"

The Earth's st

We take an in-depth look at the hidden world beneath our feet

We take the world around us for granted, but the Earth that we walk upon is a complex blend of layers that together create our planet. Thanks to research in the field of seismology, we now know the makeup of the Earth, its distances and measurements and can even compare it to other planets in our solar system.

Essentially, the internal structure of the Earth is made up of three core elements: the crust, the mantle and the core. The crust is the hard outer shell that we live on, split into Oceanic and Continental crusts, and it is comparatively thin. The first layer, the Oceanic crust, is around four to seven miles thick, made up of heavy rocks, whereas the lighter Continental crust is thicker, at approximately 19 miles.

Below the crust is the mantle, and again this is divided into two distinct layers: the inner and outer mantle. The outer mantle is the thinner of the two layers, occurring between seven miles and 190 miles below the Earth's surface. The outer mantle is made up of a bottom layer of tough liquid rock, with a temperature of somewhere between 1,400 degrees Celsius and 3,000 degrees Celsius, and a thinner, cooler upper layer. The inner mantle is deep into the Earth's structure, at between 190 and 1,800 miles deep, with an average temperature of 3,000 degrees Celsius.

Finally, we reach the Earth's core, which is 1,800 to 3,200 miles beneath our feet. The outer core is around 1,370 miles thick, encasing the inner core, which falls down to 3,960 miles below the Earth's surface. The inner core reaches a temperature high of 6,000 degrees Celsius and is made up of iron, nickel and other elements. While the outer core is liquid, the inner core is solid, and the two work together to cause the Earth's magnetism. ✿

The crust
The hard, outer shell is made up of two layers: the Oceanic crust of heavy rocks like basalt and the Continental crust of lighter rocks like granite.

Convection currents
These arrows show the convection current within the mantle. The current of heat flows upwards, cooling as it nears the Earth's surface, which causes it to drop back to the core.

Inner core
The hottest part of the planet, the inner core is literally the centre of the Earth and it's solid due to its heat, meaning that it doesn't move.

The mantle
The mantle is also made of two layers: the inner and outer mantle. These are home to liquid rock and can reach temperatures of up to 3,000 degrees Celsius.

Journey to the centre of Earth
This cutaway shows the layers that make up the Earth's interior structure

© DK Images

5 TOP FACTS
EARTH'S AXIS

Day and night
1 During Earth's year-long orbit round the Sun, it also rotates once a day round its axis, an imaginary line passing through the North and South Poles, creating day and night.

The seasons
2 Earth's axis tilts at 23.5 degrees. When Earth orbits the Sun, the North Pole spends six months leaning towards the Sun and six months leaning away from it.

The tides
3 The Earth's tides are caused by the gravity of the Moon. The Earth's water on the side nearest to the Moon is pulled causing the water to bulge, this is known as a high tide.

Spring tide
4 The Sun also affects the tides, and when the Sun and Moon are aligned with the Earth, their combined gravities create the highest tide, called spring tide.

Neap tide
5 When the Sun and Moon are not lined up but are instead at right angles to each other, their gravities cancel each other out, creating the Earth's lowest neap tides.

DID YOU KNOW? 70 per cent of the Earth's surface is covered in water

ructure

Oceanic crust
As suggested by its name, this lies underneath the Earth's oceans and commonly includes basalt in its makeup.

Water
Covering 70 per cent of the Earth's surface, resting on top of the crust, is water in the form of oceans, lakes and so on.

Landmasses
The remaining 30 per cent of the Earth's surface is made up of land – seven continents.

© DK Images

Mantle
Continuing down to the outer core, this shows the mantle, which gets hotter as you get closer to the centre.

Continental crust
The exposed crust that is part of the landmasses that cover the Earth and exposed to the atmosphere, containing rocks like granite.

Upper mantle
Also known as the asthenosphere, this is the thicker, liquid part of the mantle.

The Earth's surface
The surface of the Earth is just as complex as the interior structure

Outer core
The liquid, outer core is made up of iron, nickel, sulphur and oxygen. This outer core spins as the Earth rotates.

Crust thickness
A contour map of the globe, showing the thickness of the Earth's crust, with the numbers in kilometres.

How the Earth formed
A complicated procedure brought together the many elements of the Earth and even today the planet is adapting and changing

Accretion
Accretion describes the gradual increase in size of an object through the accumulation of additional layers. In the case of Earth, this is how rocks and metals built upon each other to form the core.

Heating and cooling
The process of creating planets via accretion causes friction and collisions that create a heat, which partly explains the temperature at the Earth's core. As this cooled in the planet's formation, the crust hardened.

Oceans and atmosphere
Steam from the crust combined with gases from volcanoes to create the atmosphere and water. As the planet cooled, clouds formed, causing rain, which in turn caused the oceans.

Today's Earth
Though we rarely see the results, the Earth's surface continues to change as landmasses collide and break apart, thanks to the dynamic properties of the Earth's interior structure, which can move land by centimetres each year.

© Side bar images: DK Images

045

A super close-up image of volcanic ash

0.05mm

© NASA

Mt Cleveland, a composite volcano, erupts sending volcanic ash spiralling into the atmosphere

Volcanic ash

What is volcanic ash, where does it come from and how did it disrupt Europe's entire airspace?

Volcanic ash consists of exceptionally small bits of pulverised rock and glass, no bigger than two millimetres in diameter, created when volcanoes erupt. The formation of volcanic ash can occur in three different ways: gas release under decompression causing magmatic (magma flow) eruptions, thermal contraction caused from quick cooling occurring on contact with water (this causes phreatomagmatic eruptions), and the ejection of entrained particles during steam-based eruption, leading to phreatic eruptions (highly explosive). In any case, the violent nature of the eruptions causes many tiny particles of rock, clay and sand to be projected in an ash plume from the volcano, as solid rock and magma is separated under the dynamic and explosive activity.

Volcanic ash is spread from its initial plume – which consists of a mixture of steam and ash particles – by weather systems, with ash often (as with the case in Iceland, Britain and Europe) being carried and sometimes deposited over hundreds of miles. If the ash is distributed in great quantity over one area then a powdery dust-layer is formed, a process referred to as ashfall. Unlike the ash typically formed when combustible materials such as wood are burned, this ashfall is hard and abrasive, and does not dissolve in water. Due to this, inhaling such ash is a severe health risk to humans and animals, with side effects including a liquid-cement substance forming in the lungs.

Importantly and topically, volcanic ash also affects aircraft in a variety of ways. First, the ash has a sandblasting effect on any aircraft, with the billions of particles colliding with its fuselage and damaging its landing lights and main body. Second, ash can clog many of the aircraft's sensors, such as the pitot tubes (pressure measurement) and, because the ash's particles are charged, communication radios. Third, and potentially with the worst consequences, ash can cause combustion power failure (see 'Power loss' boxout), leaving the plane with no engine thrust and minimal chance of landing without a catastrophic crash. ✿

Ash cloud coverage
This map illustrates just how far the ash from Eyjafjallajökull was carried by the winds.

BEFORE

© ITO World Ltd

This image shows relatively normal airspace activity for Europe (data for the south of France is absent), with hundreds of flights departing and arriving over a 24-hour period.

AFTER

© ITO World Ltd

However, this image taken on 17 April – during the heart of the ash crisis – shows how few flights were in operation, with only a couple of aircraft managing to progress as usual.

Power loss
How volcanic ash shuts down jet engines

Volcanic ash is a very fine powder that consists of tiny particles of rock and glass. These particles are normally harmless to humans. However, when jet engines are involved, they can prove a real danger to the safety of any plane. When the ash is sucked into the jet engine – a constant and large supply of air is needed for the engine to operate properly – its tiny particles are compressed and heated up within the combustion chambers, causing them to melt under the immense internal temperature and form molten glass on the turbine blades, jamming them and causing the plane to lose power.

Intake

Combustion chamber

© Jeff Dahl

Head to Head
ATMOSPHERIC LAYERS

HIGH	**Mesosphere**
	**Height:** 80 km The mesosphere extends from the ozone layer to a height of 80 km. Meteors entering the atmosphere burn up in this area. <small>Image: Jared Tennant, 2009</small>

HIGHER	**Thermosphere**
	Height: 690 km The International Space Station orbits at a height of between 320 and 380 km in this layer. The Space Shuttles fly to it.

HIGHEST	**Exosphere**
	**Height:** 10,000 km In this layer of the Earth's atmosphere particles are so widely spaced, they can travel hundreds of kilometres before hitting another particle.

DID YOU KNOW? Ozone was originally discovered and named by Christian Friedrich Schönbein in 1840

The ozone layer explained

We may hear about it a lot, and mainly how we're slowly destroying it, but just what is the ozone layer?

The ozone layer is essentially Mother Earth's safety net, residing some 50 kilometres above the planet's surface. Created from O3, or ozone gas, it is up to 20 kilometres thick and 90 per cent of this gas can be found up on the Earth's stratosphere. This protective gas is vital to the nurturing of life on our planet, and here's why.

Ozone gases act as a shield against ultraviolet, or UVB, radiation. These harmful emissions are sent through the Sun's rays, and without the ozone would severely affect the planet's ecological balance, damaging biodiversity. UVB rays reduce plankton levels in the ocean, subsequently diminishing fish stock. Plant growth would also diminish in turn disrupting agricultural productivity. This would in turn affect the human populace, who would be exposed to an increase in skin-related diseases, such as cancer.

So how does the ozone protect us? Ozone molecules consist of three oxygen atoms, hence the chemical formula O3. Stratospheric ozone absorbs UVB high-energy radiation, as well as energetic electrons, which in turn splits the O3 into an O atom and an O2 molecule. When the O atom soon encounters another O2 molecule they re-merge and recreate O3. This means that the ozone layer absorbs the UVB without being consumed. The ozone layer absorbs up to 99 per cent of the Sun's high frequency UV light rays, transforming this into heat after its combustible atomic reaction, therefore creating the stratosphere itself. This effectively incubates life on Earth.

But ozone doesn't reside only in the world above. This gas is also present in the layer around the Earth's surface. 10 to 18km above us, this is known as the tropospheric ozone or 'bad ozone', comparative to the function of the stratosphere. This ozone occurs naturally in small doses, initiating the removal of hydrocarbons, released by plants and soil, or appearing from small amounts of stratospheric ozone, which occasionally migrate down to the Earth's surface.

However, it gets a bad reputation due to its interaction of ultraviolet light, with volatile organic compounds and nitrogen oxides, emitted by fossil-fuel powered machines and internal combustion engines. This produces high levels of ozone, which are formed in high temperature conditions, ultimately toxic to all forms of organic life. ✿

A whole lot of hole
The area of depletion over the Antarctic, known as the ozone hole, is estimated at between 21 and 24 million square kilometres – enough to fit England in 161 times over!

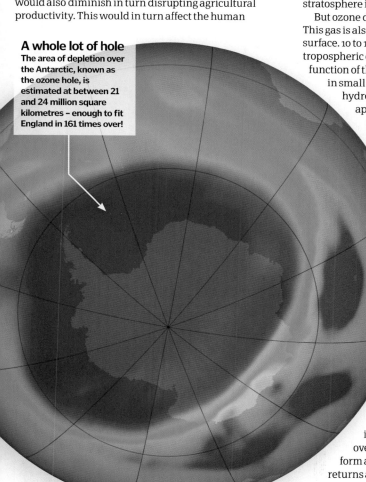

How big is the hole in the ozone layer?

The ozone hole refers to an area of depletion over the Antarctic region of Earth. The planet's ozone records a decline of four per cent per decade in total volume but much larger losses are recorded in the stratospheric ozone over Earth's polar region, but this is seasonal condition. These areas' unique atmospheric conditions see the most impact. Strong winds blow around the continent forming a polar vortex, isolating the air over Antarctica from the rest of the world. This allows special polar stratospheric clouds to form at about 24,300 metres altitude. These concentrate atmosphere pollutant. When spring returns after the sunless winter period the ozone is depleted causing the ozone hole. The largest ever recorded ozone hole occurred in 2006, at 53.3 million square kilometres. At present the ozone hole is recorded at between 21 and 24 million square kilometres.

The structure of the Earth's atmosphere
Here's how the ozone extends from the Earth's surface

Tropospheric ozone
Starts at ground level, with an altitude of up to 15 kilometres. Energy transfer from the surface heats it.

The lowest part of this is the warmest with temperature decreasing with altitude. This heat and CFC intervention produces turbulent diffusion, producing great levels of ozone, harmful to organic life.

Altitude (km): 5 10 15 20

Typical cloud altitude

Stratospheric ozone
Between ten and 50 kilometres up from the stratopause. It contains up to 90 per cent of Earth's ozone.

The stratosphere contains the highest level of ozone on the planet, with two to eight parts per million. This reacts with UVB to produce what we know as the ozone layer.

The stratosphere is layered in temperature due to UVB absorption. Heat increases with altitude, with the top of the stratosphere has a temperature up to -3°C.

"The cheetah is fast but that speed comes at a great price"

Pronghorn antelope
57mph

World's fastest animals

The arms race of hunter and hunted is a ferocious battleground, with different species furiously evolving to remain, literally, one step ahead of the competition. How It Works pits these speed demons against each other in the ultimate animal shootout

Cheetah

Accelerating to speeds of 70mph, the cheetah is the quickest on four legs!

Cheetahs are one of the fastest animals on Earth and have a terrifyingly quick 0-60 time of a mere three seconds. Cheetahs are unique in the fact they have evolved to such a degree in order to maximise their speed, that they regularly risk brain damage and starvation due to the great physical demands it places on their anatomy. The cheetah is fast, the fastest land animal on Earth, but that speed comes at a great price.

For example, lungs, nostrils and heart are all enlarged within the cheetah to ensure it can process enough oxygen and blood to maintain its explosive speed. However, it can only process this for short periods of time and at the close of a lengthy chase not only does it skirt dangerously close to oxygen deprivation but it must rest post-kill before it eats, leaving plenty of time for scavengers to surround it. In addition, while its muscle fibre is honed and holds superb elasticity, its physique is slender and lightweight, leaving it vulnerable to broken limbs and completely defenceless against a larger and heavier rival such as a lion or tiger. As a result of these facts – as well as through human-caused habitat loss and predation – cheetah numbers are dwindling and it is currently an endangered species in many African countries.

Black mamba
12mph

Tail
The cheetah's long tail acts as a counterweight, maintaining balance during sharp turns at high speed.

Lungs
Engorged lungs – and nostrils for that matter – allow for a fast and deep air intake. Maintaining a high level of oxygen is critical when the cheetah is on a chase as its breath-rate increases three-fold.

Paws
The paws are blunt and sport exposed claws that provide superior grip, increasing the forward thrust of each stride.

Heart
The heart is enlarged compared to other animals of its size, pumping a colossal amount of blood around the cheetah's body, especially during a chase.

Build
The average weight of a cheetah is 57kg (125lb) and its build is slender. It has a small head, flattened rib cage and long, thin legs that all minimise air resistance.

The Statistics

Cheetah

Family: Felidae
Genus: Acinonyx
Weight: 36-65kg
Height: 67-94cm
Length: 200-220cm
0-60mph: 3 seconds
Top speed: 70mph

Lightweight

1 The average weight of a cheetah is 125 pounds. This is actually a fraction of the weight of other big cats, with an average lion weighing more than 400 pounds.

Threat

2 All over Africa, Asia and India cheetah populations are in sharp decline. In 1990 there was roughly 100,000 individuals worldwide, now there are roughly 10,000.

Sexist

3 Baby cheetahs are brought up solely by the female parent, who raises them in isolation from any male. It takes roughly 18 months for a cheetah cub to reach maturity.

Hakuna matata

4 Cheetah's have a broad diet, ranging from antelope to springhare and game birds. However, one of their most common food supplies is the slow and fat warthog.

Habitat

5 Cheetahs tend to favour vast expanses of land where prey is abundant and easy to spot. However, cheetahs can be found in a variety of habitats including grasslands.

DID YOU KNOW? *Marine biologists postulate that the sailfish's large dorsal fin is used for cooling purposes as well as stability*

0-40 mph in three strides

Check out the three stages a cheetah undertakes to reach 40mph in just three strides

© DK Images

1. Brace
The cheetah employs its hard, ridged footpads and blunt, non-retractable claws to maximise traction with the ground. Its spine curves, coil-like, and head drops a fraction.

2. Snap
The spine uncoils and snaps straight, driving the hind legs into the earth and pushing the cheetah forward. The honed, slender muscles expand in conjunction, adding greater elasticity and drive to the forward thrust.

3. Kick
The combined spine and leg muscles give the cheetah an incredibly broad swing range and propel it 7.6 metres (25 feet) through the air in a colossal bound. At the culmination of the bound one foot is replanted onto the earth and the process is repeated. The cheetah completes three strides a second.

Cheetah anatomy

Just what makes it the fastest thing on four legs?

Eyes
The cheetah's eyes are long to provide a wide-angle view of its surroundings. This provides them with excellent vision when stalking and chasing prey in the native habitat of open plains.

Spine
The spine is incredibly flexible and has evolved so it curves with each stride, acting akin to a spring for the cheetah's hind legs.

© James Temple

The sailfish can rapidly turn its body light blue with stripes when excited, confusing its prey and making capture easier

Long nose
The sailfish's elongated bill is similar to a swordfish's and marlin's, placing it in the category of billfish.

Sailfish

Capable of swimming for long periods of time at over 40mph, and with a recorded top speed of over 70mph, the sailfish is the ocean's fastest animal

With a top speed on par with that of a cheetah, the sailfish is lightning fast and one of the most difficult-to-catch fish in the world. With its stiffened, tapered body and scissor-shaped caudal fin, the sailfish is built for speed – a speed that comes courtesy of a rapid and ferocious flicking of its tail. Indeed, during a chase to consume fish, crustaceans or cephalopods, the sailfish will flick its tail back and forth hundreds of times, utilising the powerful muscles which run down its compressed body.

As with the peregrine falcon, the sailfish's speed is also aided by its ability to retract parts of its body, in this instance its various fins (notably the large dorsal fin that adds over a foot on to its overall height). This feature helps it reduce the effects of drag and minimise resistance to its movements.

Its spine is also very flexible and as with the cheetah allows it to generate increased thrust through the rapid curves it bends its torso into while swimming.

The Statistics
Sailfish

Family: Istiophoridae
Genus: Istiophorus
Weight: 90kg
Height: 70cm
Length: 1.2-1.5m
0-60mph: Not recorded
Top speed: 70mph

Streamlined
Sailfish have an incredibly sleek, streamlined body.

© anon 09

"The peregrine does not suffer damage from oxygen deprivation at the close of its stoop"

Tiger beetle 5.6mph

Swift 106 mph

The fastest animals on Earth are...

Here's a the list of the most super-fast critters on the planet

FASTEST FISH

Sailfish	68mph (110kph)
Marlin	50mph (80kph)
Wahoo	48mph (78kph)
Tunny	46mph (74kph)
Bluefish tuna	44mph (70kph)

FASTEST LAND INSECTS

Tiger beetle	5.6mph (8.4kph)
Cockroach	3.4mph (5.4kph)

FASTEST BIRDS

Peregrine falcon	200mph (322kph)
Spine-tailed swift	106mph (171kph)
Frigatebird	95mph (153kph)
Spur-winged goose	88mph (142kph)
Red-breasted merganser	80mph (129kph)

FASTEST MAMMALS

Cheetah	71mph (114kph)
Pronghorn antelope	57mph (95kph)
Springbok	50mph (80kph)
Blue wildebeest	50mph (80kph)
Lion	45mph (72kph)

FASTEST REPTILES

Spiny-tailed iguana	21mph (34kph)
Black mamba	12mph (20kph)

Sources: American Journal of Zoology, University of Michigan, Seattle Zoo, American Journal of Physiology, National Geographic, US Fish and Wildlife Service, Forest Preserve of Illinois

© Keven Low 08

Peregrine falcon

When in free fall, the peregrine falcon is just epically quick

1. Sight
Prey is spotted while soaring and then the peregrine begins to draw its wings into its body. It also retracts its tail and tucks its feet into its body.

2. Streamline
The wings are brought right into the falcon's sternum and – thanks to their pointed, slim, stiff and unslotted feathers – begins to rapidly reduce its air resistance.

3. Velocity
Speed is increased as the falcon bombs down with little-to-zero drag, soon reaching speeds up to 200mph. Its strong keel helps maintain structural solidity during the dive and its eyes are kept clear by nictitating membranes, which act like a third eyelid.

Diving to victory

Check out the four stages a peregrine falcon undertakes to reach 200mph when diving in for a kill

If you thought the cheetah was fast, then think again. The peregrine falcon blows its top speed out of the water by over 130mph. Capable of hitting a monumental 200mph during a stoop (dive), the falcon has the highest top speed of any animal on Earth.

The peregrine's speed is caused by a combination of factors. Firstly it makes use of gravity, diving upon its prey from great height, even when they themselves are airborne. Secondly, its anatomy – as with the cheetah's – has been finely honed to maximise speed, evolving over millions of years into the swift and efficient killer it is today. For example, the peregrine's keel – which is located at its breastbone – is significantly larger than average birds', allowing for bigger muscles and a greater number to attach its wings to its body. This allows it to

generate far more power per thrust when building speed. Further, the peregrine's wings have evolved to be incredibly pointed, with slim, stiff and unslotted feathers, which helps streamlining and reducing air resistance significantly.

Unlike the cheetah, however, arguably the peregrine handles its awesome speed much better. Firstly, while having the same enlarged heart and lungs, the peregrine does

Usain Bolt **28mph** 100m in 9.58 seconds

Sailfish **68mph** Finishing time in 3.28 seconds

Cheetah **71mph** Finishing time in 3.15 seconds

Peregrine falcon **200mph** Finishing time in 1.12 seconds

Tiger beetle **720mph** Finishing time in 0.31 seconds

SLOW

1. Galapagos giant tortoise
With a top speed of 0.19mph the Galapagos tortoise is very slow. Luckily, it is protected by a shell to put off predators.

SLOWER

2. Two-toed sloth
With a top speed of just two metres per minute, they are nick-named "bicho-preguiça" in Brazil, which translates as "lazy animal".

SLOWEST

3. Snail
So slow that it was adopted by the Judeo-Christian religion as the physical manifestation of the deadly sin of sloth, the snail takes days to travel mere metres.

DID YOU KNOW? Usain Bolt currently holds the world 100 and 200-metre records

The Statistics
Peregrine falcon
Family: Falconidae
Genus: Falco
Weight: 910-1,500 grams
Height: 60cm
Length: 34-58cm
0-60mph: Not recorded
Top speed: 200mph

4. Contact
Prey is both struck and captured in mid-air. The peregrine strikes its prey with a clenched foot, which due to the immense speed either stuns or kills it, before then swooping round to catch it with its large claws. Prey is always consumed on the ground.

© DK Images

not suffer damage from oxygen deprivation at the close of its stoop. This is partly due to gravity's beneficial aid in generating its killer speed but also due to the peregrine's ability to absorb oxygen through its red muscle fibres, of which it has many. This allows it to keep a steady oxygen flow at all times and means that, consequentially, it does not need to rest post-kill, reducing its vulnerability to scavengers.

How muscles work – the contraction cycle
Muscle power is common to all these creatures so here's an explanation of how muscles provide the power that in turn provide the speed

Myosin head   Actin filament

1. Attachment
Firstly a myosin head (akin to an organic hook) attaches itself to an exposed binding site on the muscle filaments, gripping it in a cross bridge.

Actin filament is pulled

2. Power stroke
The myosin head then pulls the filament by pivoting backwards and dragging it into a compressed position.

Cross bridge detaches

3. Detachment
A molecule of ATP (adenosine triphosphate) then binds to the myosin, releasing its grip of the filament so that the cross bridge detaches.

Energised myosin head

4. Energy release
Finally, the ATP releases energy to convert the myosin head from its bent, low-energy position back to its initial high-energy configuration ready for the next cycle.

Physique
Tall height, balanced weight and powerful muscles.

Metabolism
Converting 'fuels' like glucose into power, producing adenosine triphosphate.

The Statistics
Usain Bolt
Family: Hominidae
Genus: Homo
Weight: 93.9kg
Height: 1.95m
Length: 30cm
0-60mph: Not recorded
Top speed: 28mph

Usain Bolt
The fastest human alive, Usain Bolt recently broke the world 100-metre record with a staggeringly quick time of 9.58 seconds

One of the most successful species of animal on the planet, Homo sapiens have evolved over the last 120,000 years into creatures with formidable physical abilities. Currently, the fastest human is Usain Bolt, a Jamaican-born sprinter who has won the world 100 and 200-metre gold medals.

Bolt epitomises the ideal human anatomy needed to produce such high speeds: a tall height (1.95m), balanced weight (93.9kg) and long, powerful muscles with an excellent metabolism – muscles cannot utilise energy-rich "fuels" such as glucose, instead they must convert it into ATP (adenosine triphosphate) with the amount of ATP a muscle produces directly correlating to the amount of power it can generate.

How It Works 100m final
So who would win in a 100-metre race?

NB: For the purposes of this illustration the peregrine falcon's speed is taken from a stoop and all animals begin the race at their top speed.

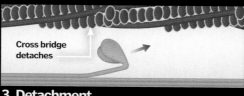

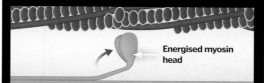

This is the speed a tiger beetle could get to if it were the same size as an average six-foot man!

TECHNOLOGY
Modern gadgetry and engineering explained

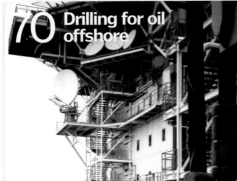

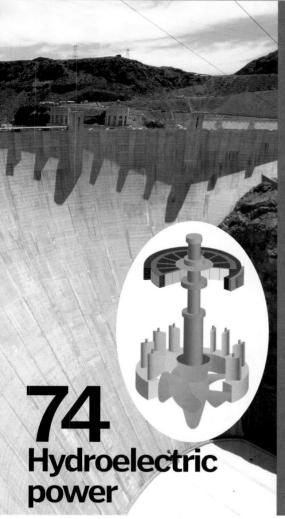

"Up close the world's tallest bridge is no less stunning"

Megastruct

Bigger, taller, longer, heavier. We explain the record-breaking engineering behind the world's biggest man-made structures

2. Making ends meet
Using hydraulic conveyors, the steel deck was glided into place from opposite directions, eventually meeting over the River Tarn.

1. World's tallest
Pier Two (P2) is the tallest support pier in the world at 244.96 metres.

Since the reign of the pharaohs, the lure of the very large has proven irresistible to visionary architects and game-changing engineers. Ancient Egypt had its pyramids, the Chinese dynasties had their Great Wall and modern Dubai has its… well, pretty much everything. At the heart of every megastructure is a dare: how far can you go? And every few years or so some ambitious billionaire ups the ante, going higher, longer, deeper and more wildly expensive.

The 828-metre Burj Khalifa tower (for more information turn to page 69) makes your palms sweat just looking at pictures from the observation deck. Not to be outdone, Dubai's Palm Islands are visible from space with the naked eye. None of these mind-blowing projects would be possible without quantum leaps in structural engineering, materials science, construction technology and logistics. On these pages, we'll explain the extreme engineering behind extraordinary structures. ✿

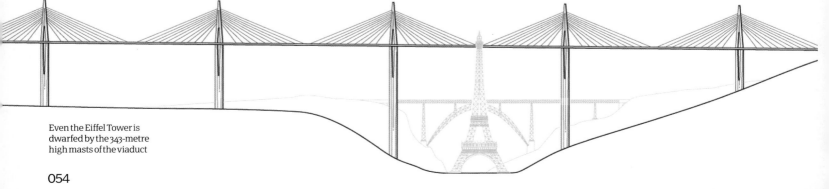

Even the Eiffel Tower is dwarfed by the 343-metre high masts of the viaduct

LONGEST SUSPENSION

1. Akashi Kaikyo Bridge
At 3,900 metres long, this masterwork of Japanese engineering can survive an earthquake up to 8.5 on the Richter scale.

BIGGEST ARCH

2. Dubai's Mile-Long Bridge
Leave it to boomtown Dubai to dream up a fantastically futuristic proposal for a mile-long double arch bridge spanning 12 lanes of traffic.

BRIDGE OF THE FUTURE

3. Bering Strait Bridge
The proposed 88-km long bridge linking North America and Asia would carry vehicle traffic, a high-speed train and pipelines for natural gas and oil.

DID YOU KNOW? The Millau Viaduct was officially opened on 14 December 2004

ures

3. Bendy bridge
Far from a straight shot, the viaduct is slightly curved and rises at a three per cent incline.

The Statistics
Millau Viaduct
Opened: 14 December 2004
Designed by: Michel Virlogeux and Norman Foster
Length: 2,460 metres
Width: 32 metres
Mast height: 343 metres

© Stephane Compoint / Foster & Partners

3. The missing link
The viaduct completes an important span of the A75 autoroute, serving 4,670,449 vehicles in 2008.

2. Tightly wound
154 stays, 11 pairs per mast, were strung and pulled to precision tautness to support the 36,000-ton weight of the steel deck.

1. No 'nosedive'
These two masts were raised first to support the overhanging noses of the decks as they slid into place.

The Millau Viaduct

Majestic and minimalist, the world's longest bridge is also one of the most beautiful

From a distance, the seven steel masts of the record-breaking Millau Viaduct in southern France look like billowing sails of a cosmic spacecraft. Up close, the tallest bridge in the world is no less stunning, a minimalist masterpiece that resembles an Apple iPad in bridge form.

The Millau Viaduct is a cable-stayed road bridge of concrete and steel with load-bearing masts stretching 343 metres into the air. Seventeen years in the making – at a cost of 400 million euros – the 2,460-metre span employed the very latest construction techniques and technologies during each of its six stages of fabrication and assembly.

First came the "legs" of the bridge, seven thick piers composed of 206,000 tons of poured concrete. The smooth, seamless surface of each pier was achieved using a machine called a self-climbing framework. Powered by hydraulic lifters, the concrete framework rises upward with the pier at a rate of three meters every three days. Pouring continuously, the piers rose from the valley floor, reaching their peak heights in ten months.

Next came the deck, built from 173 steel box beams forged in the Eiffel factory. Using two on-site metalworks, the steel floor was welded to the box beams to create 171-metre deck panels. The panels were then "launched" from both sides of the bridge using 64 hydraulic conveyors positioned atop the piers and temporary steel crutches. The two sides of the deck literally slid toward each other at a rate of 60cm per push, equal to nine metres an hour. The two sides finally met on 28 May 2004 at 2:12pm.

The seven steel masts support 1,500 tons of steel stays attached at 11 paired points. Each stay consists of up to 91 bound steel cables and each cable made from seven individual strands of steel. The stays are triply weatherproofed to avoid corrosion.

Before paving the road, workers used high-pressure blasters to scour the steel deck with millimetre-size ball bearings. Once all traces of rust were removed, special equipment laid a four-centimetre thick layer of tar thermosealed at 400°C, offering complete corrosion protection.

The bridge construction is guaranteed for 120 years and is continuously monitored for movements as small as a micrometre by dozens of fibre-optic sensors strung throughout the structure.

"A starter home begins at £1.3 million"

The Statistics
Palm Jumeirah

Nickname: The Eighth Wonder of the World
Opened/opening: Palm Jumeirah, the smallest island, was completed in 2006
Built by: Nakheel
Length: 5km
Width: 5km
Composition: 94 million m³ of reclaimed sand; 7 million tons of quarried rock
Cost: £8.14 billion ($12.3 billion)

Extreme islands

Dubai re-creates 'The World' from an ocean of sand

Sheikh Mohammed bin Rashid Al Maktoum has only one requirement for construction projects in his desert nation of Dubai: if it doesn't break a world record for tallest, biggest or most expensive, he's not interested. It shouldn't surprise, therefore, that the original design of the Palm islands – three man-made islands of colossal proportions off the coast of Dubai – came from the Sheikh's own pen.

But how do you build the world's largest man-made islands? Luckily, Dubai has almost as much sand as it does oil money. The state-run developer Nakheel hired the Dutch dredging firm Van Oord, specialists in "land reclamation", to suction up millions of cubic metres of sand from the sea floor and precision spray it into the shape of a huge date tree with 16 slender fronds extending into the sea. Van Oord's dredging equipment is guided by DGPS (differential global positioning system), NASA's new real-time positioning technology that's accurate down to ten centimetres.

The first stage of each of Dubai's artificial island projects – the three Palm islands, plus a 300-island cluster in the shape of the continents called "The World" – is to install an artificial barrier reef as a water break. The artificial wall for The World, composed of 34 million tons of carefully stacked rocks, is 27km long. The dredging team then builds each island or peninsula in stages, using heavier machinery for the island foundations and "rainbowing" sand sprayers to finish the above-water detail work.

To prevent erosion, the base of the islands is reinforced with a layer of geotextile fabric that absorbs the impact of waves. The huge piles of loose sand are also treated to vibrocompaction, a process that uses water saturation and high-intensity vibrations to "densify" the soil structure.

When complete, the Palm islands and The World will upgrade Dubai's beachfront property from a 60-km stretch of condo-clogged real estate to 965 kilometres of pristine sand. In case you're wondering, a starter home on the smallest island starts at £1.3 million ($1.9 million).

2. Life's a beach
The "rainbowing" sand sprayers on the dredging equipment are designed to create beachfront with a precise and consistent slope.

1. Meticulous
Each stone in the 11km breakwater was inspected by a diver and tagged with its own GPS co-ordinates.

3. Fresh water
Canals dug in the breakwater ensure that the water within the artificial bay circulates completely every 13 days.

Left to right: Palm Jebel Ali, Palm Jumeirah, The World and the early stages of Palm Deira, the largest of the artificial islands

Laerdal Tunnel

An ambitious dig gives drivers an unprecedented journey through the centre of the Earth

A decade ago, the drive from Oslo to Bergen, Norway required travellers to ferry multiple fjords and summit 1,600-metre peaks subject to rockslides and piles of snow. In 2000, King Harald V cut the ribbon on the Laerdal Tunnel, a 24.5km (15.2-mile) passage beneath the mountain ranges and waterways that had made travel between the two coastal cities so daunting and slow. Laerdal is by far the longest road tunnel in the world, beating the previous record-holder by seven kilometres.

Over five years, workers excavated 2.5 million cubic metres of rock. The tools of the trade were explosives and satellite-guided drilling jumbos.

The blasting crew executed over 5,000 precision explosions each requiring 100 individually drilled holes, 5.2 metres deep, filled with an explosive called Anolit. Drilling rigs were guided by satellite positioning and on-board laser beams. Without this technology, it would've been impossible for the two excavation teams to meet each other over 10km inside the heart of the mountains.

To break up the monotony of the 20-minute subterranean drive, engineers divided the tunnel into four distinct sections separated by three wide, blue-lit caverns that give the sensation of an artificial sunrise.

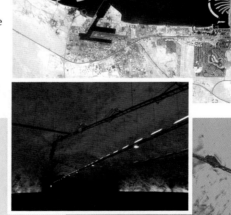

The nine-metre tunnel widens considerably in the cavernous relief areas, providing room for vehicles to turn around. The tunnel is equipped with 48 additional emergency pull-offs

A blue-lit "relief area" breaks up the mind-numbing monotony and creeping claustrophobia of a 20-minute drive through solid rock

5 TOP FACTS
GIANT STRUCTURES

Great Wall of China
1 The original megastructure, the Great Wall of China stretches an incredible 8,851km, making it easily the longest man-made structure on Earth.

Three Gorges Dam
2 The 2km dam spanning the Yangtze submerged 13 existing cities, 140 towns and over 1,300 villages, requiring the relocation of 1.5 million people.

Fresh Kills Landfill
3 This retired garbage dump covering 12 square kilometres of New York's Staten Island was once piled higher than the nearby Statue of Liberty. What a load of rubbish.

Banaue Rice Terraces
4 Built largely by hand over 2,000 years ago, these terraced rice paddies cover 10,360 square kilometres of steep mountainside in the Philippines.

Mirny Diamond Mine
5 This colossal open-pit mine located in Eastern Siberia, Russia is 525 metres deep and 1.25km wide. In the Sixties it produced two tons of diamonds per year.

DID YOU KNOW? *Taipei 101 cost approximately $1.8 billion to build*

Taipei 101

The world's second-tallest skyscraper has a 660-ton pendulum for a heart

Building a skyscraper in Taipei is like playing Jenga on a trampoline. The Taiwanese capital, located along the famed Ring of Fire, sits atop an "active" seismological zone with a very long history of deadly earthquakes. As recently as 1999, a 7.3 trembler killed over 2,400 people. As if the earthquakes aren't enough, Taipei is also directly in the path of 26 annual tropical storms and typhoons, the Pacific equivalent of hurricanes.

Why would anyone attempt to build the world's tallest building on such shaky (and blustery) ground? You obviously don't know many engineers. The challenge of building a 508-metre megastructure in such an inhospitable location calls for elegant and ingenious solutions, two words that accurately describe Taipei 101, the 101-storey superscraper that was – until the completion of the Burj Khalifa in Dubai – the tallest man-made structure in the world.

Taipei 101 was designed to resemble a bamboo shoot, rising upwards in eight sections (a lucky number in Chinese) with walls angled outward at seven degrees. Like a slender stalk of bamboo, the record-breaking tower was designed to be both strong and flexible – bendable but unbreakable.

Taipei 101's strength begins in its "roots", 380 concrete piles driven 80 metres through the island's thick clay sediment to reach solid bedrock. The building is widest at its foundation, narrowing at a five-degree angle for 25 floors before arriving at the first of the eight identical sloped sections. The tower's core stability comes from eight forged steel "megacolumns", each measuring three by 2.4 metres and filled with concrete. The megacolumns are trussed to the building's outward-sloping frame with ductile steel braces that bend in an earthquake.

At 700,000 tons of steel, concrete and glass, Taipei 101 is actually "light" for its height. To steady the tower in gale-force winds, it's equipped with an internal pendulum called a "passive tuned mass damper", whose massive weight – 660 tons – pulls instinctively in the opposite direction of swaying (see 'The Damper' boxout). The result is not only one of the tallest, but perhaps the most stable building in the world, designed to withstand a 2,500-year seismic shock.

Layers upon layers
The 660-ton ball was assembled on site using 44 layers of steel plate, each 12.5 centimetres thick.

The Damper

A massive pendulum fights the effects of skyscraper "seasickness"

Suspended from the centre of the 92nd floor of the world's second tallest building is a 660-ton, £543,000 ($800,000) steel ball hanging from four sets of steel cables. The function of the "tuned mass damper" isn't to keep Taipei 101 upright (its concrete-filled steel backbone is more than sufficient to do this), but to cancel out nausea-inducing swaying in a powerful storm.

If wind pushes the tower to the right, the dangling damper will provide an immediate and equal force to the left, cancelling out the motion. Like a shock absorber in a car, the damper is attached to a series of hydraulic pistons that convert dynamic energy – the swaying of the ball – into heat. Not only is the Taipei 101's damper the largest of its kind, but it's the only one in the world to be incorporated into the aesthetic design of the structure, easily visible from observation decks and restaurants.

Wide load
Taipei's damper is the largest in the world with a diameter of 5.5 metres and weighing as much as 10,000 people.

Cables
The damper hangs from four steel support lines, each composed of four individual steel cables.

Hydraulics
If the damper swings dramatically during an earthquake, 2m hydraulic pistons absorb and dissipate the energy as heat.

The Statistics
Taipei 101

Opened: 2004
Architect: CY Lee & Partners
Height: 508 metres; 101 stories above ground
Weight: 700,000 tons
Total floor area: 374,336m²

Go-faster swimwear

How mimicking sharkskin can give Olympic swimmers the edge

For Olympic competitors, the slightest millisecond can mean the difference between winning and losing. So if there's any legal way to enhance their performance, an athlete is going to do it.

Speedo's Fastskin technology applies some of Mother Nature's niftiest principles to cutting-edge swimwear design. Real sharkskin is covered with what are known as dermal denticles, which are tiny, grooved tooth-like projections. Using computer simulation technology called computational fluid dynamics (CFD), these ridged denticles have been proved to reduce the amount of water that comes into contact with the skin, therefore reducing the drag factor on the shark. And this is the principle behind the fabric used in Fastskin.

The Fastskin suits are also intentionally tight-fitting in order to minimise the amount of water that gets between the swimsuit and the wearer, further improving the hydrodynamics. Each seam and panel on the suit has been carefully positioned to maximise the flow of water across the body, reducing drag and promoting speed through the water. ✿

This magnified section of sharkskin reveals that the dermal denticle projections form tiny grooves, which have been proved to reduce drag in wind tunnel tests

---

The term used to describe the reduction in intensity of the light waves is attenuation

Fibre-optic internet

The next generation of communication will speed up download times using state-of-the-art fibre-optic technology

In today's culture of internet television and streaming media there's a fast-growing demand for extremely high transmission speeds to allow for such data-intensive services. Although traditional copper wire has served internet users well until now, it may just have run its course. A more reliable and efficient system of fibre-optic internet is now providing ultra-fast connection speeds while also solving the problem of increased internet traffic.

The main drawback with using copper wire is that the speed of data transmission is rapidly reduced as the length of the wire increases (this is called attenuation), meaning connection speeds can vary depending on how far away from a telephone exchange the user is located. Fibre optic cables, meanwhile, have no such restrictions. The optical fibre transmits information by a process called total internal reflection. Each fibre is made up of a transparent inner core, along which the signals are transmitted, and a casing of reflective material that bounces the signals back into the core whenever they hit the wall of the outer casing. The optical signal is neither distorted nor dramatically weakened as it travels along the fibre because the reflective casing absorbs none of the light from the core – this means the light wave can travel great distances without losing much speed or clarity. ✿

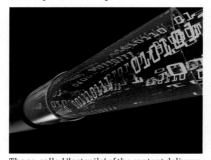

The so-called 'last mile' of the content delivery from the provider to the consumer will likely still be copper wire, rather than fibre optic cable, negating some of its advantages.

DID YOU KNOW? An optical fibre can carry 2.4 million phone calls simultaneously, while a single copper wire can carry just six phone calls.

How does your DSLR camera work?

Many camera owners are content to shout "cheese" and push the shutter button to get an image, but we go under the hood to find out exactly how it happens

Main dial
All the shooting modes are positioned on this dial including; Auto (A), Program (P), Aperture priority (AP), Shutter priority (S/Tv) and Manual (M). Some short-cut scene modes such as portrait, landscape and macro are also available here.

Built-in flash
Most DSLRs will accommodate a 'built-in' or 'pop up' flash tucked into the top ledge. In some shooting modes the flash will pop up automatically and in other scenarios photographers can activate the flash themselves. Behind this sits the flash hot shoe where external flash units can be slid into position.

Top dial
This dial allows users to alter values such as the f/stop (aperture) and shutter speed when in the appropriate modes (AP or S) or when shooting in manual.

Flash button
Depending on the shooting mode or creative purpose users may need to activate the flash manually, in which case this button should be pressed.

Lens mount
When the markers are aligned correctly, photographers can slot a lens on to the mount and twist it into a locked position.

Shutter button
Depressing this button half way will focus the lens on the scene in front of the lens when set to Auto Focus. Pressing this button completely will take the shot.

Focus Assist beam
When shooting in low light levels a light will emit from this area, illuminating the subject to help the autofocus find its focus point. In many cameras this also doubles up as the self timer indicator, where it will flash during the countdown.

Mirror system and image sensor
The mirror flips up out of the way when the shutter is released to reveal the image sensor behind it, this then electronically captures and records the picture.

Lens
The larger ring on the lens body operates the lens's focal length and the front, the smaller ring controls the focus when in manual.

Lens switches
On the side of the lens there is a switch marked AF and MF – these refer to auto and manual focus. Some lenses will also include a stabilisation switch, which can be activated or deactivated. It is recommended to have this on when shooting handheld and off when resting on a tripod.

The dawn of the digital format has revolutionised the imaging industry and in turn the way we work our cameras. Furthermore the internal DNA of the camera body has been entirely restructured to make way for the new electrical system; or has it?

In fact film and digital cameras operate in a similar manner. Varying the size of the lens's diaphragm (aperture) in tandem with the amount of time the shutter is open, focusing light on to the image detection material, the only difference being that this is now received in an electrical rather than chemical form.

A DSLR (digital single-lens reflex) camera employs a mechanical mirror system that directs the light travelling through the attached lens upwards at a 90 degree angle allowing the photographer to compose the shot through the viewfinder. As the shutter button is pressed the exposure takes place: the mirror swings out of the way and the shutter opens allowing the lens to project the light on to the image sensor. In low light scenarios the shutter will need to stay open for a longer period of time for the image to be recorded, this is why photographers support their cameras with tripods as the smallest degree of camera shake will disturb the quality.

The sensor is formed of millions of pixels laid out in thousands of rows and columns: the more pixels or dots of light, the higher the megapixel count and in theory the higher the resolution. The light travels through a colour filter above the individual sensors and is converted from light waves into an analogue signal which is then processed through a digital convertor. Next the conversion is fine tuned through a series of filters that adjust aspects such as white balance and colour. The resulting image can be made into a JPEG by compressing the file size and discarding unnecessary pixels. The final image is shown on the LCD. ✿

> "With Spotify, you don't need to download music to listen to it. Instead, you can stream it over the internet"

How Spotify works
A quick guide to the ins and outs of Spotify

1. Log in & share
As user one logs on, the contents of their Spotify cache are indexed and sent to the Spotify streaming hub when they connect to the service. Music files are stored to their cache as they play them.

User 1

2. Search for music
User two performs a search for a song or artist. This request is then processed by the hub against the index that it compiles from all users.

User 2

3. Process the request
The Spotify hub responds to a search by first requesting the first piece of the song file from the Spotify servers. Meanwhile, it searches the peer-to-peer network for the remainder. It then switches back and forth between Spotify servers and peers as needed.

Music streaming in is stored in cache
Index info and music files going out

Music files streaming in
Sending search request

4. Share & share alike
The hub then streams the requested song from either the servers or via peer to peer from other users, back to user two's computer where he can listen to it.

Spotify™
Stream hub

6. Pay the premium
As a paying premium subscriber, user four can do all this at faster connection speeds and without the adverts between songs.

5. Listen & share
As user three launches the Spotify app, their computer also starts listening for incoming connections from other Spotify users, as well as intuitively connecting to other users to exchange songs as appropriate.

Outgoing music, requests and index info
Incoming connections

Outgoing data
Faster 320kb connection

JARGON EXPLAINED

Hub
A hub is a common connection point for devices in a network. It can receive information from a connected computer and forward it to another on the network.

Peer-to-peer
A method of sharing files and information directly between two computers without the need to access a central server.

Streaming
Playing audio or video immediately as it is downloaded from the internet, rather than storing it in a file on the receiving computer first.

User 3

User 4

NEWEST

1. Spotify
The pairing of a minimal UI and instant musical gratification, thanks to audio being streamed instead of downloaded, makes Spotify a real contender for the crown.

BIGGEST

2. iTunes
With no monthly subscription, the best UI on the net, fantastic pairing with iPhones and iPods, as well as the ability to buy single tracks, iTunes is rightly the market leader.

MOST CUSTOMISABLE

the social music revolution

3. Last.fm
Last.fm is a popular internet radio and music service which uses a music recommender system call 'Audioscrobbler' to custom build a profile for each of its users.

DID YOU KNOW? Spotify has been active in various European countries since October 2008

What is Spotify?

Seen by many to be the next stage in the evolution of music distribution and reproduction, Spotify is bringing music to the world of cloud computing

Spotify is a new application that is available for PC and Mac – along with some modern smartphones – which allows you to stream music from a vast catalogue distributed through the Spotify central hub and sourced from every other Spotify user.

To use Spotify you would first need to download the Spotify software from www.spotify.com, currently you can only do this if you have an invite from an existing Spotify user. Once installed, Spotify looks a lot like other media players such as iTunes, but there is a big difference. With Spotify, you don't have to download the music in order to listen to it (although this is also possible). Instead you can simply stream it over your internet connection.

How does this work? Well, Spotify delivers music to your PC using a combination of peer-to-peer sharing and streaming from its servers (see the jargon boxout on the previous page for an explanation of these terms). When a Spotify user opens the application it makes an index of the contents of their Spotify cache and sends this to the Spotify streaming hub. The cache contains all the music files or pieces of music files that Spotify sends when a user is listening to tracks. The streaming hub can then use this index to share these music files and pieces of files with other Spotify users. So while you are receiving the music stream, your computer is also sending music to other users on the network and it's this combination of peer-to-peer sharing and streaming from a server that gives Spotify its famously fast response time.

In other respects, Spotify works like many other media players and online music stores, allowing users to browse its 6 million tracks via name, genre, artist etc, as well as allowing custom playlists to be created and random radio lists to be constructed. Individual tracks, albums, playlists, as well as money to extend subscriptions or buy downloads, can also be shared easily from user to user and there are community forums in order for users to stay in touch with each other.

Spotify makes money through both interspersing music tracks with advertisements (the frequency of these ads can vary depending on time-frames and last between 10-30 seconds), or by getting its users to sign up as a premium user, which costs £9.99 per month. If users take up a premium subscription then there are no advertisements between tracks, allowing for continuous playback. ✿

ON THE MAP

Where is Spotify available?
Currently it can be used in:
- United Kingdom
- France
- Sweden
- Spain
- Norway
- Finland

It will also be available in:
- Italy
- Portugal
- Germany
- Denmark
- Netherlands
- Estonia
- Poland
- Belgium
- Austria
- Switzerland
- Romania
- Greece

Cofounders of Spotify Daniel Ek and Martin

Side view of a pinsetter

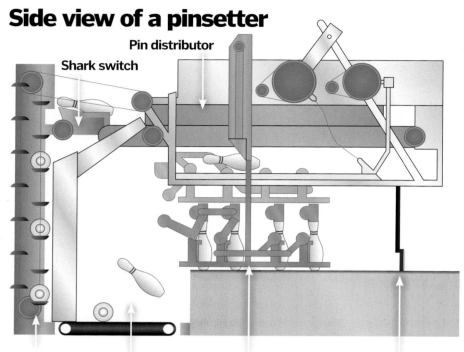

Shark switch

Pin distributor

Pin elevator

Ball pit

Pin table

Sweep

How a bowling alley works

The workings of a ten-pin bowling alley

Any bowling alley works through a combination of a wooden or synthetic lane flanked by semicylindrical gutter channels, an automated pinsetter machine and ball sorter, and a return ball gully and stacker. The glossy, 60-foot lane is normally constructed out of 39 strips of sugar maple wood, which itself is coated with varying layers of oil down its length. This coating is often heavy towards the bowler end, before dissipating down the alley, allowing any spinning ball more purchase in the final quarter of its journey allowing pro-bowlers to hit the pins at varying angles. At the pin end of the alley, starting at the termination of the lane, lays the pin-deck. This deck is where the pins are set-up and knocked down, and thanks to this constant activity, it is coated with a durable impact-resistant material.

Behind the deck lies the first part of the mechanical pinsetter machine. The pit and shaker collects both the fallen ball and pins before shuffling them to its rear and into mechanical lifts that raise them to above the alley. Once there, the ball is then funnelled onto a metal track which then descends back under the lane to the conveyer belt gully and back to the bowler. The pins on the other hand get dropped from this elevated position into the pinsetter's turret, where their bottom-heavy weight ensures that they drop base first. Once filled, the turret then waits for the sweep – a mechanical bar that literally 'sweeps' any still-standing pins backwards into the pit – to operate before dispensing a freshly ordered set of pins into the spotting table. This table then lowers the pins gently back onto the pin deck ready for the process to begin again.

In addition, returned balls are automatically slowed and filtered by spinning rubberised pads as they reach the docking station and ball stacker at the bowler end of the lane, as well as scores being automatically logged and recorded by the lane's in-built computer system and displayed on a screen. ✿

What's inside a vacuum flask?

How to keep hot things hot and cold things cold

Vacuum flasks use thermodynamic principles to keep the hot or cold contents of a vessel warmer or cooler than the temperature outside. A glass of cold water left on a table will eventually warm up till it's room temperature, and likewise a hot cup of coffee will cool down until it's the same temperature as the room. Creating a vacuum between the contents in a sealed vacuum flask and the outside environment provides thermal insulation, preventing heat transfer and therefore temperature change.

Because there are so few atoms inside a vacuum, heat transfer via conduction and convection is limited, meaning the temperature within the flask remains the same for longer. The heat will eventually become the same temperature as that of the outside environment but only really through the weaknesses of the seal at the top of the vessel and the cap. ✿

Inside a vacuum flask

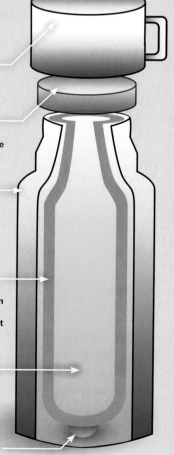

5. Cup
A handy cup is usually screwed on the top of the flask.

1. Cap
The only place where heat transfer can potentially take place is through the limitations of the seal.

2. Outer casing
The outer materials are made of either metal or plastic and serve to protect the fragile inner glass.

3. Vacuum layer
A double-walled glass envelope contains a vacuum that forms a barrier separating the inner content from the temperature outside.

4. Contents
The hot or cold contents will maintain the same temperature for far longer inside a vacuum flask.

Insulated support

MOST EXPENSIVE

1. Batman Begins
Batman's suit is £300,000 worth of armour, but it doesn't work against dog bites as we see in *Dark Knight*.

LEAST EFFECTIVE

2. Iron Man
Tony Stark's vest probably didn't come cheap but it still didn't stop the shrapnel from an exploding shell that landed nearby.

MOST EIGHTIES

3. Back To The Future
As well as nearly snogging his own mum, Marty McFly was also able to warn Doc of his would-be assassins.

DID YOU KNOW? *Scientists are implementing nanomaterials into the next generation of body armour*

Bulletproof vests explained

How does armoured apparel stop a bullet?

There are two different types of bullet-resistant vests – soft and hard – with many varieties using a combination arrangement to absorb the impact from firearm-fired projectiles and shrapnel from explosive devices. So-called 'soft' bulletproof vests are made from multiple layers of woven, interlaced laminated fibres, which prevent bullet penetration by spreading its impact force throughout its layers and dispersing the energy that would otherwise have punctured the target. Of course, the material used to create the finely woven fibres needs to be exceptionally strong also, and in the majority of modern day vests Kevlar is the material of choice as it offers five times the strength of steel. Further, Kevlar is lightweight, allowing the wearer to retain maximum mobility. Soft bulletproof vests provide protection from the majority of pistol rounds, shotgun shrapnel and knife attacks.

There are natural limits to a soft vest however, with super-hard rounds fired at high velocity capable of tearing its material and breaching its critical kinetic energy threshold. For these, 'hard' bulletproof vests are required, which use the same technology as the soft suits, yet have integrated ceramic (usually alumina) and hard-metal plates to halt and deflect larger, quicker rounds. These plates are designed to slow or deform any bullet that comes into contact with them, often mushrooming the bullet's shape and dispersing its energy. In addition, while soft vests have a certain knife tolerance, these plates provide added protection against bladed weapons. Hard vests are usually integrated into military outfits.

Current advances into personal bullet-resistant body armour have seen the rise of fully ceramic vests, which use two and three-dimensional arrays of ceramic elements that can be rigid, semi-flexible or flexible, as well as providing a high-calibre multi-hit threshold. Further, at the cutting edge of this rapidly advancing field, vests are now being created out of nanomaterials, utilising the fine weaves of carbon and tungsten nanotubes to provide protection from projectiles of velocities up to 1.5kmps, as well as withstanding impact pressure up to 250 tons per square centimetre. Unfortunately, however, despite the phenomenal stopping power that these vests can achieve, the materials needed to create them are currently prohibitively expensive for a mass-market release. ✿

A SWAT Marine posing in full body armour

Plastic film (green)

Outer cloth material (blue)

Woven Kevlar (red)

"Now hold still, this won't hurt a bit…"

Bulletproof vests are now often given to dogs that are operating in war zones

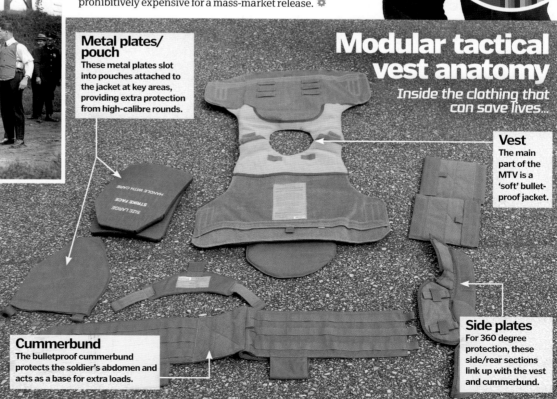

Metal plates/pouch
These metal plates slot into pouches attached to the jacket at key areas, providing extra protection from high-calibre rounds.

Cummerbund
The bulletproof cummerbund protects the soldier's abdomen and acts as a base for extra loads.

Modular tactical vest anatomy
Inside the clothing that can save lives…

Vest
The main part of the MTV is a 'soft' bullet-proof jacket.

Side plates
For 360 degree protection, these side/rear sections link up with the vest and cummerbund.

HOW IS FIBRE OPTIC BROADBAND USHERING IN A NEW ERA OF COMMUNICATION?

Superfast broadband

Remember dial-up internet? Most of us do and it's not so very long ago that speeds of 56K were considered fast when it came to accessing the delights of the world wide web. And while it may have been fine for checking GeoCities pages and bulletin boards, as our demands and uses of the internet became more complex so higher speeds became more necessary, can you imagine using iTunes or YouTube on a 56K modem? Neither could the service providers who now vie for our attention, trying to find the balance between faster connections and lower prices.

Currently the fastest speed on offer in the UK and US and most of Europe lie somewhere between 2MB and 10MB while China, South Korea and Japan lead the way in 'fibre-to-the-home' broadband lines. However many western nations such as America, Sweden and Romania are following close behind. Over the next few pages we'll be explaining fibre optics, the amazing technology behind the new generation of internet connections, so read on to find out just how it works, where you can find it and why some countries are faster than others. ✿

5 TOP FACTS
INTERNET

WWW
1 The man credited with inventing the internet is Sir Tim Berners-Lee, a British computer scientist and professor at the Massachusetts Institute of Technology.

Dominant
2 The prevalent language of communication on the internet is English, followed by Chinese and Spanish. This is despite 42 per cent of total users being based in Asia.

Modal
3 Currently, in the UK the fastest commercial fibre optic line broadband connection is an 'up to 50MB' connection. The lines are available in selected areas only.

VIP
4 The first switched telephone network arrived in Britain in 1879 when The Telephone Company Ltd opened its first exchange in London. It served just eight subscribers.

Victorian
5 Many copper-based communication lines in the UK can trace their origins back to Victorian and Edwardian times, especially in built-up areas around major cities.

DID YOU KNOW? *Currently all new undersea cables are made of optical fibres*

A standard transceiver used to send and receive data

A laser bouncing down a Perspex rod demonstrating the total internal reflection of light in an optical fibre

Reflection
Light enters the Perspex line and is reflected throughout.

Exit
Data leaves the other end at the speed of light.

Superfast broadband explained

The brand new breed of superfast broadband connections is made possible by switching from copper telephone wires to new fibre optic cables. Fibre optic broadband essentially works by transmitting data as pulses of light from an exchange throughout an optical fibre – a cable consisting of a light-carrying glass core, light-reflecting cladding (to ensure total light retention) and protective buffer coating – before then receiving and decoding that information at the far end with a transceiver.

A fibre optic line is an excellent medium for communication purposes as it holds numerous advantageous properties over the existing copper-based wiring networks. Most notable is its long-distance data delivery speed, a factor made possible because light propagates through fibre with little attenuation and, obviously, at the speed of light. Further, each fibre optic cable can carry many independent channels of information, each using a different wavelength of light, so the sheer amount of data is increased also.

Broadband now

In most countries, broadband is delivered down copper telephone wire, which suffers from speed, range and breadth restrictions. The wire, which is prevalent across most networks, often dates from the early 20th or even late 19th Century and carries information through electric pulses. This is problematic in terms of maintaining speed at long ranges as all electrical transmissions are subject to high electrical resistance, and information effectiveness is compromised. In addition, electrical transmission lines suffer when tightly packed from crosstalk – a phenomenon by which a signal transmitted on one circuit or channel of a transmission system creates an undesired effect in another circuit or channel. In short, the system is an ageing one, unable to meet today's demands.

Delivery

A diagram illustrating how broadband architectures vary depending on the distance between the optical fibre end-point, existing copper-based network and the user. The building on the left is the communications exchange; that on the right is representative of one of the buildings served by it.

FTTN
(Fibre-to-the-node)
Optical fibre is terminated at a node multiple miles from the user's residence, with the connection from it to the premises being copper-based.

FTTC
(Fibre-to-the-cabinet)
Similar to FTTN, this configuration sees any optical fibre terminated at a street cabinet closer to the user's house. The connection from it, though, is still copper.

FTTB
(Fibre-to-the-building)
Used in apartment and office blocks, this sees the optical cable stop at the boundary of the structure, the final connection being delivered by other means.

FTTH
(Fibre-to-the-home)
Here an optical fibre line enters the user's premises like a regular copper connection. No copper connections are necessary in the 'last mile' and speed is vastly increased.

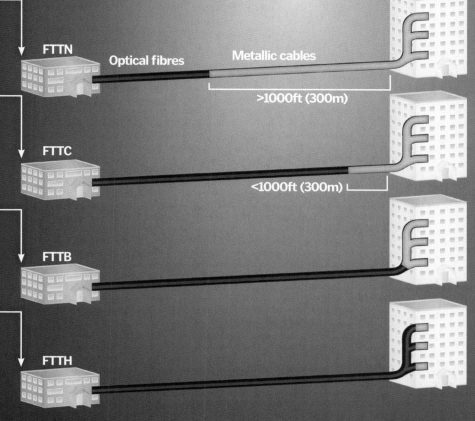

FTTN — Optical fibres — Metallic cables — >1000ft (300m)

FTTC — <1000ft (300m)

FTTB

FTTH

The last mile

The term 'the last mile' refers to the final leg of delivering broadband communications from a provider to a user. In reality, the last mile may in fact be considerably further than a mile, with many miles separating the two. This is because at this late stage any main cable must be fanned out and split to service numerous separate clients, often living far apart. This is time-consuming and carries a large expense, however, if the 'last mile' is too great a distance, then the cable infrastructure is rendered useless as it cannot sustain information flow due to speed loss.

To address these connectivity issues many operators share and splice networks to reach customers, with cabling varying in type and length depending on where the user is based. This has the obvious drawback that while initially a line from a provider may be fibre optic (carrying data faster and further with less speed loss), at the users' end, in the 'last mile', it may be fanned out onto an old, pre-existing copper line, which as aforementioned in this article, sustains high-speeds poorly, especially over large distances.

"More and more countries are rolling-out extensive optical networks"

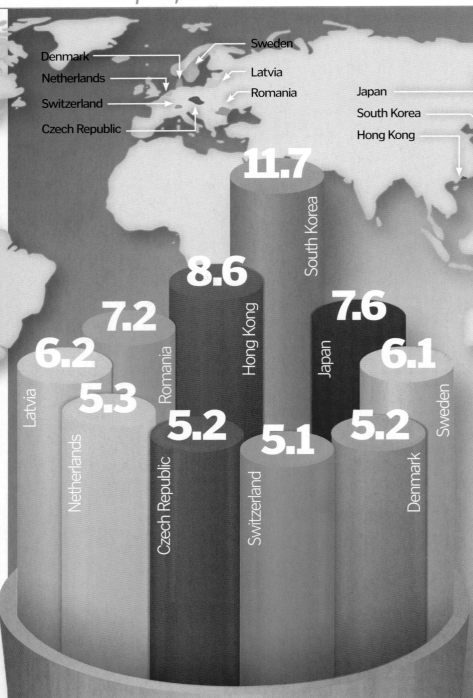

An underground fibre optic splice enclosure opened for splicing

Sweden
Denmark
Netherlands
Latvia
Switzerland
Romania
Czech Republic

Japan
South Korea
Hong Kong

11.7 — South Korea

8.6 — Hong Kong

7.2 — Romania

7.6 — Japan

6.2 — Latvia

5.3 — Netherlands

6.1 — Sweden

5.2 — Czech Republic

5.1 — Switzerland

5.2 — Denmark

1. South Korea – 11.7 Mbps
2. Hong Kong – 8.6 Mbps
3. Japan – 7.6 Mbps
4. Romania – 7.2 Mbps
5. Latvia – 6.2 Mbps
6. Sweden – 6.1 Mbps
7. Netherlands – 5.3 Mbps
8. Czech Republic – 5.2 Mbps
9. Denmark – 5.2 Mbps
10. Switzerland – 5.1 Mbps

THE TOP 10 LOCATIONS WITH THE FASTEST AVERAGE SPEED

The United States is ranked 22nd, with the average broadband connection speed of 3.8Mbps, while Britain is ranked even lower at 26th with an average of 3.5Mbps

United States
22 **of America**
26 **Great Britain**

Why are some countries faster than others?

If you've been looking at the speeds on offer in Asian countries and experiencing an extreme case of broadband envy then you might be wondering just why the services on offer in South Korea, Hong Kong and even Sweden are better than those in the US or UK. Part of the answer lies in financial outlay; Japan, South Korea and Sweden have all made significant investment in fibre optic networks.

Urban density plays its part in the disparity too. Much of the population in South Korea live in very dense apartment complexes. Most of the superfast broadband service has been delivered by fibre optic connections into the basements of buildings like these, then to the individual apartments by fast DSL. So while the fastest broadband connection in the world currently resides in the UK (see below) this is unlikely to see domestic role-out soon due to the prohibitive nature of upgrading the existing network.

The fastest broadband in the world

From the 20 March 2010, the title of world's fastest broadband supplier was awarded to Virgin Media after it demonstrated its 200Mbps service trials at Earls Court, London. That speed is four times faster than its current top-end 50Mbps connection and twice that of the already reported 100Mbps connection due at the end of 2010. Virgin achieved this record speed by using the DOCSIS 3 (Data Over Cable Service Interface Specification) international telecommunications standard that allows for high-speed data transfer over an existing hybrid fibre coaxial infrastructure. Despite the epic speed, the service is not currently commercially available, however, and an early estimate has put it being introduced, depending on demand, in mid 2012.

Top five fastest places for broadband

Region: United States City: Berkeley, CA KBPS: 18,730	Region: United States Town: Chapel Hill, NC KBPS: 17,483	Region: South Korea City: Masan KBPS: 14,969	Region: United States CDP: Stanford, CA KBPS: 16,956	Region: Great Britain City: Oxford, England KBPS: 14,463

What can superfast broadband be used for?

New devices are making the most of increased bandwidth

Cloud computing, online gaming, digital downloads and live streaming of television and films are but a selection of the possible services fibre optic broadband can be utilised for. Indeed, already a host of applications and services are being set up to exploit the benefits fibre optic broadband brings. NetFlix, for example, allows for an unprecedented selection of titles – both from the current season of television, classical film archives and new Hollywood releases – to be instantly streamed live over the internet with no waiting or downloading. Gaming services like Steam allow for titles to be bought online, then downloaded and played instantly without the buyer ever needing to leave the house. Online gaming is also quicker and users experience lower ping rates and reduced lag.

Cloud computing
Content stored online and accessed remotely from hardware devices will be advanced with widespread superfast broadband.

How radar finds objects

How sound inspired radiowave observation

Radar uses a radiowave-based version of echo location to find moving and stationery objects. When you make a noise in a space that echoes, the sound is bounced back to you – you hear it again a moment or so later. If the sound is moving, somebody standing still and listening to you will hear the sound go up and down as it moves past them. This is called the Doppler effect.

We can't go around shouting at aeroplanes in order to find them, no matter how frustrating Terminal 5 can be, so instead radiowaves are used. They produce exactly the same phenomenon as sound. For example, an aircraft is fitted with a radar transmitter. When another transmitter sends a burst of radiowaves in its direction, they're bounced back. The speed with which they bounce back, and the wavelength of the waves, determine where the aircraft is and the rate at which it's moving relative to the transmitter.

"Sir, what are all those green lines coming out of Russia?"

Understanding digital sound

We've come a long way from the gramophone, but what exactly is digital sound?

Record collections may still be en vogue, but both vinyl and cassette mediums represent an archaic analogue technology that has been superseded since compact discs came to the fore. Imagine the pits and grooves in a record or the magnetically charged surface of tape that store the information as a variable wave: in contrast, digital sound is stored as a series of distinct peaks and troughs, rather like the battlements of a castle. Translating from analogue to digital is called encoding and in terms data storage, it saves an enormous amount of space.

This is the basis of Dolby's digital audio technologies and the encoding process allows companies like Dolby to tease apart digital sound into separate channels for a surround sound experience: 5.1 surround, for example, consists of a left and right channel communicating movement, a focused centre channel for dialogue, a pair of surround channels and a resonant low-frequency bass.

DID YOU KNOW? It's not carbon dioxide that actually makes the bubbles in a drink – it's dirty glasses. CO_2 is invisible; what you see is its silhouette outlined by trace elements.

Starting your car without a key

Keyless car ignition is becoming more common – but how does it work?

Necessity is the mother of invention and these days, gadgets are necessary. Keyless ignition simply allows the motorist to come within range of their vehicle then press a button to start the engine. It uses a technology called radio frequency identification (RFID). An RFID chip (the lock) is placed inside the car that will unlock the ignition system when activated. Only its corresponding fob (the key) can activate the chip using a radio signal, which works like a barcode in a supermarket. RFID used to use a 40-bit encryption system that wasn't particularly strong and proved fallible, with high-profile victims of failed RFID security that include David Beckham, who lost two BMW X5s with keyless ignition to thieves.

On the plus side, there's no physical key to replicate, keyless systems include security measures that prevent you from locking your key inside and it has more practical significance for disabled drivers.

Creating the perfect frothy beer head

Two pints of CO_2 and a shot of liquid nitrogen

A widget is a small plastic ball with a hole in one end, which is added to a beer can. Beer is loaded with gaseous nitrogen and carbon dioxide, and a chaser of liquid nitrogen just before canning. When these elements are under pressure they're relatively inert, but remove the pressure (by pulling the ringpull) and they expand. If they evaporate in a thick liquid they don't get through as much of the liquid as they would in a thin one before they've been dissipated, because the speed of evaporation is constant, but the distance they travel depends on how fast they can move. This movement creates the head on your beer. The nitrogen-filled widget pulls beer into it and shoves it back out again at high speed when the pressure of the can is released, exciting both elements to move through the liquid faster and aerating it with the evaporating gases.

Head to Head
SKYSCRAPERS

The world's tallest building

Piercing the sky, Burj Khalifa is currently the world's tallest man-made structure

TALLEST

1. Burj Dubai
Location: Dubai, United Arab Emirates
Height: 828m
Floor count: 160

TALLER

2. Taipei 101
Location: Taipei, Taiwan
Height: 509m
Floor count: 101

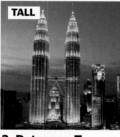

TALL

3. Petronas Towers
Location: Kuala Lumpur, Malaysia
Height: 452m
Floor count: 88

©Nicolas Lannuzel

In 2004 construction began on the world's tallest skyscraper. Due to open in December, Burj Dubai is a mammoth feat of human engineering and design. Located in downtown Dubai, the tower forms the eye-catching heart of a huge development venture that has seen investment reaching into the billions of dollars.

As you can imagine, there are major logistical obstacles associated with erecting a mega high-rise tower: it must be lightweight yet resistant to the elements, durable yet aesthetically pleasing, and built to last yet affordable. The Burj tower comprises a mind-blowing 160 floors. Just take a moment to consider the immense weight bearing down on the foundations. So how have the Burj Dubai engineers managed to create a structure so much taller than anything else like it?

Y-shaped foundations, inspired by the hymenocallis plant native to the region, give the building a sturdy base. Parts of the structure are helical in shape with 26 stepped terraces snaking round the outside. The core of the building is hexagonal and surrounded by high-performance reinforced concrete with steel piles sunk 50 metres into the ground. A blend of additives make the concrete heat, fire, and crack resistant. Pumping the concrete to extreme heights before it sets is a major complication, and for the Burj Dubai the builders employed some innovative chilling techniques with the mixture.

Very tall structures generate a massive amount of heat energy, so the Burj required a state-of-the-art cooling system. However, together with high outside humidity, this creates condensation, which must be piped to a tank in the basement. The Burj Dubai's facade is clad with a reflective glass designed to keep the building cool while also allowing plenty of light in. A staggering 20.7 acres of glass have been used for the outer shell of the tower. Of course, you wouldn't take the stairs in a 160-storey skyscraper so a reliable and fast elevator system is essential to any super-tall structure. Like most of the Burj's features, the elevator installation is the tallest in the world, and features double-decker cabs that travel at 64 kmph.

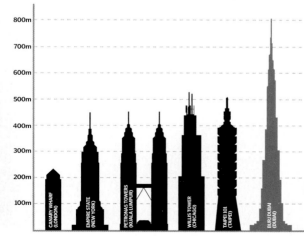

Drilling for oil offshore

The world produces over 82 million barrels of oil every day, much of it in harsh conditions, miles from shore and safety if an emergency happens. So how is it done?

Oil has been around for millions of years, located deep below the land or sea where it became trapped under layers of permeable rocks or slowly seeping to the surface. Although examples of oil drilling were documented in 4th Century China, the first modern oil gathering structure was built in 1897 and by 1928 mobile rigs consisting of a simple barge with a drill mounted on top had set the scene for a revolution that fuelled Western industrial dominance for the next century.

Over 82 million barrels of oil are produced every single day, a process that usually starts with a range of surveys; from geographical and geomagnetic surveys to the deep echo sounding or seismic reflection surveys that pinpoint the likely location of a substantial deposit. Only then, and after the necessary permits have all been obtained of course, can the rigs move in – multi-million pound structures and teams of professionals that locate, make the well safe and finally drill down to its precious commodity.

Today, there are over 40,000 oil fields around the world, with most offshore drilling undertaken in the Continental shelf – the sunken perimeter of a continent's original glacial shape. From the $100 million monsters that plumb the deepest waters in the Gulf of Mexico, to the smaller North Sea structures that nevertheless have to withstand 90-knot winds and 20 metre waves. Mobile rigs are usually reserved for exploratory work, owned by private contractors and leased to the oil companies who then have limited time to find, tap and process their precious bounty. Larger manned platforms and spars can service up to 30 wellheads, tapping into multiple wells up to 8 km from the platform itself. ✿

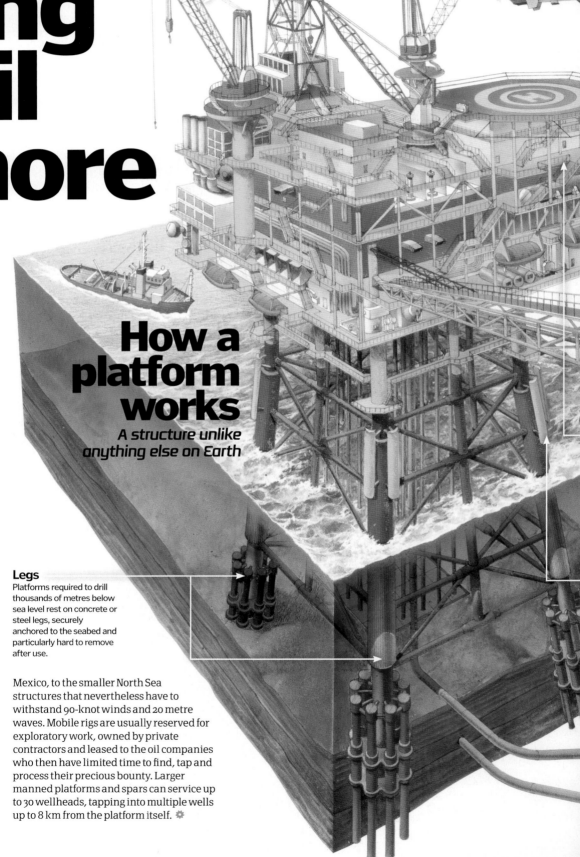

How a platform works
A structure unlike anything else on Earth

Legs
Platforms required to drill thousands of metres below sea level rest on concrete or steel legs, securely anchored to the seabed and particularly hard to remove after use.

DID YOU KNOW? As North Sea reserves run dry, the estimated cost of removing the structures would exceed £621 billion

Life on an oil rig

Required to work for up to six months a year, oil workers are well compensated for the undeniably hazardous conditions they work in. Wages are typically higher than in similar engineering disciplines and the larger platforms and spars come complete with facilities more appropriate to a cruise ship than a floating factory. These can include private rooms for the 100+ crew, cinemas, 24-hour restaurants and even gyms. Supplies are usually brought in by helicopter or ship, making oil platforms better stocked than most workplaces and significantly more important to the local economies they reside in. It is estimated that every offshore worker supports up to ten more in local industries such as food, transport or maintenance. However, the dangers are constant and largely unpredictable. Offshore drilling involves not just dealing with highly flammable oil and gas, with the added danger of this being pumped out at exceptionally high pressures, but also extreme wind and sea conditions. When danger strikes, support is often miles away by helicopter or ship and despite the high levels of training and increasingly safe equipment, offshore fatality rates have been on the rise in recent years. In addition to this, workers are often prone to alcoholism or drug abuse to overcome the isolation and gruelling 12-hour shifts.

Above: Accommodation decks of a North Sea oil platform
Below: A worker checks the drilling head on a tower

Deck
The working space aboard an offshore platform where drilling rigs, production facilities and crew quarters are located. Larger platforms may use nearby 'flotels' for crew quarters.

Jacket
Jackets are usually vertical steel sections piled into the seabed, protecting the central drill shaft against damage or interference.

Wells
With each platform needing to service up to 30 wells at different depths and positions, flow lines and umbilical connections are required to connect them all to the main rig.

© DK Images

Oil rig teamwork
The men and women who make it all possible

Offshore installation manager
Also known as the Man in Charge (MIC) the installation manager makes all key production decisions, both before, during and after drilling. He has usually worked his way through the other drill team roles.

Driller
A highly specialist discipline, drillers are the ones who operate the drilling equipment, including making the initial hole in the seabed. He is effectively in charge of everything that happens on the rig floor.

Derrickman
So called because of their position at the top of the derrick, derrickmen are usually working roughnecks responsible for the guiding of pipe into the drill as well as operating mud pumps and other such machinery.

Roughneck
The grunts of the oil business, roughnecks work in teams of three and are mainly responsible for manual work both during and after drilling. They can also be called on to operate other equipment such as mud shakers.

Tool pusher
On an offshore rig, tool pushers tend to be department heads in charge of drilling or other essential functions such as engineering or operations. They may also assist with administrative work such as payroll or benefits.

THE RIGHT RIG FOR THE JOB

Drill Ships
Designed for speculative or deep-water mining, these vessels are converted to include a drilling platform in the centre. Drill ships use sophisticated sensors and satellite tracking to keep them moving while lined up to the well.

Semi-submersibles
Made up of floating pontoons and columns able to sink in the water where they are anchored to the sea floor or kept in place by steerable thrusters. Effective at drill depths of up to 1,800 metres, they're designed for quick deployment.

Jack-up
Mobile platforms can be raised above the sea on extendable steel legs. Designed for depths of 500 metres or less, they are useful for small to mid-sized deposits and typically only support smaller crews.

Rig
An immovable structure of concrete and steel that rests on the seabed with deck space for multiple rigs, crew quarters and production facilities. Their design and expense makes them appropriate for larger offshore deposits.

Spar
Perfect for major oil fields such as the North Sea, spars are drilling platforms fixed to giant, hollow hulls that can descend up to 250 metres, still above the ocean floor and secured by cables.

"Radar-based speed cameras work by projecting a continuous radar signal over a set stretch of road"

How speed cameras work

Recording your speed in a flash

Speed cameras come in a variety of flavours. However, the most common is the radar-based variant. Radar-based speed cameras work by projecting a continuous radar signal over a set stretch of road, which as a vehicle passes by alters the returning signal's frequency, indicating the presence of the vehicle and its speed.

In addition to the continuous radar signal, the area of road which the camera is pointed at is often covered with either inductive loops or piezoelectric strips, which initiate once passed over by a moving vehicle and, due to their set distance apart, allow speed to be measured against distance travelled. Further, another central technology evident in radar-based speed cameras is its automatic number plate recognition (ANPR) system. This system uses a form of optical character recognition (OCR) – an electronic conversion and translation of image data to typewritten characters – to log and determine the plate number and subsequently the owner of the vehicle in question.

Most speed cameras (there are over 6,000 speed cameras in Great Britain) are distributed at the sides of roads and are largely rearward facing in order to prevent drivers being blinded by their flash. However, present developments have seen cameras positioned on overhead gantries, central reservation hubs and even custom-built docking stations. These fixed speed cameras are connected to a central system and storage database (where recorded images and data are processed ready for prosecution) and each installation costs between £20,000-£40,000 ($30,000-$60,000). When first installed, radar-based cameras used film in order to process the images they took. However, film variants are now sidelined in favour of digital processing procedures, as the film limit of 400 images is made obsolete by digital storage.

Despite their huge cost, the money required to install a speed camera is often quickly recouped through the fines that caught drivers are required to pay by law. In Great Britain the average penalty for speeding is £60 ($90) and three points on a licence, meaning that a single camera requires 300 to 600 speeding offences to recoup its cost.

An image of a speeding car taken from a roadside speed camera

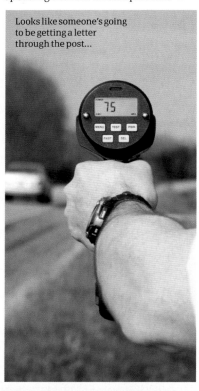

Looks like someone's going to be getting a letter through the post...

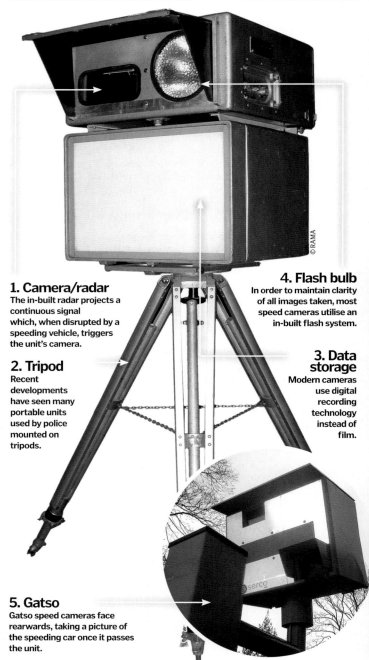

1. Camera/radar
The in-built radar projects a continuous signal which, when disrupted by a speeding vehicle, triggers the unit's camera.

2. Tripod
Recent developments have seen many portable units used by police mounted on tripods.

4. Flash bulb
In order to maintain clarity of all images taken, most speed cameras utilise an in-built flash system.

3. Data storage
Modern cameras use digital recording technology instead of film.

5. Gatso
Gatso speed cameras face rearwards, taking a picture of the speeding car once it passes the unit.

DID YOU KNOW? A temporary speed camera placed on the M62 motorway in West Yorkshire, England, accrued more than £1 million in fines over an 18 month period

BEGINNER

1. Tandem jump
Attached to an experienced instructor, the novice can enjoy an exciting tandem jump, sitting back and letting the instructor take complete control.

INTERMEDIATE

2. Formation skydiving
Formation skydiving uses aerodynamic techniques, timing and co-ordination to create spectacular aerial displays.

EXPERT

3. Wingsuit skyflying
Advanced parachutists can fly with an outfit called a wingsuit, which acts as a personal parachute shaped like an airfoil to create lift.

© SBirdman Inc/Mark Harris, www.bird-man.com

DID YOU KNOW? *The first successful parachute jump was completed by balloonist André Garnerin in 1797*

Getting down
The steps to land safely

Jump
With the need for additional oxygen, the typical altitude you would choose for your jump is 3,960 m.

Freefall
'Freefall' begins the second you step off the plane and will last about a minute. 762 m from the ground is a good time to deploy the parachute.

Landing
The ground exerts an upward force on you, stopping motion and bringing you down to Earth with a bump.

Ram-air canopy
Made of coated nylon so as not to let air through, the main canopy of a ram-air parachute (the rectangular kind) is composed of two layers of fabric divided into cells that are filled (or 'rammed') with high-pressure air when deployed.

Pilot chute
This mini parachute releases quickly and, when inflated, tugs hard on a long bit of nylon called a bridle that pulls the main canopy out of its container.

Reserve (inside container, not seen)
As a back-up in case your main parachute fails to deploy properly, a reserve can be triggered using the traditional ripcord method used before the pilot chute.

Container
Until they are required, all the essential chutes and lines are kept neatly in a container, which is basically a carefully packed backpack that the parachutist straps themselves into (including their legs).

Slider

Risers

Steering toggles (brake)

Lines
Five sets of durable but lightweight lines connect the parachute and the container via straps called risers. The lines are referred to as A, B, C, D, and the brake line.

Automatic activation device
If the parachutist gets distracted, an automatic activation device (AAD) will step in and automatically activate the reserve when 228 m from the ground.

Friction

Terminal velocity

Gravity

Parachutes, falling with style
Friction versus gravity in a battle to the ground

When you jump out of a plane, two major forces are competing for attention: friction (or drag) between you and the air whizzing past, and gravity pulling you down. When freefalling, you will experience acceleration because the force of friction is initially much weaker than the force of gravity. Eventually, the downward force of gravity will equal the upward force of drag and you will stop accelerating and fall at a constant speed – usually around 193 kmph. This is known as terminal velocity: the point at which no force is acting upon your body.

While gravity is a constant force, the force of friction changes with velocity and surface area. For example, stick your hand out the window of a stationary vehicle and you'll not experience friction. However, stick your hand out the window of a moving vehicle and you'll experience a large force of friction. Upon opening the parachute, the frictional force is greater than the force of gravity because the canopy has increased your cross-sectional area – this is what slows you down. As your acceleration drops so, too, does the force of friction until it is equal to the force of gravity and again you descend at a constant rate.

Precise control

Steering a parachute is remarkably easy with the use of two handheld toggles to control the lines. The parachute canopy behaves like a wing due to the airfoil shape created by the air-filled cells. To turn left, you should pull on the left-hand toggle because this lowers the back-left section of the parachute, which also slows down that side of the 'wing'. The same goes for turning right, except that you tug on the right-hand toggle instead of the left. Pulling on both at the same time has a braking effect and will slow the whole parachute down.

Head to Head
DAMS

BIGGEST

1. The Three Gorges Dam

Location: Yangtze River, China
Size: It's 2,335 metres long, 101 metres wide and 115 metres at its thickest point. It took 15 years, approximately £25 billion and nearly 14 million tons of cement and materials to construct it.
Facts: 34 turbines weighing in at a 6,000 tons each generate 22,500 megawatts for an annual output of 60.7 terawatt hours per year in 2009. It is the world's largest electricity-generating plant of any kind.

TALLEST

2. Nurek Dam

Location: Vakhsh River, Tajikistan
Size: The Nurek is an earth fill dam finished in 1980 when the Soviet Union had control of Tajikistan. At 300 metres it is the tallest dam in the world, though the Rogun Dam has a taller proposed height for when it's eventually completed.
Facts: A comparatively modest nine hydroelectric turbines have a total power output of three gigawatts, but amazingly, since 1994 this has been enough to supply 98 per cent of the nation's total electricity needs.

MOST FAMOUS

3. Verzasca Dam

Location: Lago di Vogorno, Switzerland
Size: Neither the largest nor the tallest dam at 220 metres high.
Facts: The site of the scene where Bond dove off into the Verzasca river below in *GoldenEye*, it's one of the most famous dams worldwide.

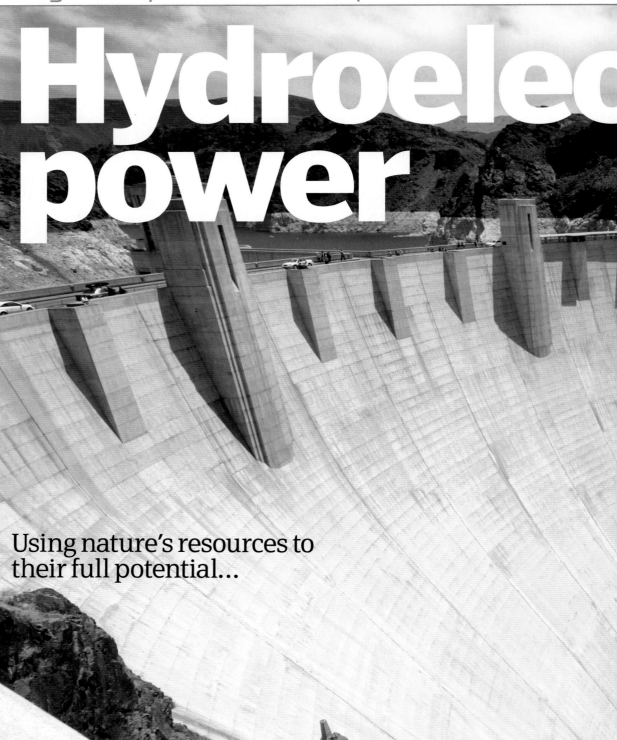

Hydroelec

power

Using nature's resources to their full potential...

Water has been used to power man-made mechanisms for hundreds of years, mostly in food production in the form of a mill wheel to grind corn. But using the kinetic energy of water probably became a reality earlier than you thought. In 1878, inventor Lord Armstrong lit his home in Northumberland using only the power of a nearby waterfall. It's not until the latter half of the 20th Century that we began to take advantage of the massive potential of hydroelectric power.

Intriguingly, both the dirty and environmentally unfriendly coal power plants and clean, green hydro-power use almost identical technology to generate power. Central to a coal-fired plant is a turbine: coal is burned to produce heat energy, which is used to boil water into steam to drives a turbine. Hydroelectric power removes the coal and steam elements and instead, flowing water turns the blades of each installed turbine.

By damming a river next to a drop in elevation and releasing a controlled flow (and creating a large body of water behind the dam called a reservoir), you can effectively harness the Earth's gravity as an energy source. It's based on the principles discovered by physicist Michael Faraday: when a magnet moves past a conductor, it creates electricity. When the water flowing

tric

The huge generators inside the Hoover Dam

Inside the dam

The main components that allow water to create electricity

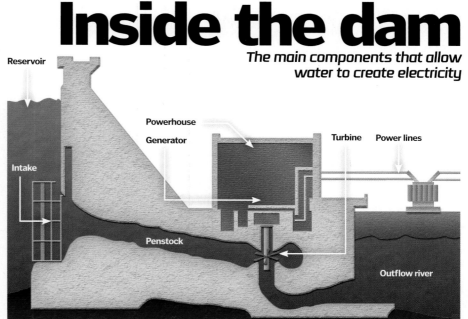

Reservoir

Intake

Powerhouse

Generator

Turbine

Power lines

Penstock

Outflow river

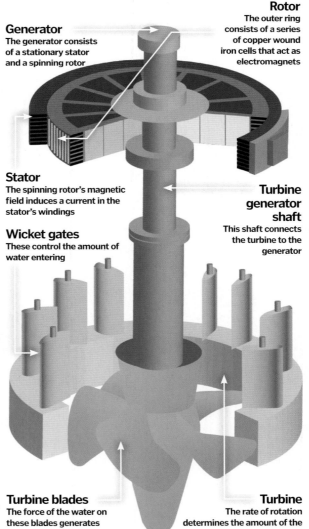

Generator
The generator consists of a stationary stator and a spinning rotor

Rotor
The outer ring consists of a series of copper wound iron cells that act as electromagnets

Stator
The spinning rotor's magnetic field induces a current in the stator's windings

Wicket gates
These control the amount of water entering

Turbine generator shaft
This shaft connects the turbine to the generator

Turbine blades
The force of the water on these blades generates movement

Turbine
The rate of rotation determines the amount of the power produced

through a hydroelectric turbine turns the blades it rotates a shaft attached to a large disk called a rotor at the opposite end. The rotor is made up of loops of wire with current circulating through them, wound around stacks of magnetic steel. When active, the turbine propeller turns the rotor past the conductors located in the static part of the turbine, known as the stator.

Modern technology in even a single large turbine (which can weigh thousands of tons) can generate an enormous amount of power, but the cost-effectiveness of building the dam as well as the environmental and economic impact of flooding the area behind it can prohibit such ventures. ✿

TYPES OF... DAM

1 Saddle
Often constructed as an auxiliary to the main dam, at a dip (or saddle) where water would otherwise escape.

2 Diversionary
Often a controversial construction, these are created with the pure intention of diverting a river from its course.

3 Dry
These are designed to control flooding, allowing the river to flow freely except in times of intense rainfall where flooding is most likely.

4 Overflow
These are made with the intention of the river flowing over the top of the dam, usually to measure the flow and for drinking water.

5 Check
Check dams are used to slow the rate of flow of the river with the express intention of controlling soil erosion.

 Learn more

For more information about the Hoover Dam visit **http://www.pbs.org/wgbh/americanexperience/hoover/** where you can watch a video on how the dam was built and witness the mammoth undertaking that was.

Solar panel technology

How sunlight is transformed into electrical energy

Solar panels – also known as photovoltaic (PV) cells – convert the Sun's energy into electricity, which is a great alternative to costly, less environmentally friendly methods of powering your home. PV cells consist of two layers of a semiconductor material, such as silicon, and when sunlight shines on the cell it creates an electrical field between the layers.

This amazing conversion of sunlight into electricity takes place because when the Sun's energy hits a cell, some of it is absorbed – and transferred – into the semiconductor material. The energy loosens the electrons in the material, which, due to the electric fields, flow as electrical current. An inverter then converts this direct current into alternating current so it can be used in the home.

To be able to store all this lovely solar energy for a rainy day would require batteries, which are pretty expensive to buy and maintain. So one solution is to hook up with the National Grid and buy power from there when you need it but sell it back when you're producing more than you can use.

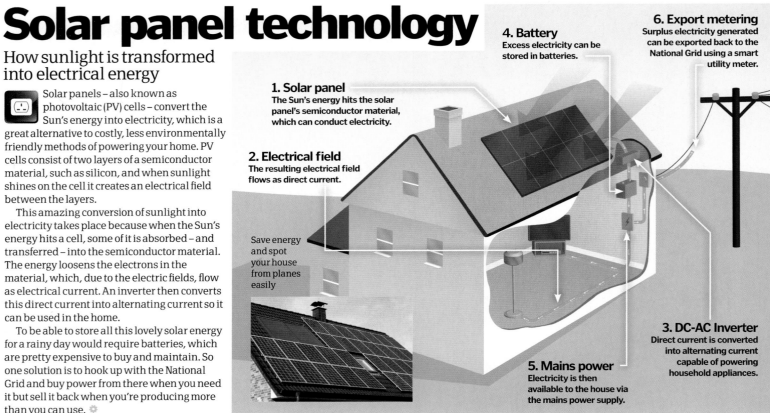

4. Battery
Excess electricity can be stored in batteries.

6. Export metering
Surplus electricity generated can be exported back to the National Grid using a smart utility meter.

1. Solar panel
The Sun's energy hits the solar panel's semiconductor material, which can conduct electricity.

2. Electrical field
The resulting electrical field flows as direct current.

Save energy and spot your house from planes easily

3. DC-AC Inverter
Direct current is converted into alternating current capable of powering household appliances.

5. Mains power
Electricity is then available to the house via the mains power supply.

Pet ID chips explained

If Lassie had one of these she'd have come home a lot sooner...

When a cherished pet goes missing, any caring owner will do all they can to get their beloved animal back. And a popular way of improving your chances of seeing old Fido again is getting him chipped – that is, having a tiny microchip implanted just under the skin between the shoulder blades. The chip is programmed with a unique identifying number that refers to the owner's details stored in a nationwide database. This ID number will permanently identify the pet and its owner. So, should a chipped pet end up at an animal rescue shelter, it will be scanned revealing the unique number.

Identification chips use passive (ie no power source) radio frequency identification (RFID) technology. They consist of a silicon chip, containing the ID number and a circuit that relays information to the scanner, a coil inductor (or radio antenna) to receive the signal from the scanner, and a capacitor, which – together with the inductor – picks up the signal from the scanner.

The chips are only slightly larger than a grain of rice

Image: courtesy of Destron Fearing

"Tower to Rex, you are cleared for take off"

Image: TheGiantVermin, 2008

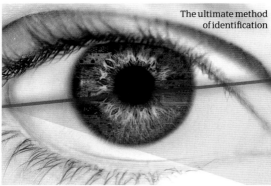

The ultimate method of identification

Iris scanning

Why iris scanning is more secure than fingerprint recognition systems

Iris scanning is the latest buzzword in biometrics for fast, secure identification. It's so accurate – 1,000 times more so than fingerprint scanning – that the UK Border Agency is introducing the Iris Recognition Immigration System (IRIS) where people can enter the UK through barriers equipped with scanners.

Iris scan cameras are used to take digital high-resolution images of the iris with visible and infrared light, which are then converted via a computer into a digital template, known as an IrisCode, which stores the exact position of unique patterns and features.

Everyone displays different iris patterns and the first time you have your eyes scanned, an IrisCode will need to be generated. Future scans will be compared to a database and your digital template is located in seconds.

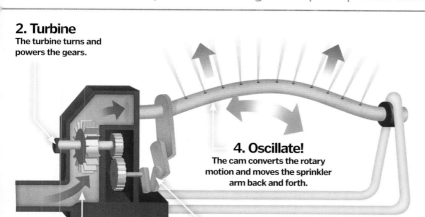

2. Turbine
The turbine turns and powers the gears.

4. Oscillate!
The cam converts the rotary motion and moves the sprinkler arm back and forth.

1. Water
Water enters from the hose with enough power to turn the turbine.

3. Cam
The gears reduce the speed of revolution and power the cam.

Sprinklers

Arguably crucial in maintaining a luscious lawn, oscillating sprinklers can offer hands-free water distribution

 It's August and sprinklers on the lawn will be a common sight in yards and gardens the world over, so long as there's no hosepipe ban. The sprinkler is a simple but no-less ingenious device that harnesses the power of the water that it distributes to the lawn, and the key to its success is a turbine and a cam.

So, the sprinkler is attached to a hosepipe, the water runs through the hosepipe and is sprayed from the sprinkler arm. But how does it move back and forth? Well, as the water enters it turns a turbine, usually a cylindrical, bladed piece of plastic. The force of the water turns the turbine at a very high rate, so a system of gears are employed to slow the revolution speed.

Once slowed the rotating motion needs to be transferred to a linear one so that the arm will move back and forth. This is achieved by use of a cam which is, if you didn't know, a device that does just that. A cam can be an irregularly shaped wheel or other shape that produces a smooth reciprocating (back and forth) motion in the follower, which is a lever making contact with the cam. This back and forth motion is what causes the sprinkler arm to move and spray a fine arc of water across the surface of the lawn.

Another force called "Sod's Law" dictates that the arm will always swing towards you when you try to move the sprinkler to another part of your garden or yard... ✿

Sprinklers can water the lawn and amuse the kids!

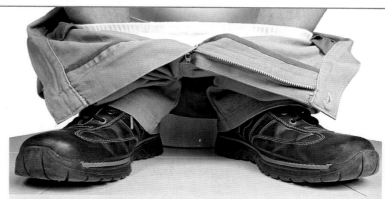

Ball cocks

How do they both refill and stop your toilet from overflowing?

 A ball cock is a simple float valve that moderates the amount of water in your toilet's cistern. It both opens a water-in valve when the water level in your tank is low, and shuts off that valve when the water reaches a pre-set point called the toilet's fill line. A ball cock's construction is usually characterised by a hollow spherical plastic balloon on the end of a metal rod, which in turn leads to the cap of the flow valve. The plastic balloon sits on the surface of the tank's water at the fill line and when the toilet is operated and the water level in the tank reduces the balloon drops with it, lifting the valve cap in a seesaw motion. Only when the level of water in the tank is returned to the fill line does the ball cock rise to a level where the valve cap is replaced, shutting off the water supply. ✿

Ball cock
A simple float valve, the ball cock floats at the cistern's fill line when the toilet is not in use and prevents extra water entering the system from the fill valve.

Fill line
The fill line in a cistern dictates at what height the ball cock should close the fill valve, stopping the tank from overflowing. The higher the fill line the more water is allowed into the tank.

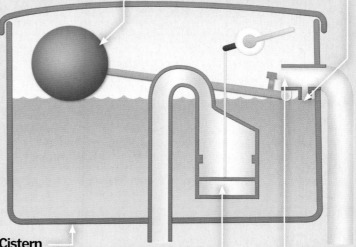

Cistern
The main tank found on flush-based toilets, the cistern houses the other mechanisms of the flush system as well as a set amount of water to be released down the flush tube when the toilet's handle is pressed.

Flapper
When the handle of the toilet is flushed the flapper, which is directly connected to it via a metal chain, is opened releasing the tank's contents down the flush tube.

Fill valve
Connected to the plumbing network of the building, the fill valve is the part of the system in which fresh water enters the tank when it is empty post-flush. It is directly controlled by the level of the ball cock.

> *"No longer was music trapped in the present. Now it could be recorded, stored and replayed in the future"*

Audio reproduction

Since the creation of the phonograph in the late-19th Century, sound reproduction systems have evolved massively, culminating in the hi-tech audio and loudspeaker systems we use today

© Monitor Audio

The recording and reproduction of audio undertook sweeping changes throughout the late 19th and 20th Centuries, offering numerous new storage mediums, playback systems and methodologies that allowed humans to control the sound wave like never before. At first relying on mechanical inscription and re-creation techniques, before advancing on to electrical methods, the analogue and digital recording of speech, music and environmental noise has brought sounds never before heard to the masses, and created two of the most dominant entertainment businesses on the planet: music and film.

Indeed, when the phonograph (the earliest form of audio recording and reproduction system, partnered with a horn loudspeaker) was invented in the latter half of the 20th Century, it advertised a system that could 'transport you to the realms of music' and that it could 'bring the theatre or opera to your home' after a hard day's work. It was a revelation. The sound wave had been captured and harnessed by man. No longer was music and speech trapped in the present. Now it could be recorded, stored and replayed in the future. Higher forms of musical entertainment were no longer the reserve of only the rich and powerful, with the best opera and ballet scores transported to the homes of many.

Since then techniques and machines used to record and reproduce audio have progressed rapidly, and with them have the loudspeakers necessary to output their signals. Most early phonographs or gramophones used horn loudspeakers, which acted like modern-day amplifiers, and worked by increasing the coupling efficiency (akin to increasing the surface area of an object) between the system's driver, which was often a small metal diaphragm, and the surrounding air. This mechanical amplification effectively increased the volume of the outputted vibrations emanating from the diaphragm, and made the sound audible to listeners over a wider area.

Now, of course, amplification is normally achieved through electrically driven amplifiers, and the complex loudspeaker systems in use today rely on more than just spreading the surface area of sound waves. Here we take a closer look at how modern loudspeakers work. ⚙

History of audio systems

Audio systems have evolved massively since their creation in the late-19th Century

Cylinder phonograph

Date made: 1877

By rotating cylindrical records on which audio was engraved, these engravings would, via the medium of a stylus, vibrate a diaphragm at the base of a metal horn, which would in turn amplify the sound.

© Holger Ellgaard

Gramophone

Date made: 1892

Gramophones read the grooves in the circular disks by their needle – like the cylindrical phonograph did with its stylus – amplifying sound by horn and later electronic amplification technology.

© HGeorges Jansoone

5 TOP FACTS
SPEAKERS AND AUDIO

Feel the base
1 At 190 decibels the human eardrum has a 50 per cent chance of rupturing, and this can result in loss of hearing and take weeks before the eardrum heals completely.

Maximum power
2 The world's loudest speaker is the Wyle Labs' WAS 3000, which can produce a sound level of 165 decibels, five times louder than a space shuttle taking off.

Do you retro?
3 The last mass-market cylindrical phonograph record was produced as late as 1929, while today they are still made by specialist audio companies for collectors.

Crossed channels
4 During WWII the residents of Dover reported that they could hear the sound waves emanating from warfare across the channel in France, a distance of 34 km away.

Can't keep it down
5 Despite the dominance of the CD, over 1.8 million vinyl records were sold in the United States in 2008, an increase of over 800 thousand from 2007.

DID YOU KNOW? German scientist Johann Philipp Reis created the original loudspeaker in 1861

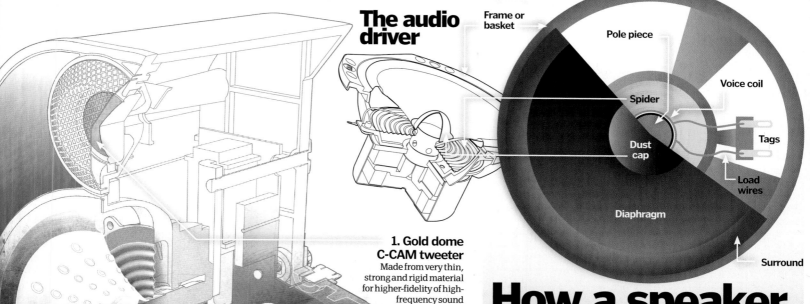

The audio driver

Frame or basket

Pole piece

Voice coil

Spider

Tags

Dust cap

Load wires

Diaphragm

Surround

© Monitor Audio

1. Gold dome C-CAM tweeter
Made from very thin, strong and rigid material for higher-fidelity of high-frequency sound reproduction.

2. C-CAM RST driver
A classical driver, though lighter and stronger to prevent distortion of mid and low-tonal frequencies when driven hard at its limits.

4. Single through-bolt fixings
These allow the drivers to float freely within the system, eliminating a major source of distortion in common speakers.

3. HiVe port
A technically advanced input port ensuring air movement is consistently rapid, improving bass speed and punch.

Inside a speaker
A closer look at the Apex 10 speaker

How a speaker works

Even the clearest of recordings are useless without a good loudspeaker

The modern loudspeaker, as demonstrated by the Monitor Audio Apex series, produces sound by converting electrical signals from an audio amplifier into mechanical motion, from which sound waves emanate. Loudspeakers can consist of an individual transducer (audio driver) or a series of drivers encased within large chassis, each dealing with a certain frequency band to improve the overall gamut and fidelity of reproduced sounds.

For example, larger subwoofer speakers deal with low frequencies, while smaller speakers called tweeters deal with high frequencies. These various drivers are controlled by a filter network, which organises the different frequency signals coming from the amplifier and directs them to the driver most suitable to deal with it.

The construction of a single loudspeaker driver is a complex process, the central element of which is a concave plastic or paper conical disc. This is the part that moves backwards and forwards in the generation of sound, fixed in the centre of a concave metal frame. Attached to the cone is a hollow cylinder of aluminium and a pair of wire coils suspended by a flexible fabric disc. These coils are attached to the amplifier and positioned inside a narrow cylindrical groove in the centre of a magnet. By doing this, every time a signal travels through the wires, the coil emits a magnetic field that pushes or pulls the cone backwards or forwards, forming sound waves.

Tape player
Date made: 1950
The invention of magnetic tape lead to the creation of reel-to-reel tape players. Magnetic tape allowed large recordings to be stored for lengthy periods of time and done so in multiple takes.

© Nixdorf

CD player
Date made: 1982
With the introduction of compact discs, CD players took over as the dominant audio system. CD players work by rotating a disc between 200 and 500rpm, reading the encoded information contained on it with a laser beam.

© Les Chatfield

MP3 player
Date made: 1997
The current player of choice, these work by converting an audio wave into a sequence of binary numbers, which can then be stored in a digital format such as MP3, before utilising audio codecs.

DID YOU KNOW?

Speaker placement can alter sound quality

Due to the fact that sound bounces off of the objects in your room, where you position your speakers will directly effect the quality of the sound that you hear. For instance, placing speakers too close to the wall will increase the bass sound, making it too loud or boomy. In general try to keep the speaker 8 cm from the wall, the speakers' distance from the side wall should be 1.6 times the distance from the front wall. Angle the speakers inwards towards the general listening spot.

Inside a freestanding speaker

The Monitor Audio PL300 demonstrates what lies inside the cabinet

1. Bitumastic damping
This adhesive is applied to all internal cabinet walls to reduce resonance damping as well as aiding structural rigidity.

5. Tapered Line Enclosure (TLE)
Formed from a ARC thermo-set polymer, the Tapered Line Enclosure houses all of the mid-range drivers in the PL300, preventing the propagation of standing waves and modal resonances.

2. Polymer casing
Almost all elements of the PL300 loudspeaker's case, including front baffles, plinths and mid-range driver housings, are cast from a thermo-set polymer characterised by its high mineral content.

3. Steel 'pin hole' brace
A set of four steel braces, tightened to a specific torque, run through the polymer casing to further reduce unwanted resonance

4. HiVe II high velocity reflex ports
Twin HiVe II ports allow maximum airflow in and out of the cabinet quicker than a conventional port as well as reducing turbulence, providing super-powerful bass and a superior transient response

6. Composite plinth
Raising the casing from the floor, the composite plinth helps prevent vibration distortion as well as reducing resonance

The PL300 from Monitor Audio represents the current pinnacle of multi-driver, loudspeaker technology

1. The Who
Where: London, England
When: 31 May 1976
How loud: 126dB

2. Manowar
Where: Hanover, Germany
When: 8 March 1984
How loud: 129.5dB

3. Kiss
Where: Ottawa, Canada,
When: 15 July 2009
How loud: 136dB

DID YOU KNOW? *The speed of sound varies depending on temperature and altitude*

Multi-driver loudspeaker enclosures

Floor-standing loudspeakers are now being produced which combine multiple audio drivers with audio-friendly, structurally complex cases

The enclosure of any loudspeaker plays a highly significant role in the reproduction of sound, as well as providing a unit in which the speaker's drivers, electronic circuitry, crossover control and amplifier are all mounted.

Current state-of-the-art enclosures are built from composite materials and include numerous struts, baffles air ports and acoustic insulation materials and adhesives. These work together to reduce echo and reverberation caused by rearward sound waves generated by the speaker's drivers reflecting off the back and sides of the case. This is important for audio fidelity and accuracy of reproduction, as rogue or errant sound waves can interfere with forward-generated waves, distorting them

and adding effects not part of the original recording. The enclosure, thanks to its complex construction, is also the key factor in reducing vibrations caused by the back and forth movement of the driver diaphragm, shake of the driver chassis and rumble of any subwoofer.

Historically, in early forms of loudspeaker, drivers were often left exposed completely or partially due to heat-related issues with their electronics, as well as because of the fixed, unsuspended nature of the driver chassis and the difficulty in securing a consistent airflow. Further, the materials used in these early loudspeakers (usually heavy metals) were prone to vibration issues and did little to prevent standing waves, while their chunky

and bulky designs caused diffraction of sound waves from their sharp edges.

Today, these flaws are minimised by audio-friendly, lightweight polymer casing materials, which are manufactured with smooth edges to reduce refraction and coated with resonance and vibration damping adhesives. Single component plinths, baffles and struts, as well as lightweight driver chassis also aid the accuracy of sound reproduction and, thanks to the inclusion of transmission lines (an internal structure within the loudspeaker enclosure designed to guide up to 90 per cent of a driver's rear wave output away from distortion-prone areas) in modern cabinets, has allowed sleeker and more compact driver arrays.

An example of an older, metal-framed, audio driver chassis

Head to Head
SPEAKER DRIVERS

TOP END

1. Tweeters
Tweeters are much smaller units, designed to produce the highest frequencies typically from around 2,000Hz to 20,000Hz. Some tweeters can manage response up to 45kHz. Nearly all tweeters are electrodynamic drivers, using a voice coil suspended within a fixed magnetic field. The name is derived from the high-pitched sounds made by birds.

MIDDLE

2. Midrange
As the name suggests, midrange drivers produce a range of frequencies in the middle of the sound spectrum, with a frequency range from approximately 300–5,000Hz. Midrange drivers handle the most significant part of the audible sound spectrum. For this reason the midrange speaker must be good quality or discrepancies will be heard.

BASS IN YER FACE

3. Woofer
Designed to produce low frequency sounds, typically from around 40Hz up to about a kilohertz or higher. The most common design for a woofer is the electrodynamic driver, which typically uses a stiff paper cone, driven by a voice coil which is surrounded by a magnetic field. The voice coil is attached by adhesives to the back of the speaker cone. Woofers are generally used to cover the lowest octaves of the system's frequency range although subwoofers are also sometimes employed.

Polar frequency patterns

Frequency has dynamic effects on loudspeakers

Composite images of six loudspeaker polar patterns taken at six frequencies over a five octave range. The speaker is a Bosch 36 watt column with four four-inch drivers arranged in a columnar enclosure 841mm high. The Polar prediction software used is CLF viewer and loudspeaker information was gathered by the manufacturer.

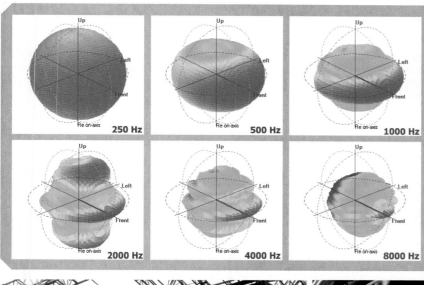

250 Hz · 500 Hz · 1000 Hz · 2000 Hz · 4000 Hz · 8000 Hz

Suspended stadium loudspeakers

Where does he put the luggage?

How an elevator works

The lift was a world-changing invention because it enabled the creation of today's stunning skyscrapers, not to mention saving an incredible amount of time and effort. Imagine a world with just stairs...

Most modern lifts use a cable system. The lift car runs up and down rails within a shaft, and at the top of the shaft is an electric motor that turns a large wheel, or sheave. Cables run over this, one end of which is attached to the car, the other end to a counterweight.

The counterweight weighs the same as the car plus a typical half load, which means that the two structures balance each other out, so the motor doesn't need to work very hard to move the lift; it just needs to overcome the friction within the system. Of course, the motor must be strong enough to cope with the lift being fully loaded, but this only happens occasionally.

A number of cables are used as back-up in the rare event of one failing. In addition, an automatic brake activates if the lift falls too fast. So those horror-movie scenes of plummeting lifts and flailing cables can never become reality.

Inside a lift shaft

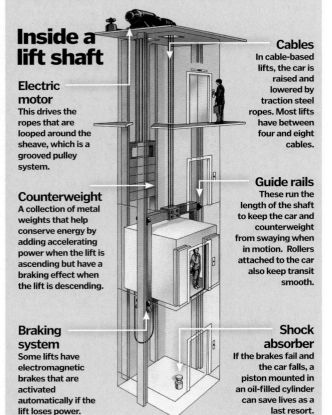

Electric motor
This drives the ropes that are looped around the sheave, which is a grooved pulley system.

Counterweight
A collection of metal weights that help conserve energy by adding accelerating power when the lift is ascending but have a braking effect when the lift is descending.

Braking system
Some lifts have electromagnetic brakes that are activated automatically if the lift loses power.

Cables
In cable-based lifts, the car is raised and lowered by traction steel ropes. Most lifts have between four and eight cables.

Guide rails
These run the length of the shaft to keep the car and counterweight from swaying when in motion. Rollers attached to the car also keep transit smooth.

Shock absorber
If the brakes fail and the car falls, a piston mounted in an oil-filled cylinder can save lives as a last resort.

IBM's Roadrunner

How many processors does it require to compute at the speed of 10,000 PCs?

IBM's Roadrunner supercomputer is one of the fastest on the planet. It's designed to run at 1.7 petaflops although the maximum it has achieved is 1.4. But don't think that's below standard – take a look at how its speed is measured.

FLOPS, which stands for FLoating-point Operations Per Second, is the unit of measurement that governs how much data a computer can crunch, measured by the quantity of a particular kind of sum it can do (a floating-point operation) every second. Your average desktop Mac or PC can do a gigaflop or so – that's about a billion floating point operations a second. To understand the power of the Roadrunner, you need to multiply that by roughly a thousand, and a thousand again – a teraflop is equal to 1,024 gigaflops, and a petaflop is equal to 1,024 teraflops.

The Roadrunner can get nearly 445 megaflops for every watt of power it uses, making it the fourth most energy-efficient computer in the world. This may be thanks to its design: Roadrunner is made out of lots of other computers which have been stripped down to remove non-essentials. Powered by nearly 18,000 processors, Roadrunner is a mixture of IBM's own brand and AMD's dual-core Opteron chips. Despite its sci-fi looks and super speed, much of it is made from off-the-shelf parts. This is what's called a cluster computer – a supercomputer made of other computers – and it's configured in a way known as Triblade: made up of sections comprising two AMD chips and eight IBM ones with 16GB of RAM apiece. The Roadrunner has a total of 3,240 clusters working concurrently, which powers its awesome number-crunching speed.

Noise-cancelling headphones

The way we listen to music has changed dramatically in recent years, making noise-cancelling headphones more important... and expensive

Noise-cancelling technology is not to be confused with noise reducing, although the best examples use a combination of both. Noise reducing – a 'passive' solution that relies on insulating the ears against unwanted sound – tends to be cheaper and applies to both earphones and headphones. Noise cancelling, meanwhile, employs Active Noise Control (ANC) to create sound waves of the opposite frequency to those you wish to block out – also known as anti-noise. This is achieved by positioning tiny microphones close to each earpiece, fast-reacting amplification circuitry to create the anti-noise and a battery for power.

Most studies indicate that ANC is more effective with continuous low-frequency sounds (such as traffic) than rapidly changing mid-frequency ones (such as human conversation) and may also create its own high-frequency hiss. Design-wise they can either sit around or on the ear with prices as high as £400 a pair.

5 TOP FACTS
CRANES

Mobile crane
1 The most versatile crane for both small and large jobs is simply a telescoping hydraulic boom attached to the bed of a heavy-duty construction vehicle.

Overhead crane
2 Shaped like an upside down 'U', this small but powerful crane rolls along tracks on factory floors to lift car engines and other heavy parts into place.

Self-erecting cranes
3 This crane rolls onto the work site as a compact, foldable unit only 13.6m long. The crane rises and extends its jib 32m out with a holding capacity of 4,000kg.

Luffing tower crane
4 The jib arm of this tower crane – which can still carry 35 tons – can be raised from a flat horizontal position to an 85-degree angle using a special jib cable and motor.

Hammerhead tower crane
5 The classic T-shaped tower crane with a fixed horizontal jib and counterweight arm. The hammerhead lacks freedom of movement, but can carry more weight.

DID YOU KNOW? Tower cranes are designed to withstand wind gusts up to 150kph

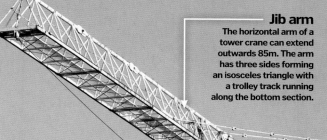

Load and stability

Hold a 10kg weight close to your body. Now try to extend your arms without tipping over. Tough, isn't it? Tower cranes have the same problem. A large tower crane can handle loads up to 16 tons, but that's only at a horizontal distance that's very close to the tower. At 80 metres out on the jib, the most that the same crane can carry is 3.9 tons. Tower cranes are preloaded with multiple slabs of concrete counterweights to maintain the overall equilibrium of the arm. A crane that carries heavy loads at 80 metres from the tower requires 31 tons of counterweight.

Jib arm
The horizontal arm of a tower crane can extend outwards 85m. The arm has three sides forming an isosceles triangle with a trolley track running along the bottom section.

Trolley
The trolley and hook are connected by cables to a trolley motor mounted on the upper side of the jib arm. The operator can roll the trolley back and forth with hand controls.

Cat head tower
On hammerhead tower cranes, the cat head tower reinforces the jib arm and counterweight jib using thick steel cables called pendants.

Machinery arm
The power to raise and lower the load line is supplied by a huge winch located along the counterweight jib or machinery arm.

Operator's cab
It's a long climb to the cab, where the crane operator has a bird's-eye view of the construction site through floor-to-ceiling windows.

How tower cranes work

These big birds of sky-high construction are engineering marvels

Tower cranes flock to money. During the economic boom years, high-rise construction cranes migrated from Beijing to Shanghai to Dubai, where it was estimated in 2006 that there was one tower crane for every 44 residents of the desert boom-opolis.

Tower cranes are feats of structural engineering that often outshine their creations. They are designed to stand 80 metres tall and reach 80 metres out supported only by a narrow steel-frame mast, a concrete foundation and several counterweights.

The engineering principle that keeps the twiggy tower crane from tipping over is something called a 'moment'. If you hang a weight from the crane's jib arm, it exerts a rotational force or torque where the arm connects to the top of the mast. The magnitude and direction of this force (clockwise or anti-clockwise) is called the moment. If the weight is hung close to the mast, the magnitude of the moment is lower than if the weight is hung far out on the jib. To keep the crane upright, counterweights are used to create a moment of equal magnitude in the opposite direction, balancing out the rotational forces.

Once a tower crane meets its maximum unsupported height, it can be tethered to the building itself and continue to grow with the rising skyscraper. The tower cranes that rose with the construction of the record-breaking Burj Khalifa skyscraper in Dubai reached a truly dizzying height of 750 metres. ✿

The tower
Also known as the mast, each 2.8-metre tower section has four sides, each with vertical, horizontal and diagonal trusses that give them full structural integrity.

Slewing unit
This motorised pivot allows the jib arm to rotate nearly 360 degrees to lift and drop materials all across the construction site.

Counterweights
Multiple concrete slabs – each weighing several tons – are hung or piled on the very back end of the counterweight jib to overcompensate for the crane's lifting capacity.

Hydraulic climbing section
The hydraulic unit attaches to the outside of the tower. A powerful hydraulic arm lifts the entire top section of the crane just enough for the crane to insert a new section beneath.

Concrete foundation
Large tower cranes get their core stability by burying the bottom of the tower in several metres of concrete weighing 185 tons.

Self-assembling crane

One of the most remarkable engineering feats of tower cranes is that they can literally build themselves. With help from a large mobile crane, construction workers secure the base sections of the tower and assemble the top unit of the crane – the slewing unit, jib and machinery arm.

But before the top section of the crane is attached, workers slide a hydraulic climbing unit around the base of the tower. Once everything is in place, the hydraulic climbing unit lifts the entire top section of the crane (including the horizontal jib and operator's cab) just enough to slide in a new section of tower beneath. Once the new section is secured, the hydraulic unit continues to climb up, section by section, as the crane slowly builds itself higher.

© Nebrot 08

"The Airblade takes just ten seconds to dry your hands, whereas a conventional dryer will take up to 44 seconds"

Conventional warm-air hand dryers never seem to do a great job of actually drying your hands. That's because they simply blow out a low-power stream of warm air that slowly evaporates the water from your wet hands.

Indeed, inventor Sir James Dyson was so fed up with having to wipe his hands down his trousers after using a dryer, that he took a fresh look at the problem and came up with the Dyson Airblade – the dryer that works much faster, more efficiently and without spreading nasty germs.

To use the Airblade, simply place your hands in it and draw them slowly up. 'Blades' of cool air travelling at 643 kmph and driven by a special digital motor scrape the water from your hands, leaving them dry. And the Airblade takes just ten seconds to dry your hands, whereas a conventional dryer will take up to 44 seconds.

What's more, because the air has been effectively filtered as it entered the Airblade, it's free from bacteria, which makes it more hygienic. In fact, the Airblade is said to be the world's only dryer that has been certified as hygienic by NSF International, the public health specialist. Other dryers simply suck in germ-filled air from the washroom, warm it up and blow it back out, germs and all. ✿

Inside the Airblade
The Airblade combines high technology within a remarkably compact and stylish package

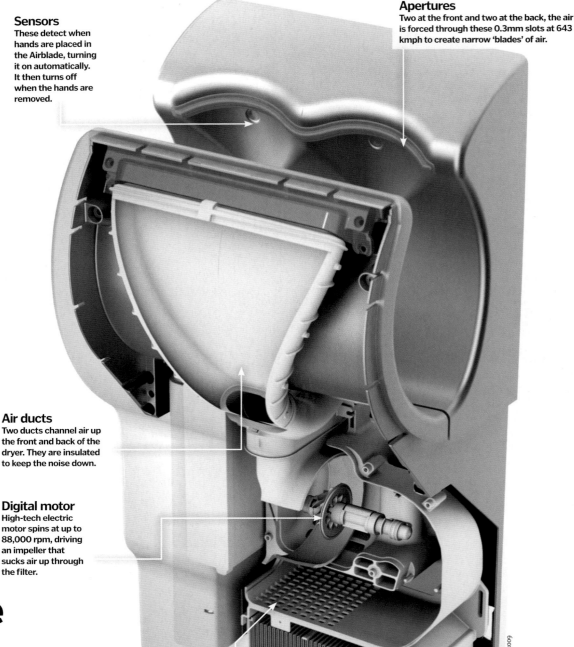

Sensors
These detect when hands are placed in the Airblade, turning it on automatically. It then turns off when the hands are removed.

Apertures
Two at the front and two at the back, the air is forced through these 0.3mm slots at 643 kmph to create narrow 'blades' of air.

Air ducts
Two ducts channel air up the front and back of the dryer. They are insulated to keep the noise down.

Digital motor
High-tech electric motor spins at up to 88,000 rpm, driving an impeller that sucks air up through the filter.

HEPA filter
High efficiency particulate air or HEPA filter consists of fine fibres that remove at least 99.7 per cent of airborne bacteria from the washroom air.

All images © Dyson 2009

The Dyson

DID YOU KNOW? *The Airblade is accredited by the British Skin Foundation and the Royal Institute of Public Health*

The Dyson digital motor

Impeller and vane diffuser
The three-dimensional impeller is designed to suck air in and through the vane diffuser in an efficient manner.

Neodymium magnet
Neodymium is a very strong magnetic material. The rapidly alternating electromagnetic field of the stator causes the magnet to spin at up to 88,000 revolutions per minute.

The secret of the Airblade lies in a special electric motor developed by Dyson's engineers. Conventional electric motors use brushes, which create friction, wear out and produce carbon dust. They also have heavy, bulky magnets and windings.

The Dyson digital motor, on the other hand, dispenses with brushes and instead uses digital pulse technology to spin at high speed. Because they don't have such large windings and magnets, digital motors are lighter and smaller than conventional ones. Similar motors are also used in Dyson's famous vacuum cleaners.

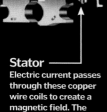

Stator
Electric current passes through these copper wire coils to create a magnetic field. The polarity of this field switches rapidly from north to south.

Circuit board and capacitors
The circuit board controls the motor timing and speed, making adjustments up to 3,000 times a second. The capacitors supply current to the circuit board.

How it dries your hands

The blasts of air dry your hands as you place them into the dryer

Not only does the Airblade dry your hands, it's the only dryer that's been certified hygienic by NSF International

Impeller factor
The impeller's aerodynamic design means that its continuously curving blades spin at phenomenal speeds. The airflow produced is then channelled up and through the vane diffuser, as well as cooling other components of the system.

5 TOP FACTS
DYSON AIRBLADE

1 **High tolerance**
There is just 0.3mm clearance between the impeller and its housing.

2 **Super strong magnet**
The neodymium magnet is ten times stronger than a typical everyday magnet.

3 **Super sucker**
The Airblade sucks in 37 litres of air every second.

4 **Efficiency dryer**
The Airblade uses up to 80 per cent less energy than a conventional dryer.

5 **Cheaper than paper**
For the price of one paper towel, the Airblade dries up to 19 pairs of hands.

At last, a hand dryer that doesn't leave you wiping your hands down your trousers

Airblade

Using barcodes

How this printed version of Morse code has revolutionised the checkout

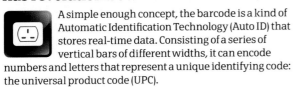

A simple enough concept, the barcode is a kind of Automatic Identification Technology (Auto ID) that stores real-time data. Consisting of a series of vertical bars of different widths, it can encode numbers and letters that represent a unique identifying code: the universal product code (UPC).

The barcode can then be read and interpreted by an electronic scanner, which electro-optically converts bars and spaces into numbers – the alphanumeric version below the barcode can also be read by the human operator. Information can then be transferred to a data-processing system directly.

This method of representing data has automated the supermarket checkout so that whenever we purchase an item, all the product details are catalogued every time a product's barcode is scanned. This allows retailers instant access to information about the item, enabling them to keep track of prices and price changes, product descriptions, stock levels and automatic re-ordering. A very useful everyday cryptogram. ❂

Impressive technology that we take for granted

How do flash drives work?

Find out how these versatile plug-and-play devices can store your data

Similar in nature to a conventional hard drive, a flash drive is a very convenient device capable of not only storing data, but also transferring it quickly between computers and digital devices. A form of solid-state storage (electronic, with no moving parts), flash drives are both robust and small enough to fit in your pocket and yet can hold vast quantities of data – up to 16GB – depending on how great their storage capacity. Flash memory is a type of EEPROM (Electrically Erasable Programmable Read-Only Memory) stored as small blocks. The chunks of data stored using flash memory can be erased and re-programmed electronically, making it a quick, effective way of transferring files.

Insert the flash drive into the computer's USB port and the computer will automatically detect the device. It will then act like an external hard drive, allowing you to immediately begin storing and retrieving data. The internal workings of a flash drive consist of a small printed circuit board (PCB) that features some power circuitry and a few mini integrated circuits: one of these circuits provides an interface to the USB port, one drives the memory, and another – perhaps the most important – is the flash memory as you can see from our annotation. ❂

Stun guns

What happens if you're zapped by one of these electrifying weapons?

A stun gun is a non-lethal personal protection device that generates a high-voltage, low-amperage electrical charge. Stun guns operate on nine-volt batteries and have the power to deliver up to 300,000 volts to the body. It sounds like a lot, but our nervous system creates natural electrical impulses that enable us to move, think and feel – the electrical charge of a stun gun simply over-stimulates these nerves.

The battery sends power to a circuit, consisting of transformers that transfer electrical energy from one circuit to another. The transformers boost the voltage and yet reduce the amperage as an oscillator varies the current, creating pulses of electricity. The pulsed current charges a capacitor that builds the charge released to a pair of electrodes. These are spaced apart so the current doesn't flow until a conductor completes the circuit. Humans can conduct electricity so if the electrodes make contact with a person, the circuit is complete and the shock delivered. ❂

© junglecat 2008

TASER X26

How the flash memory chip works

Inside your storage device

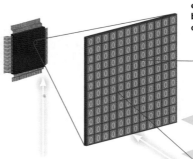

3. Electrical charge
Once data enters via the USB, electrical energy (controlled by the gate transistors) charges certain cells.

4. Thin oxide layer
The electrical charge pierces the oxide layer until it is drained away by opening the floating gate.

1. Flash memory chip
Inside this memory chip is an array of memory cells and two gates – a floating gate (electrically separate from the rest of the device and surrounded by a thin oxide layer) and a control gate transistor that affects the flow of electricity.

2. Enlarged memory cell
Each memory cell contains binary code in the form of 0s and 1s. When no data is stored, the cells are all set to 0 because the voltage on the gate is blocked.

5. Stored data
The charge becomes trapped on the oxide and the cells become 1s. This pattern of 0s and 1s are stored as data in the memory.

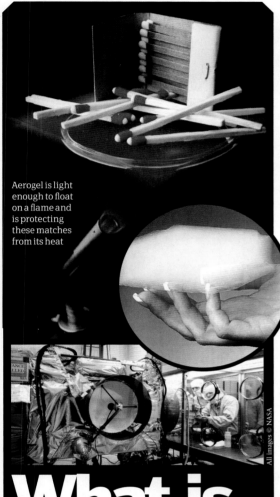

Aerogel is light enough to float on a flame and is protecting these matches from its heat

All images © NASA

What is aerogel?

The strongest, lightest material known to man is just three times the density of air

Aerogel is a highly porous sponge-like solid, usually formed from silica gel. In 1930, American chemist Samuel Kistler created the world's first aerogel using a process called supercritical fluid drying, during which the liquid part of the gel is carefully transformed into gas. Sometimes referred to as frozen smoke, aerogel is surprisingly strong considering it has an extremely low density. Such porous substances are often exploited for their useful insulating properties.

NASA's Stardust spacecraft even used aerogel to catch tiny interstellar dust and comet particles from the Comet Wild 2. When a particle strikes the aerogel, it is slowed to a gradual stop and becomes buried in the incredibly light yet incredibly durable material. Scientists are then able to locate and examine the tiny comet particles upon their return to Earth. ✿

In the spin

How do washing machines clean our clothes?

Most homes are lucky enough to have one, but have you ever wondered how a washing machine works? After separating your laundry into whites and colours – so as to protect your whites from colour run – load your clothes into the main drum and close the door. Once you've programmed the machine to tell it what sort of wash you require – temperature, speed, length and so on – the machine then adds water and detergent and sloshes the clothes around. After a time, the drum will spin really fast – up to 130 kmph – creating a centrifugal force that extracts most of the water out of the clothes and out through the holes in the inner drum where it is then pumped away. ✿

2. Detergent
The water washes through a tray containing detergent. Laundry detergent contains surfactant molecules, which are attracted to water, reducing the water's surface tension. This allows the soap to better penetrate the clothes and lift stains away.

6. Centrifugal rinsing
A pump then extracts the dirty water, and the clothes are then rinsed. The drum then spins up to 1,400 times per minute, extracting as much water from the load as possible before the cycle finishes.

1. Water inlet
Water enters the machine via inlet pipes. Modern machines endeavour to use as little water as possible in order to be environmentally friendly. Some models even have the capacity to weigh the load to assess how much water is required.

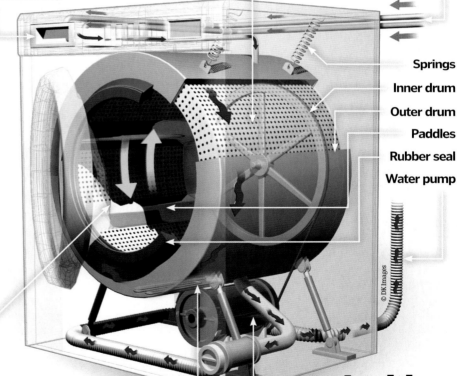

Springs
Inner drum
Outer drum
Paddles
Rubber seal
Water pump

© DK Images

5. Washing motion
The cyclical motion of the spinning drum ensures the clothes get good and soapy, and paddles around the sides of the drum scoop up the soapy water and distribute it all over the clothes. The spinning creates a lot of vibration, which can be partly absorbed by the springs located between the main drum and the outer structure.

3. Heating element
The soapy water then drains into the outer drum and through tiny holes down the sides of the inner drum where it collects at the bottom. Here the water is heated by a heating element. As less water is used in modern machines, less electricity is needed to heat it.

Inside a washing machine

4. Motor
Once the water is the right temperature – as indicated by the program selected – a motor then drives the inner drum round inside the larger outer drum. The motor is attached to a large wheel at the back of the machine.

> "In its simplest terms, a lens is a tube containing a set of glass elements"

Camera lenses

How a tube and some glass combine to resolve a photographer's creative vision

The lens is one of the most important components of any camera. In its simplest terms, a lens is a tube containing a set of glass elements (or lenses), each of which is positioned precisely to channel light through the tube, focusing it on to your camera's sensor or film plane, and resolving an image of the outside world as a result.

Zoom ring
Only found on a zoom lens – rotating this moves the lens elements to increase or decrease the lens's magnifying power.

Focusing ring
The photographer turns this to fine-tune the space between the front and rear elements in order to focus the image.

Front element
The point where light enters the lens. Front elements often have a special coating to reduce problems like ghosting or flare.

Inside a camera lens
The parts that produce the ideal picture

AF motor
Lenses with built-in AF (autofocus) motors can focus automatically rather than having to be adjusted manually.

Elements
Small lenses arranged in groups that refine the path of the light travelling through the lens to help focus the image on the sensor.

Contacts
These electronic contacts allow the camera and lens to communicate with each other, and so the lens can be controlled via the buttons and dials on the camera body.

Aperture
An adjustable opening that controls how much or little light is allowed through the lens and on to the camera's sensor. Sometimes referred to as the diaphragm or iris.

Lens mounting
The internal elements are mounted on a platform which – in a zoom lens – is adjustable, allowing for them to be moved.

© Canon

Optical vs digital zoom

If you look at any compact or superzoom digital camera's specifications, chances are it'll state values for both optical and digital zoom capability. Optical zoom refers to the ability of a camera's lens to shift its internal elements, magnifying the subject you're trying to photograph as the lens zooms to the telephoto (longest) end of its focal range. All non-fixed focal length DSLR lenses zoom optically. Digital zoom, on the other hand, involves no physical zooming mechanism at all; rather the camera crops into your image, making your subject appear to fill more of the frame. Overall image quality is reduced as the camera makes up (interpolates) pixels to create the impression of magnification, which may produce less-than-satisfactory results.

Wide
The wide-angled shot ready for some serious zooming.

Optical
Keeps quality high, found on all non-fixed focal length DSLRs.

Digital
Focuses in-depth on a specific area but loses overall quality.

3 x images © Josie Reavely

GOOD

1. 18-250mm f/3.5-6.3 DC OS HSM
Costing £573, this lens covers a decent focal range but a non-fixed aperture means less light-gathering ability as you zoom.

BETTER

2. 50-500mm f/4.5-6.3 DG OS HSM
Priced at £1,400 this telephoto lens also spans a wide focal range, but it's heavy, and can suffer from loss of sharpness.

BEST

3. 70-200mm f/2.8 EX DG MACRO HSM II
This impressive lens costs £817 and has wide fixed maximum aperture, meaning it stays the same even if you zoom in.

DID YOU KNOW? *The glass used for lenses must be completely colourless*

Different lenses

Knowing which lens to use for which shot is the key to a perfect picture

Focal length example 50mm

A standard or 'normal' lens typically has focal length equal to the diagonal of the focal plane, which is around 35mm on a 'cropped' (APS-C) sensor DSLR or 50mm on a full frame camera. The front element of a standard lens is fairly flat, so light is not significantly bent internally, and the image projected onto the sensor should roughly fill it, without any overlap. The standard lens is considered ideal for portraits as – when engineered correctly – they generate little, if any, distortion and tend to perform well in low light.

USE LENS WHEN...

... trying to capture flattering portraits with minimal distortion.

Focal length example 24mm

Wide-angle lenses have a short focal length (roughly less than 35mm on a full frame camera) and have curved front elements, which give them a wide angle of view. The fact that the glass at the front of the lens is curved outwards means the light rays enter the front element at a sharper angle, spreading light across a smaller area of the camera's sensor and therefore producing a wider angle of view in your final image. This has the effect of allowing the lens to 'see' more around it and exaggerating the wide perspective of a scene.

USE LENS WHEN...

... photographing groups of people, tall buildings or sweeping landscapes.

Focal length example 200mm

A telephoto lens covers the longer end of the focal ranges – with around 200-300mm being the most popular among enthusiasts, but professionals often use much longer optics. The front group of elements in a telephoto lens gather and project light on to a rear group of elements, which magnify the image transmitted and spread it across a wider area of the image sensor, creating a magnified version of your distant subject. This design allows the lens elements to be closer together, helping to keep the physical length of the lens barrel compact in relation to its focal length.

USE LENS IF...

... you have to shoot from a distance, such as at sporting events or when photographing wildlife and candid portraits.

Other lenses

Macro

Macro optics are highly specialised lenses with powerful magnification capabilities. They feature a flat image plane and, usually, very high-grade glass elements which are highly corrected to minimise any distortion. Most produce a 1:1 (life-size) reproduction of a subject, although some can magnify by up to five times.
USE LENS WHEN...
... you want to make small things look big.

Fisheye

A fisheye lens is an extreme version of a wide-angle lens. The front element is bulbous, literally like a fish eye, which diverges light. These lenses produce a great deal of distortion, with objects being 'pulled' away from the centre of the frame, but give a very wide angle of view – often around 180-degrees or more.
USE LENS WHEN...
... you want to get everything into your shot, or for comic effect in portraits.

Teleconverter

Teleconverters are basically tubes that contain predominantly diverging lens elements. These are attached to your existing lens and increase its magnification power, allowing you to zoom further with a telephoto lens or magnify your subject more with a macro optic, for example. The downside is they reduce the lens's maximum aperture and can reduce image quality.
USE LENS IF...
... your telephoto lens isn't quite long enough to fill the frame with your subject.

089

> "The three key benefits to OLED displays all stem from that lack of a backlight"

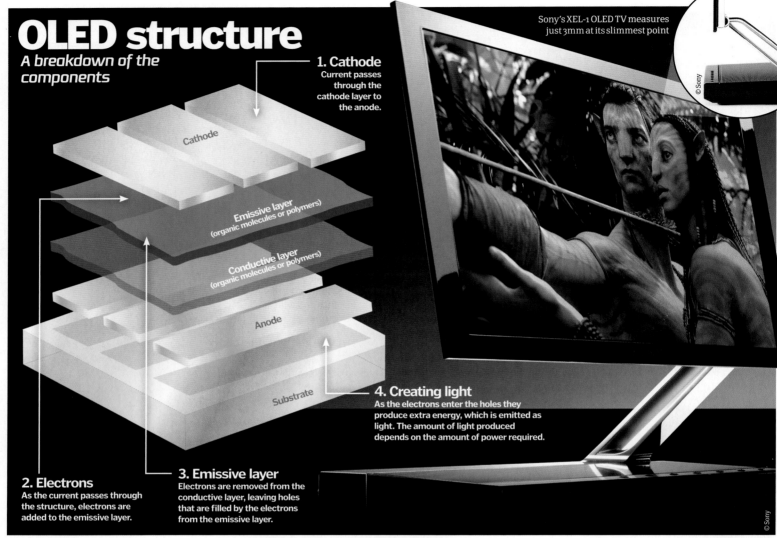

OLED structure
A breakdown of the components

1. Cathode
Current passes through the cathode layer to the anode.

Cathode

Emissive layer
(organic molecules or polymers)

Conductive layer
(organic molecules or polymers)

Anode

Substrate

Sony's XEL-1 OLED TV measures just 3mm at its slimmest point

4. Creating light
As the electrons enter the holes they produce extra energy, which is emitted as light. The amount of light produced depends on the amount of power required.

2. Electrons
As the current passes through the structure, electrons are added to the emissive layer.

3. Emissive layer
Electrons are removed from the conductive layer, leaving holes that are filled by the electrons from the emissive layer.

How OLEDs work

Measuring just 3mm thick, OLED displays are changing the face of our TVs and mobile phones

TVs have come a long way since the massive boxes hogging the corner of your living room. Yet even your current flat-screen LCD TV will soon look unwieldy compared to the next generation of products. With OLED (organic light-emitting diode) technology TVs, computer monitors, mobile phones and pretty much anything else with a screen are set to become thinner than ever before.

OLED is a major step on from the LCD technology that is currently used. In simple terms, it is created from organic materials that emit light when power is passed through it. An OLED display contains thin films of organic materials placed between two conductors; as the current passes through, the display lights up. This self-illuminating function removes the need for the backlight that is an essential requirement of a traditional LCD screen.

There are two kinds of OLED display, of which AMOLED (active matrix) is the most important. Designed for larger displays (of over about three inches), it allows for each individual pixel on the screen to be controlled separately.

The three key benefits to OLED displays all stem from that lack of a backlight. The immediate consequence is that devices can be made thinner – a 40-inch LCD TV needs a backlight large enough to span and light the entire surface of the screen evenly. Without this problem, the same sized OLED-based TV could be little more than a inch thick, and as miniaturisation of the other components powering devices develops further, they will only continue to get thinner.

The next benefit is that without that backlight, the screens draw far less power. While a black image on an LCD display is backlit to the same degree as a

white screen, the light on an AMOLED display directly corresponds to the brightness of each individual pixel. For devices that run on battery power, like mobile phones, this is a massive boon. The final benefit comes in the form of a massive improvement in image quality, with greater contrast between light and dark colours thanks to the absence of the backlight that turns blacks into dark greys on a traditional LCD.

Of course, thinner hardware is only the first step in what OLED technology will bring us. Through nanotechnology companies like Sony and Toshiba have created screens that measure less than half a millimetre thick, making them extremely flexible. Imagine a mobile phone with a large screen that can be folded to keep it pocketable, or even wearable computers built into clothing – this is no longer just the stuff of science fiction. ✿

DID YOU KNOW? The first refrigerator to see widespread use was the General Electric refrigerator introduced in 1927

How fridges cool

Fridges are one of the most important kitchen appliances, but how do they work?

To achieve a cooling effect, the fridge relies on the simple notion of evaporation, absorbing heat when a liquid changes its state. This evaporation is the central principle of the refrigeration cycle, a perpetual loop in which a refrigerant is forced to change state in order to invoke heat absorption.

The cycle begins with the refrigerant in a vapour state, which is then pressurised in an internal compressor. This compression forces the refrigerant to heat up before being sent outside the fridge into a condenser and expelled into the surrounding area, cooling the refrigerant vapour in the process and condensing it into a highly pressurised liquid state. This liquid is then sucked through an expansion valve and back into the low-pressure fridge compartment causing the refrigerant to boil, vaporise and drop in temperature, cooling the compartment in the process. The cycle then begins again, with the low-pressure refrigerant vapour being sucked up into the compressor. ✿

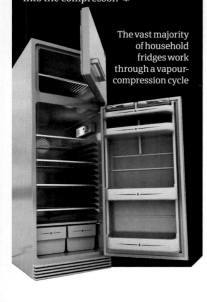

The vast majority of household fridges work through a vapour-compression cycle

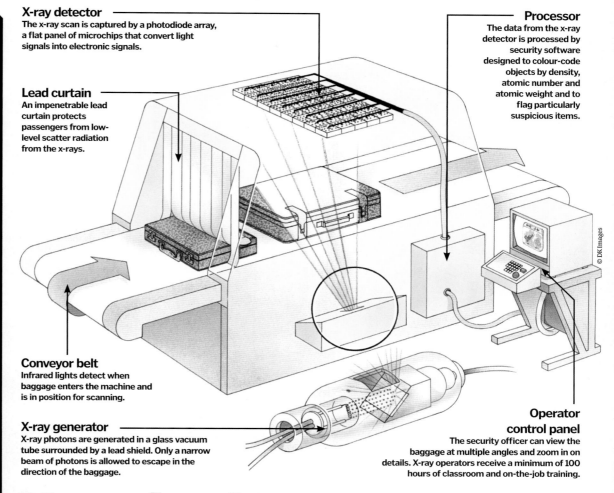

X-ray detector
The x-ray scan is captured by a photodiode array, a flat panel of microchips that convert light signals into electronic signals.

Processor
The data from the x-ray detector is processed by security software designed to colour-code objects by density, atomic number and atomic weight and to flag particularly suspicious items.

Lead curtain
An impenetrable lead curtain protects passengers from low-level scatter radiation from the x-rays.

Conveyor belt
Infrared lights detect when baggage enters the machine and is in position for scanning.

X-ray generator
X-ray photons are generated in a glass vacuum tube surrounded by a lead shield. Only a narrow beam of photons is allowed to escape in the direction of the baggage.

Operator control panel
The security officer can view the baggage at multiple angles and zoom in on details. X-ray operators receive a minimum of 100 hours of classroom and on-the-job training.

© DK Images

How do airport scanners check our bags?

The technology behind the long queues at the airport

It's every traveller's nightmare – gridlock in the airport security area. Like a dutiful patriot, you remove your shoes, belt, wallet, mobile phone, watch and loose change and shuffle through the endless line. Finally you make it to the machine. The laptop comes out of its case, the jacket is laid flat on the conveyor, then – beep – your bag is flagged for inspection.

X-ray baggage scanners are based on the same technology as x-ray machines in hospitals. An x-ray generator emits a beam of high-energy x-ray photons that pass through the baggage towards a detector plate. X-rays have very short wavelengths, so they easily pass through low-density materials (like skin and clothing) but get absorbed by higher-density materials with larger atoms (like bone and metals).

In a baggage scanner, the x-rays are captured by an internal detector plate and relayed as digital data to the security officer's computer. The computer takes all of the information from the x-ray scan – including the relative density, atomic number and atomic weight of every item in the bag – and uses software algorithms to colour-code objects as organic, inorganic, liquid, precious metals, currency, drugs, weapons and even explosives. Newer x-ray machines use dual scanners to produce two simultaneous images of the bag: top-down and from the side.

It's the security officer's job to interpret the red, brown and blue blobs on the screen and quickly decide if a suspicious rectangle is peanut butter or plastique. That's why so many pieces of innocent baggage get flagged for hand checks – the cost of getting it wrong is too high.

Staring at x-rays of sweaters and shaving kits can be mind-numbing work. To keep security officers on their toes, the latest x-ray scanners are loaded with something called TIP (Threat Image Protection), which digitally superimposes images of suspicious items onto random bags. The poor officer thinks it's a real knife or detonator until his presses his alert button, then the software lets him off the hook. ✿

"The iPad's design oozes the smart, sophisticated architecture for which Apple has become synonymous"

Inside the iPad

Will the iPad change the world?

iPad. A new breed of computer brought to us by Apple, the masters of must-have multimedia devices. Just as iPhone before it spawned a brand-new class of mobile phone so, too, does iPad have its heart set on inciting the gadget-buying public to embrace this potentially genius fusion of laptop and smartphone.

The first-generation model launched on 3 April in the US had Wi-Fi but no 3G connectivity and yet it still cleared a colossal 300,000 units on day one. Apparently Apple's tablet has charmed a significant number of curious consumers all eager to adopt this convenient photo frame/eBook reader/laptop/app resource/tea tray. So why – if you haven't already done so – should you too look into splashing out on one of these stylish Apple devices?

Clearly the iPad's design oozes the smart, sophisticated architecture for which Apple has become synonymous, the signature Home button the only sign of life beneath a dead display. And yet there's much more going on under the skin of this super-slick tablet. Discover for yourself exactly what lurks beneath this unfeasibly polished plate as we delve inside the iPad. ✿

The glass
Apple's touch devices use optical grade glass, which is tough and scratch resistant. For iPad Apple has also added an oleophobic coating which prevents fingerprint marks appearing.

The Statistics
Apple iPad
Height: 242.8 mm
Width: 189.7 mm
Depth: 13.4 mm
Weight: 0.68 kg Wi-Fi model; 0.73 kg Wi-Fi + 3G model
Display: 24.6 cm (diagonal) LED-backlit Multi-Touch with IPS technology and fingerprint-resistant coating
Processor: 1GHz Apple A4 custom-designed, high-performance, low-power system-on-a-chip
Memory: 16GB, 32GB, or 64GB flash drive
Battery: Built-in 25-watt-hour rechargeable lithium-polymer battery (ten hours of surfing the web on Wi-Fi, watching video, or listening to music). Charge with power adaptor or USB to computer system
Pricing: £429-£699 ($499-$829)

Full screen
With iPad it's all about the screen, and at 9.7 inches Apple's display practically takes up the whole front side.

Window on the world
At 1.18mm the glass panel is thicker than that of the iPhone (1.02mm).

In-plane switching
A technology more at home in LCD TVs, IPS improves the viewing angle by aligning the crystal molecules so their motion is parallel to the panel.

Screen

The 9.7-inch display is particularly interesting because it falls just short of full HD, but at the same time boasts some incredible technology, which means that the iPad benefits from incredible viewing angles. The resolution is 1024 x 768 pixels at 132 pixels-per-inch (ppi) and it uses a system called IPS (in-plane switching) to get that great 178-degree viewing angle. The display also uses the same fingerprint-resistant oleophobic coating that resides on the iPhone.

iPod

1 This dynamic MP3 player has changed the face of music content delivery forever, and rekindled our love affair with Apple. iPod's integration with iTunes was pure genius.

Apple II

2 1977 saw the introduction of one of the world's earliest and most popular PCs. Apple II's pioneering software, unique hardware and affordable price tag was a milestone.

OS X

3 Launched in 2001, Mac OS X was Apple's tenth and finest incarnation of the company's operating system, bringing with it both an appealing appearance and ease of use.

iMac

4 Apple's products are renowned for their cool and clean designs and the iMac changed the appearance of people's workspaces with this stylish all-in-one Macintosh.

iPhone

5 Released in 2007, iPhone is one of Apple's most functional product innovations. An invaluable piece of kit, it reshaped smartphone consumer expectations.

DID YOU KNOW? iPad uses just 2.5 watts – just one fifth of the power of a compact fluorescent bulb

1. Bezel
A lot of discussion surrounds the inclusion of such a wide bezel. Design-minded people say it's ugly, but if its presence prevents unwanted or accidental touches on the screen, surely it's a price worth paying.

5. Software
iPad uses the same software that is used in the iPhone and iPod touch. While this does restrict the use of the iPad in that it's not a Mac, the App Store does mean that there will be plenty of apps you can run on it.

7. Screen lock
This prevents the screen from rotating between landscape and portrait.

6. Sleep/wake
The iPad also comes with the same sleep/wake button as the iPhone and iPod touch.

9. 3G plastic
The 3G version of the iPad comes with a plastic area, which allows for much better reception of a 3G signal.

12. Apple apps
Apple has repurposed a number of apps to suit the larger screen on the iPad. iTunes, the App Store, Calendar, Photos, YouTube and Contacts all get new interfaces and greater functionality. And not only that, but the iWork suite has been completely repurposed, making the iPad an ideal choice for business users wishing to travel light.

3. Display
The iPad display is a 9.7-inch (diagonal) LED-backlit glossy widescreen Multi-Touch display with IPS technology. The IPS technology allows for an incredibly wide viewing angle and makes the iPad great for sharing movies and pictures.

2. Apps
The iPad works in the same way as the iPhone and iPod touch, allowing you to download and organise your apps on a number of Home screens.

8. Volume up/down
There is also a hardware button to turn the volume up and down.

4. Dock
It's possible to fit six apps on the iPad's dock.

10. Unibody
The outer casing of the iPad utilises Apple's unibody construction method. This is where Apple takes a single piece of pressed aluminium and uses it as a single back cover.

11. Dock connector
The iPad uses the same connection that the iPhone and most iPods use. There are also some interesting peripherals stemming from it. Apple itself has created a dock connected to a physical keyboard. The 802.11n Wi-Fi/Bluetooth card is integrated into the dock connector cable.

The processor

For the first time in its own device, Apple has made its own processor. In April 2008 Apple acquired chip-making company PA Semi – a sign that the company was looking to bring that side of computing in-house. This chip is based on an ARM design, which is the same chip inside the current iPhone. Apple describes the chip as a "1GHz Apple A4 custom-designed, high-performance, low-power system-on-a-chip".

The A4 is Package-on-Package (POP), with at least three layers of circuitry on top of each other. It's packaged just like the iPhone processors: microprocessor in one package and two memory modules in the other package – all sandwiched together in a thin POP.

The iPad RAM is *inside* the A4 processor package – something that was confirmed by x-raying the processor. The x-ray showed two layers of RAM. As well as the ARM processor, the A4 package contains two stacked Samsung dies.

"There's an empty space where the 3G version's cellular communications board will live"

The iPad teardown

Cracking open the iPad to discover what's inside

It's a sad sight to see such a beautiful piece of kit in pieces on the table before you, but it also gives a fascinating insight into the technology inside. Although the 3G-enabled iPad won't be available in the US till late-April, there are telltale signs of future 3G integration, including an empty space where the cellular communications board will live.

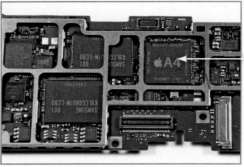

Logic board
Decoding the A4's part number revealed 2GB of memory inside, which translates into 128MB of memory per die, for 256MB total (not 512MB, as previously reported).

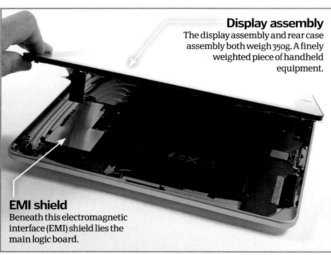

Display assembly
The display assembly and rear case assembly both weigh 350g. A finely weighted piece of handheld equipment.

EMI shield
Beneath this electromagnetic interface (EMI) shield lies the main logic board.

Ambient light sensor
Where you might have been expecting to see a camera, instead sits an ambient light sensor to automatically adjust the display brightness.

Audio-out jack

What comes as standard?
Out-of-the-box apps

The larger screen size of the iPad means Apple could redesign the standard apps that come on the iPhone to better suit the new tablet device. Here is a breakdown of what has changed...

Contacts
The new address book interface looks like an actual address book.

Photos
This has been redesigned so that albums can be explored using the pinch gesture.

iBooks
iBooks is a brand new eBook reading app for the iPad that includes the iBookstore.

Calendar
The calendar has been reinvigorated – a great improvement.

Mail
Very smart and will reconfigure itself according to the orientation of the iPad.

YouTube
A revised interface has also been created for YouTube, but there's no video capability.

Maps
The same Google system, but with a much faster processor.

Safari
Apple touts the web-surfing skill of the iPad as a major selling point.

iPod
Browse artists and, with iTunes LP, look at excellent extra content.

Apps you wouldn't want to run:

Facebook ■ eBay ■ Amazon
These apps were created to make the functionality of the websites fit into a more appealing system on a smaller iPhone screen. With the iPad, this isn't necessary.

Up to 10 hours battery life

Battery life – lithium-polymer

The iPad features a built-in 3.75V, 24.8 watt-hour rechargeable battery that allows up to ten hours of use without a charge. With a much larger space available, the battery is much bigger than that of the iPhone or iPod touch, and therefore lasts longer even when in use.

Unibody

Apple has used its unibody production system to create the iPad, which means that the entire back panel is a single piece of aluminium. This makes the overall weight and depth of the iPad much thinner than rival makers can achieve with plastics, while maintaining a solid exterior.

EBOOK READER

1. Amazon Kindle
Considering the extensive support pledged to Apple's iBookstore, the Kindle should be shaking in its monochrome boots.

PURE GAMING

2. DS XL
With an excellent catalogue of brain-tickling titles, an intuitive control system and a new XL screen, Nintendo's handheld joy stands firm.

LOOKALIKE

3. JooJoo
Although the Linux-operated JooJoo has a bigger screen size than iPad (12.1" to iPad's 9.7"), it doesn't have anywhere near the same app availability.

DID YOU KNOW? There's space in the upper-right corner for the cellular communications board of the 3G iPad

What's inside the iPad?
iPad components laid bare

Display assembly
The touch circuit design is more akin to the 2G and 3G iPhones than today's 3GS. Its size meant there was no need to use small chips.

Display data cable connector

Unibody
The rear case is machined from a single billet of aluminium, increasing weight while also greatly improving the rigidity of the iPad.

Wi-Fi antenna
Dense antennas should mean decent wireless reception.

Lithium-ion polymer batteries
The iPad battery has 5.5 times the capacity of the iPhone battery. These two batteries are wired in parallel, for a total of 24.8 watt-hours.

Wi-Fi/Bluetooth card

Apple A4 system-on-a-chip

Speaker assembly
Dual speakers provide mono sound. Two small sealed channels direct sound towards three audio ports carved into the bottom edge.

EMI shield

Dock connector cable

Speaker/microphone
The inclusion of a speaker and a microphone on the iPad, coupled with the recent SDK unlocking of the VOIP protocols, means that the iPad could easily be used as an internet phone. The omission of a camera on the device makes video chat less likely. More recent rumours that the iPad is ready to house a camera add even more weight to this argument.

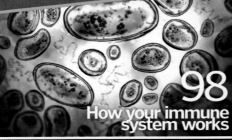
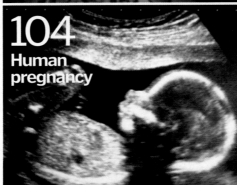
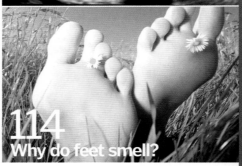

136
Electricity explained

130
Why do we get fat?

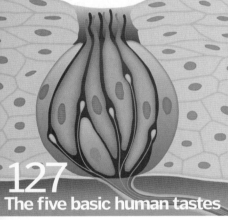

127
The five basic human tastes

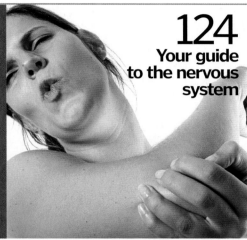

124
Your guide to the nervous system

"Dangerous bacteria release toxins in the body that cause diseases"

How your immune system works

Physical defences

Human anatomy subscribes to the notion that good fences make good neighbours. Your skin, made up of tightly packed cells and an antibacterial oil coating, keeps most pathogens from ever setting foot in body. Your body's openings are well-fortified too. Pathogens that you inhale face a wall of mucus-covered membranes in your respiratory tract, optimised to trap germs. Pathogens that you digest end up soaking in a bath of potent stomach acid. Tears flush pathogens out of your eyes, dousing bacteria with a harsh enzyme for good measure.

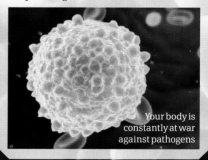

Your body is constantly at war against pathogens

Your body is locked in a constant war against a viscous army

It's true: while you're sitting around watching TV, trillions of foreign invaders are launching a full-scale assault on the trillions of cells that constitute 'you'. Collectively known as pathogens, these attackers include bacteria, single-celled creatures that live to eat and reproduce; protists, larger single-cell organisms; viruses, packets of genetic information that take over host cells and replicate inside them; and fungi, a type of plant life.

Bacteria and viruses are by far the very worst offenders. Dangerous bacteria release toxins in the body that cause diseases such as E coli, anthrax, and the black plague. The cell damage from viruses causes measles, the flu and the common cold, among numerous other diseases.

Just about everything in our environment is teeming with these microscopic intruders... including you. The bacteria in your stomach alone outnumber all the cells in your body, ten-to-one. Yet, your scrappy microscopic soldiers usually win the day against pathogens, through a combination of sturdy barriers, brute force, and superior battlefield intelligence, collectively dubbed the immune system. ✿

5 TOP FACTS
IMMUNE SYSTEM

The cure can sometimes hurt
1 Sneezing, coughing, a sore throat, and fever are all means of expelling pathogens, so as annoying as they are, each one is necessary.

Immunity soldiers are everywhere
2 A single drop of blood contains around 375,000 white blood cells, and blood constitutes seven per cent of your total body weight.

You can 'borrow' immunity
3 Antibodies in breast milk give babies temporary immunity from diseases their mother is immune to, preventing infancy infection.

It deals with internal troubles too
4 In addition to fighting pathogens, T-cells fight the body's own cancerous cells and some cancer therapies boost the number of T-cells.

It has trouble with change
5 Unfortunately, you cannot develop immunity to the flu and common cold because the viruses are constantly changing and mutating.

DID YOU KNOW? Dr Karl Landsteiner first identified the major human blood groups – A, B, AB and O – in 1901

The adaptive immune system

Fighting the good fight, and white blood cells are right on the front line...

When a pathogen is tough, wily, or numerous enough to survive non-specific defences, it's up to the adaptive immune system to clean up the mess. The key forces in the adaptive immune system are white blood cells called lymphocytes. Unlike their macrophage cousins, lymphocytes are engineered to attack only one specific type of pathogen. There are two types of lymphocytes: B-cells and T-cells.

These cells join the action when macrophages pass along information about the invading pathogen, through chemical messages called interleukins. After engulfing a pathogen, a macrophage communicates details about the pathogen's antigens – telltale molecules that characterise a particular pathogen. Based on this information, the immune system identifies specific B-cells and T-cells equipped to recognise and

battle the pathogen. Once they are successfully identified, these cells rapidly reproduce, assembling an army of cells that are ready and equipped to take down the attacker.

The B-cells flood your body with antibodies, molecules that either disarm a specific pathogen or bind to it, marking it as a target for other white blood cells. When T-cells find their target, they lock on and release toxic chemicals that will destroy it. T-cells are especially adept at destroying your body's cells that are infected with a virus.

This entire process takes several days to get going and may take even longer to conclude. All the while, the raging battle can make you feel terrible. Fortunately, the immune system is engineered to learn from the past. While your body is producing new B-cells and T-cells to fight the pathogens, it also produces memory cells – copies of the B-cells and T-cells, which stay in the system after the pathogen is defeated. The next time that pathogen shows up in your body, these memory cells help launch a counter-attack much more quickly. Your body can wipe out the invaders before any infection takes hold. In other words, you develop immunity.

Vaccines accomplish the same thing by giving you just enough pathogen exposure for you to develop memory cells, but not enough to make you sick.

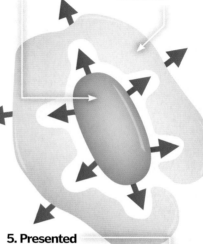

1. Bacterium
Any bacteria that enter your body have characteristic antigens on their surface.

2. Bacterium antigen
These distinctive molecules allow your immune system to recognise that the bacterium is something other than a body cell.

3. Macrophage
These white blood cells engulf and digest any pathogens they come across.

4. Engulfed bacterium
During the initial inflammation reaction, a macrophage engulfs the bacterium.

5. Presented bacterium antigen
After engulfing the bacterium, the macrophage 'presents' the bacterium's distinctive antigens, communicating the presence of the specific pathogen to B-cells.

6. Matching B-cell
The specific B-cell that recognises the antigen, and can help defeat the pathogen, receives the message.

7. Non-matching B-cells
Other B-cells, engineered to attack other pathogens, don't recognise the antigen.

9. Memory cell
The matching B-cell also replicates to produce memory cells, which will rapidly produce copies of itself if the specific bacteria ever returns.

'Tis but a scratch but can your immune system cope?

Non-specific defences

As good as your physical defence system is, pathogens do creep past it regularly. Your body initially responds with counterattacks known as non-specific defences, so named because they don't target a specific type of pathogen.

After a breech – bacteria rushing in through a cut, for example – cells release chemicals called inflammatory mediators. This triggers the chief non-specific defence, known as inflammation. Within minutes of a breach, your blood vessels dilate, allowing blood and other fluid to flow into the tissue around the cut.

The rush of fluid in inflammation carries various types of white blood cells, which get to work destroying intruders. The biggest and toughest of the bunch are macrophages, white blood cells with an insatiable appetite for foreign particles. When a macrophage detects a bacterium's telltale chemical trail, it grabs the intruder, engulfs it, takes it apart with chemical enzymes, and spits out the indigestible parts. A single macrophage can swallow up about 100 bacteria before its own digestive chemicals destroy it from within.

How B-cells attack
B-cells target and destroy specific bacteria and other invaders

11. Phagocyte
White blood cells called phagocytes recognise the antibody marker, engulf the bacteria, and digest them.

10. Antibodies
The plasma cells release antibodies, which disable the bacteria by latching on to their antigens. The antibodies also mark the bacteria for destruction.

8. Plasma cell
The matching B-cell replicates itself, creating many plasma cells to fight all the bacteria of this type in the body.

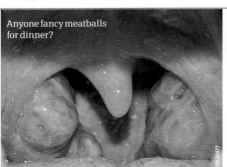

Anyone fancy meatballs for dinner?

© Klein 2007

1. Tonsils
Lymphoid tissue loaded with lymphocytes, which attack bacteria that get into the body through your nose or mouth.

2. Left subclavian vein
One of two large veins that serve as the re-entry point for lymph returning to the bloodstream.

3. Right lymphatic duct
Passageway leading from lymph vessels to the right subclavian vein.

4. Right subclavian vein
The second of the two subclavian veins, this one taking the opposite path to its twin.

5. Spleen
An organ that houses white blood cells that attack pathogens in the bloodstream.

© Ed Uhtman, MD

6. Lymph node cluster
Located along lymph vessels throughout the body, lymph nodes filter lymph as it makes its way back into the bloodstream.

7. Left lymphatic duct
Passageway leading from lymph vessels to the left subclavian vein.

8. Thymus gland
Organ that provides area for lymphocytes produced by bone marrow to mature into specialised T-cells.

9. Thoracic duct
The largest lymph vessel in the body.

11. Peyer's patch
Nodules of lymphoid tissue supporting white blood cells that battle pathogens in the intestinal tract.

12. Bone marrow
The site of all white blood cell production.

Disorders of the immune system
Who watches the watchmen?

The immune system is a powerful set of defences, so when it malfunctions, it can do as much harm as a disease. Allergies are the result of an overzealous immune system. In response to something relatively benign, like pollen, the immune system triggers excessive measures to expel the pathogen. On the extreme end, allergies may cause anaphylactic shock, a potentially deadly drop in blood pressure, sometimes accompanied by breathing difficulty and loss of consciousness. In autoimmune disorders such as rheumatoid arthritis, the immune system fails to recognise the body's own cells and attacks them.

In an allergic reaction, the body may resort to sneezing to expel a fairly harmless pathogen

In rheumatoid arthritis, the immune system attacks joint linings

10. Lymph vessels
Lymph collects in tiny capillaries, which expand into larger vessels. Skeletal muscles move lymph through these vessels, back into the bloodstream.

The lymphatic system

The lymphatic system is a network of organs and vessels that collects lymph – fluid that has drained from the bloodstream into bodily tissues – and returns it to your bloodstream. It also plays a key role in your immune system, filtering pathogens from lymph and providing a home-base for disease-fighting lymphocytes.

© DK Images

Lymph nodes explained
Lymph nodes filter out pathogens moving through your lymph vessels

Your immune system depends on these 1 cm-2.5 cm swellings to fight all manner of pathogens. As lymph makes its way through a network of fibres in the node, white blood cells filter it, destroying any pathogens they find.

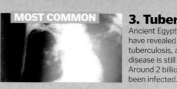

1. Influenza
The flu kills hundreds of thousands of people – and that's a conservative estimate. Every once in a while, a virulent form can take out tens of millions.

2. Measles
One person infected with measles will spread the virus to just about every unvaccinated person they encounter. Luckily, the vaccine is very effective.

3. Tuberculosis
Ancient Egyptian mummies have revealed evidence of tuberculosis, and this deadly disease is still thriving today. Around 2 billion people have been infected.

DID YOU KNOW? In 2008, approximately 33 million people worldwide were living with HIV or AIDS

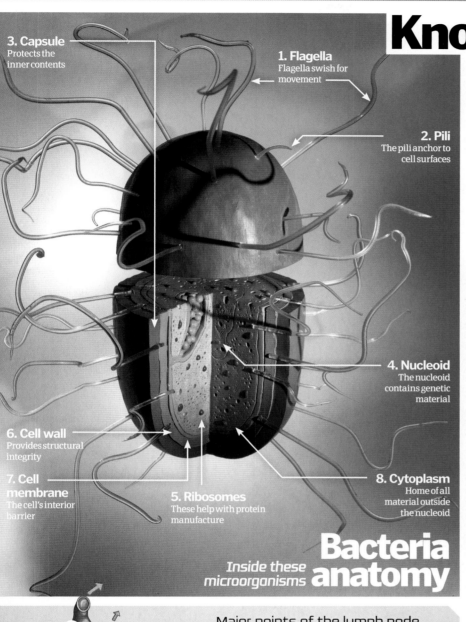

3. Capsule
Protects the inner contents

1. Flagella
Flagella swish for movement

2. Pili
The pili anchor to cell surfaces

4. Nucleoid
The nucleoid contains genetic material

6. Cell wall
Provides structural integrity

7. Cell membrane
The cell's interior barrier

5. Ribosomes
These help with protein manufacture

8. Cytoplasm
Home of all material outside the nucleoid

Bacteria anatomy
Inside these microorganisms

Know your enemy:
Bacteria

Bacteria are the smallest and, by far, the most populous form of life on Earth. Right now, there are trillions of the single-celled creatures crawling on and in you. In fact, they constitute about 1.8 kilograms of your total body weight. To the left is a look at bacteria anatomy...

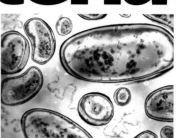

Free HIV particles, with protruding antigens that bind to CD4 molecules on helper T-cells

What is HIV...
... and how does it affect the immune system?

The human immunodeficiency virus (HIV) is a retrovirus (one carrying ribonucleic acid, or RNA as it's known), transmitted through bodily fluids. Like other deadly viruses, HIV invades cells and multiplies rapidly inside. Specifically, HIV infects cells with CD4 molecules on their surface, which includes infection-fighting helper T-cells. HIV destroys the host cell, and the virus copies go on to infect other cells. As the virus destroys helper T-cells, it steadily weakens the immune system. If enough T-cells are lost, the body becomes highly susceptible to a range of infections, a condition known as acquired immune deficiency syndrome (AIDS).

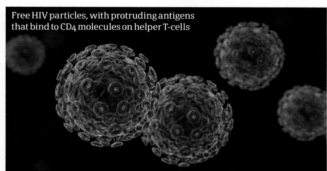

Major points of the lymph node

1. Outgoing lymph vessel
The vessel that carries filtered lymph out of the lymph node

2. Valve
A structure that prevents lymph from flowing back into the lymph node

3. Vein
Passageway for blood leaving the lymph node

4. Artery
Supply of incoming blood for the lymph node

5. Reticular fibres
Divides the lymph node into individual cells

6. Capsule
The protective fibres surrounding the lymph node

7. Sinus
A channel that slows the flow of lymph, giving macrophages the opportunity to destroy pathogens

8. Incoming lymph vessel
A vessel that carries lymph into the lymph node

9. Lymphocyte
The T-cells, B-cells and natural killer cells that fight infection

10. Germinal centre
Site of lymphocyte multiplication and maturation

11. Macrophage
Large white blood cells that engulf and destroy pathogens

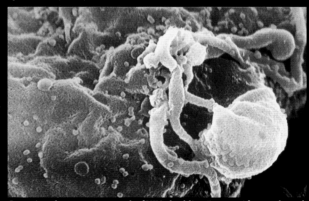

Scanning electron micrograph of HIV-1 budding (in green) from cultured lymphocyte. This image has been coloured to highlight the most important features. Multiple round bumps on the cell surface represent sites of assembly and budding of virions.

How do allergies affect us?

Hay fever is seen to be becoming more common, but how and why do allergens cause our bodies to react?

Allergic reactions occur in response to specific environmental stimuli called allergens, such as pollen, dust, bee stings and food, and the reaction displayed in individuals is normally due to an immune system disorder. Most allergies are mild, but some can be severe and even fatal depending on the reaction and treatment received following exposure to the allergen.

Allergies are actually caused by the immune system being hypersensitive to elements within the environment, rather than – as many people suppose – it being under active. Large numbers of antibodies are produced in response to the allergen, which then cause an over-reaction in the immune system when the individual next comes into contact with the allergen – so creating the allergic reaction. ✿

Allergen
This is the environmental substance that is absorbed into the body, which the body then reacts to.

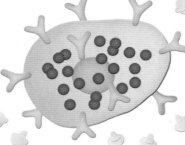

Mast cell
This is the cell where IgE receptors are situated.

IgE antibodies
These are formed in response to the initial contact with the allergen. They attach to mast cells.

Histamines (and other chemicals)
These are released when the allergen is present and cause the symptoms of the allergic reaction.

IgE receptors
Antibodies attach to these, and the cell reacts by releasing histamines and other chemicals when the individual comes into contact with the allergen.

Head to Head
ALLERGIES

MOST COMMON

1. Allergic rhinitis (hay fever)
This common allergy is a reaction to pollens and other airborne particles. It causes sneezing and itchiness of the eyes.

COMMON

2. Peanut allergy
This food allergy can cause a range of different reactions from rashes and mild swelling to causing the throat to close, potentially suffocating the individual.

RARE

3. Red meat allergy
This extremely rare allergy has attracted much interest recently due to a number of cases in Stockholm. Chest pain and breathing issues are said to be caused by this allergy.

3. Parts of the brain
The areas involved are the left dorsolateral prefrontal cortex, the pregenual rostral right anterior cingulate, the right anterior insular cortex and the left nucleus accumbens.

Another victim of *Heroes'* Sylar...

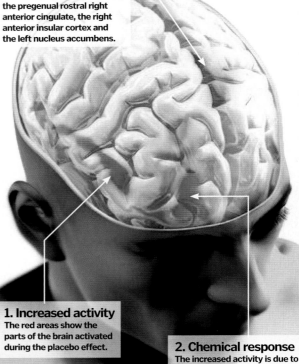

1. Increased activity
The red areas show the parts of the brain activated during the placebo effect.

2. Chemical response
The increased activity is due to the release of endorphins, the body's natural painkillers.

Placebos – do they work?

What are placebos, how do they actually work, and can they really cure disease?

The placebo effect occurs when a patient with a condition responds positively to a treatment that doesn't have any medical value. It is thought to alleviate conditions due to the patient believing they are being treated, and psychologically they start to feel better.

It is thought that the improvements often seen with placebos might be due to conditioned responses (for example, taking medicines makes you feel better, therefore you feel better because you're taking medicine). However, sceptics commonly state that the so-called placebo effect is actually only seen because patients want to please the doctors or testers, and that in truth placebos have no effect whatsoever.

Ultimately, placebos will not cure physical conditions – they can only affect the individual's mental state, which may be seen to then aid physical and mental recovery. With some patients and some illnesses, a placebo is potentially a very powerful mental and psychological tool for use in a number of cases, but often is not a valid replacement for treatment. ✿

QUICK

1. Tesla Roadster
One of the world's fastest electric cars, the TeslaRoadster can accelerate to 60 mph in four seconds.

QUICKER

2. Koenigsegg CCX
The Koenigsegg CCX is sharp even by Jeremy Clarkson's standards, hitting 60 mph in a mere 3.2 seconds. Blimey!

QUICKEST

3. Bugatti Veyron 16.4 Grand Sport
The daddy of them all, the beautiful Bugatti Veyron screams past the others at 60 miles per hour in a superfast 2.4 seconds.

DID YOU KNOW? The cheetah is the world's fastest land mammal, accelerating to 60 mph in just three seconds.

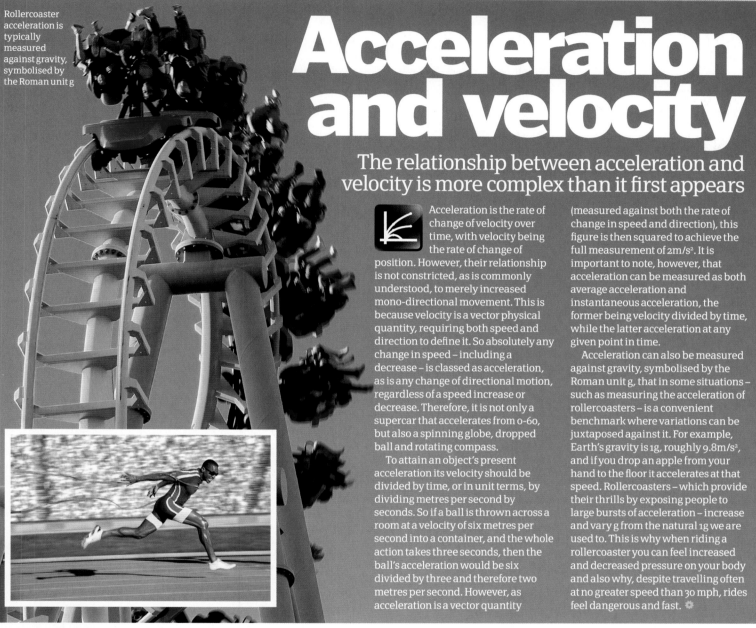

Rollercoaster acceleration is typically measured against gravity, symbolised by the Roman unit g

Acceleration and velocity

The relationship between acceleration and velocity is more complex than it first appears

Acceleration is the rate of change of velocity over time, with velocity being the rate of change of position. However, their relationship is not constricted, as is commonly understood, to merely increased mono-directional movement. This is because velocity is a vector physical quantity, requiring both speed and direction to define it. So absolutely any change in speed – including a decrease – is classed as acceleration, as is any change of directional motion, regardless of a speed increase or decrease. Therefore, it is not only a supercar that accelerates from 0-60, but also a spinning globe, dropped ball and rotating compass.

To attain an object's present acceleration its velocity should be divided by time, or in unit terms, by dividing metres per second by seconds. So if a ball is thrown across a room at a velocity of six metres per second into a container, and the whole action takes three seconds, then the ball's acceleration would be six divided by three and therefore two metres per second. However, as acceleration is a vector quantity (measured against both the rate of change in speed and direction), this figure is then squared to achieve the full measurement of 2m/s². It is important to note, however, that acceleration can be measured as both average acceleration and instantaneous acceleration, the former being velocity divided by time, while the latter acceleration at any given point in time.

Acceleration can also be measured against gravity, symbolised by the Roman unit g, that in some situations – such as measuring the acceleration of rollercoasters – is a convenient benchmark where variations can be juxtaposed against it. For example, Earth's gravity is 1g, roughly 9.8m/s², and if you drop an apple from your hand to the floor it accelerates at that speed. Rollercoasters – which provide their thrills by exposing people to large bursts of acceleration – increase and vary g from the natural 1g we are used to. This is why when riding a rollercoaster you can feel increased and decreased pressure on your body and also why, despite travelling often at no greater speed than 30 mph, rides feel dangerous and fast. ⚙

I can see a rainbow

A meteorological phenomenon – we investigate how rainbows take shape

Marvelled for their beauty, rainbows have been inspiration for folk tales, but how are they made? Well, rainbows are refractions of light and are made of a series of colours: red, orange, yellow, blue, green, indigo and violet. As light travels in waves the colour of light that is emitted depends on the light's wavelength. When light travels through an object such as crystal or an individual raindrop, it bends and refracts. As light hits the water it bends according to its wavelength and refracts at separate angles. Drops at different angles send different colours to the eye. To see a rainbow you must have your back to the Sun and rain must be falling nearby – since each raindrop is lit by the white light of the Sun a spectrum of colours is produced. ⚙

OMG! Double rainbow. What does this mean?

1. Angles
No two observers will witness the exact same rainbow because each will view a different set of drops at different angles.

2. Wave lengths
As light enters a raindrop the different wavelength colours bend at separate angles.

Human pregnancy

Nine months of change and growth

Pregnancy is a unique period in a woman's life that brings about physical and emotional changes. When it occurs, there is an intricate change in the balance of the oestrogen and progesterone hormones, which causes the cessation of menstruation and allows the conditions in the uterus (womb) to become suitable for the growth of the fetus. The lining of the uterus, rather than being discharged, thickens and enables the development of the baby.

At first, it is a collection of embryonic cells no bigger than a pinhead. By week four the embryo forms the brain, spinal cord and heart inside the newly fluid-filled amniotic sac. Protected by this cushion of fluid, it becomes recognisably human and enters the fetal stage by week eight.

Many demands are put upon the mother's body and she is likely to experience sickness, tiredness, lower-back pain, heartburn, increased appetite and muscle cramps, as well as the enlargement of her breasts and stretch marks. Her blood-sugar levels, heart rate and breathing will also increase in order to cope with the growing demands of the fetus.

As the date of labour approaches, the mother feels sudden contractions known as Braxton-Hicks, and the neck of her uterus begins to soften and thin out. Meanwhile, the lungs of the fetus fill with surfactant. This substance enables the lungs to soften, making them able to inflate when he baby takes its first breath of air. Finally, chemical signals from the fetus trigger the uterus to go into labour.

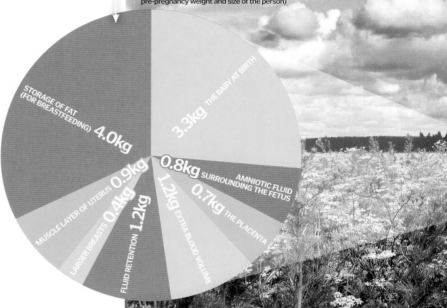

Weight gain
The average woman gains 12.5kg during pregnancy. This consists of...
(These figures vary according to several factors including the age, race, diet and the pre-pregnancy weight and size of the person)

- STORAGE OF FAT (FOR BREASTFEEDING) 4.0kg
- 3.3kg THE BABY AT BIRTH
- 0.8kg AMNIOTIC FLUID SURROUNDING THE FETUS
- 0.7kg THE PLACENTA
- 1.2kg EXTRA BLOOD VOLUME
- FLUID RETENTION 1.2kg
- LARGER BREASTS 0.4kg
- MUSCLE LAYER OF UTERUS 0.9kg

FIRST TRIMESTER (0–12 weeks)

This begins after the last menstrual period, when an egg is released and fertilised. It takes about nine weeks for the resulting embryo to develop into a fetus. During this period, the mother will be prone to sickness and mood swings due to hormonal changes.

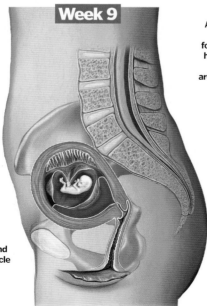

Week 9

Head
Face begins to look human and the brain is developing rapidly.

Heart
All the internal organs are formed and the heart is able to pump blood around its body.

Movement
Fetus moves around to encourage muscle development.

Weight
10g

Length
5.5cm

4 x trimester images © Science Photo Library

SECOND TRIMESTER (13–27 weeks)

The fetus grows rapidly and its organs mature. By week 20 its movements can be felt. At week 24 it can suck its thumb and hiccup, and can live independently of the mother with medical support.

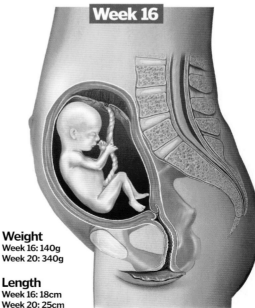

Week 16

Hair and teeth
At 16 weeks, fine hair (lanugo) grows over the fetal body. By 20 weeks, teeth start forming in the jaw and hair grows.

Movement
By week 16 the eyes can move and the whole fetus makes vigorous movements.

Sound and light
The fetus will respond to light and is able to hear sounds such as the mother's voice.

Vernix
By 20 weeks, this white, waxy substance covers the skin, protecting it from the surrounding amniotic fluid.

Sweating
An increase in blood circulation causes mother to sweat more.

Weight
Week 16: 140g
Week 20: 340g

Length
Week 16: 18cm
Week 20: 25cm

MEN ONLY

1. Seahorses
The female seahorse deposits her eggs in the pouch of the male seahorse. He fertilises the eggs and carries them for the full term of three weeks.

VIRGIN BIRTH

2. Komodo dragons
Female komodo dragons can give birth to male babies without fertilisation from a male partner. This is known as parthenogenesis.

JUST PLAIN WEIRD

3. Spotted hyenas
Female spotted hyenas have genitalia like a penis. It stretches to allow the insertion of the male penis during copulation, and stretches again when giving birth through it.

DID YOU KNOW? 200 extra calories a day are needed in mid-pregnancy, which is 10 per cent more than the usual daily requirement

The placenta

The placenta is an essential interface between the mother and fetus. When mature it is a 22cm diameter, flat oval shape with a 2.5cm bulge in the centre. The three intertwined blood vessels from the cord radiate from the centre to the edges of the placenta. Like tree roots, these villous structures penetrate the placenta and link to 15 to 20 lobes on the maternal surface.

The five major functions of the placenta deal with respiration, nutrition, excretion of waste products, bacterial protection and the production of hormones.

Placenta body
Is firmly attached to the inside of the mother's uterus.

Maternal surface
Blood from the mother is absorbed and transferred to the fetal surface.

Fetal surface
Blood vessels radiate out from the umbilical cord and penetrate the placenta. The surface is covered with the thin amnion membrane.

Umbilical cord
Consists of three blood vessels. Two carry carbon dioxide and waste from the fetus, the other supplies oxygen and nutrients from the mother.

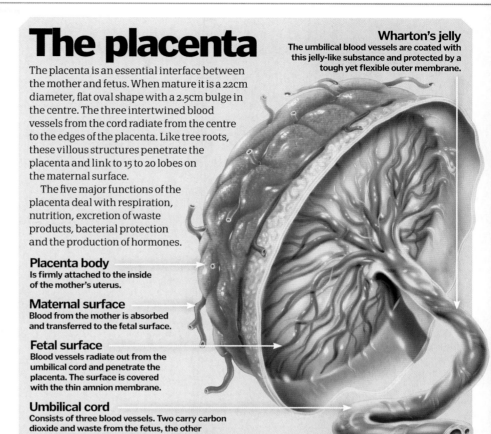

Wharton's jelly
The umbilical blood vessels are coated with this jelly-like substance and protected by a tough yet flexible outer membrane.

© Science Photo Library

THIRD TRIMESTER (28–40 weeks)

Breathlessness
The increased size of the fetus by 24 weeks causes compression of rib cage and discomfort for mother.

Movement
By the 28th week, due to less room in uterus, the fetus will wriggle if it feels uncomfortable.

Hands
The fetus can move its hands to touch its umbilical cord at 24 weeks.

Position
By 28 weeks, the uterus has risen to a position between the navel and breastbone.

Head
The head can move at 28 weeks and the eyes can open and see.

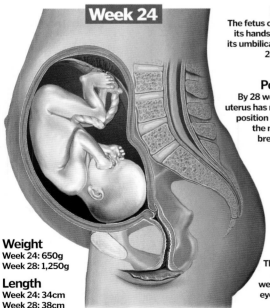

Week 24

Weight
Week 24: 650g
Week 28: 1,250g

Length
Week 24: 34cm
Week 28: 38cm

Now almost at full term, the fetus can recognise and respond to sounds and changes in light. Fat begins to be stored under the skin and the lungs are the very last organs to mature.

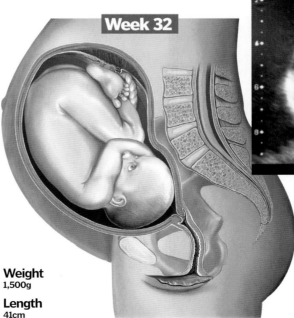

Week 32

Weight
1,500g

Length
41cm

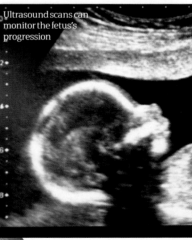

Ultrasound scans can monitor the fetus's progression

Under pressure
Pressure on the diaphragm and other organs causes indigestion and heartburn in the mother. She will find it difficult to eat a lot.

Position
Head positions itself downwards, in preparation for labour.

Sleep patterns
Fetus will sleep and wake in 20-minute cycles.

"The only scientific method to avoid hangovers is to moderate the amount of alcohol consumed"

Chlorine

The ultimate pool cleaner

Chlorine is a successful cleansing agent because on contact with water it breaks down into several different chemicals including hypochlorite ion and hypochlorous acid, both of which kill bacteria by attacking their cell walls and destroying the enzymes and structure of the bacteria, oxidising them and rendering them harmless. Interestingly, this happens at different times depending on what compounds it is, with hypochlorous acid oxidising in seconds while hypochlorite ion can take up to half an hour.

There are some problems to using chlorine though, ranging from its smell to the fact that certain skin types can have a strong reaction to it. Even worse, high levels of chlorine gas collecting above a pool can be actively hazardous to the health of its users and the hypochlorite is actively hazardous to fabrics, causing many to fade if not washed off quickly after leaving the pool.

Head to Head
WATER PURIFICATION

EASIEST

1. Boiling
Boiling will kill bacteria but it's not a permanent solution as new bacteria can enter the water once it's cooled.

EASY

2. Granular activated carbon filtering
Carbon with a high surface area can absorb many pollutants and toxic compounds and is often used in fish tanks.

NOT EASY

3. Reverse osmosis
A flashback to those science lessons at school, an impure solution is forced through a semi-permeable membrane, filtering out many of the impurities.

Hangovers

What are they, what causes them and can they be avoided?

A 'hangover' is the common term used to describe a delayed negative reaction by the human body to excessive exposure to alcoholic substances.

Symptoms generally include myriad physiological effects such as headaches, nausea, tiredness, dysphoria, diarrhoea and severe thirst, as well as many psychological symptoms including depression and anxiety. Current scientific theory states that the main chemical causes of a hangover are a mixture of hypoglycemia (low blood sugar), dehydration, acetaldehyde intoxication (a chemical compound produced by the oxidation of ethanol) and vitamin B deficiency.

Currently, the only scientifically backed method to avoid hangovers is to moderate the amount of alcohol the human body is exposed to, reducing the negative effects. However, it is commonly accepted that through a mixture of rehydration and replenishment of vitamin B, the length and severity of a hangover can be mitigated.

Someone had one Babycham too many last night...

DID YOU KNOW? The ancient Romans treated hangovers by consuming raw owl's eggs and fried canaries.

Transformers

Hundreds of thousands of volts are passing above your head, right now

The power lines that crisscross the country can carry up to 750,000-volt charges, an astonishing amount of raw power that's extremely dangerous. So how do you transmit the power from the lines to the electrical wiring and appliances of a house without destroying them? Simple, by using a transformer. These work off the principle of electromagnetic induction, where an alternating electrical field or AC current in a coil of wire will generate an electrical current in a second coil placed next to it. If the number of coils of wire is the same, the current will be virtually the same, and it can be increased or decreased by changing the number of coils. In this way, current can be 'stepped down' to levels where it can be used safely.

If you're waiting for it to come alive you're thinking of a different type of transformer

BIGGEST

1. NASA's Ames Research Center
Silicon Valley, California
The world's largest wind tunnel has a test section 36.5 m wide and 24.3 m high – enough to test a full-sized Boeing 737.

FASTEST

2. LENS-X wind tunnel
Calspan University, NYC
The world's fastest wind tunnel can momentarily deliver airflow at Mach 30 and was used to test NASA's Orion spacecraft.

LONGEST SERVING

3. Langley, Virginia
Opened in 1931, the world's first wind tunnel for testing full-scale aircraft remained in operation for 78 years until September 2009.

DID YOU KNOW? The pressure the wind puts on an object can be measured with fluorescent paint

Wind tunnels

Allowing engineers to test aircraft designs in the lab, wind tunnels are invaluable to scientific research

A wind tunnel simulates in a laboratory the flow of air around, for example, an aeroplane or a building. This allows designers to work out the impact this airflow will have on the finished product and make cars and planes more aerodynamic and structures more wind resistant.

Wind tunnels are large circular tubes through which air is blown in one direction by giant fans: the test object – usually a scale model of the actual design – is mounted in the centre. In the case of an aircraft or a plane, in reality the object will be moving while the air stays still, but this doesn't matter as long as the relative velocity between the air and the object is the same. An enclosed cylinder is needed to allow for uniform airflow in one direction (known as laminar flow), simulating the airflow past a plane moving in a straight line or the wind hitting a skyscraper. ✿

Testing in the supersonic wind tunnel at NASA's Lewis Flight Propulsion Laboratory

Both photographs © NASA

Anatomy of a wind tunnel

The role of each section explained

Closed loop
Most – but not all – wind tunnels save energy by feeding the moving air from the exhaust back to the input.

Fans
Most wind tunnels use fans or banks of fans, although the very fastest use explosive expansion of compressed air.

Internal casing
Kept as smooth as possible to minimise friction between the wind tunnel and air, which would introduce turbulence to airflow.

Lighting
Illumination is usually provided by shining light in through windows – lighting would heat up air and produce turbulence.

Settling chamber
Air produced by fans is highly turbulent. Metal grating with a series of holes filters air current to create stable, uni-directional flow.

Test object
As some drag from walls is inevitable, the object is mounted in the centre of a wind tunnel where air stream is most stable.

Observation windows
Kept level with the inside of wind tunnel and usually curved to keep inside as smooth as possible and prevent introduction of turbulence.

"The bubble, many times smaller than a single proton, contained all matter and radiation in our current universe"

As an elegant explanation of the origins of both atoms and galaxies, the big bang is the ultimate theory of everything

The big bang theory begins with a simple assumption: if the universe is expanding and cooling – something Edwin Hubble and company proved at the beginning of the 20th Century – then it must have once been very small and very hot. From then on, the simple becomes infinitely complex. Big bang theory is nothing less than the summation of everything we've learned about the very big (astrophysics) and the very small (quantum physics) in the history of human thought.

Cosmologists – people who study the origin and evolution of the universe – theorise that 13.7 billion years ago, a bubble formed out of the void. The bubble, many times smaller than a single proton, contained all matter and radiation in our current universe. Propelled by a mysterious outward force, the bubble instantaneously expanded (it didn't explode) by a factor of 1,027, triggering a cosmic domino effect that created the stars, the galaxies and life as we know it. ✿

The big bang

The Planck era   Time: Zero to 10^{-43} seconds

The Planck era describes the impossibly short passage of time between the absolute beginning of the universe (zero) and 10^{-43} seconds (10 trillionths of a yoctosecond, if you're counting). In this fraction of an instant, the universe went from infinite density to something called Planck density ($1093g/cm^3$), the equivalent of 100 billion galaxies squeezed into the nucleus of an atom. Beyond the Planck density, rules of General Relativity don't apply, so the very dawn of time is still a complete and utter mystery.

ERA

Inflation era

In the Eighties, cosmologists theorised a period of spontaneous expansion in the very early moments of time. Instantaneously, every point in the universe expanded by a factor of

TIME 10^{-36} to 10^{-32} after big bang

1,027. The universe didn't get bigger, it just was bigger. Because the universe got so big, so fast, its naturally spherical shape appeared flat to objects on the surface, solving one of the early problems with big bang theory.

Quark era

After the explosive inflation period, the universe was a dense cauldron of pure energy. Under these conditions, gamma rays of energy collided to briefly form quarks and anti-quarks, the fundamental building blocks of matter. Just as quickly, though, the quarks and anti-quarks collided in a process called annihilation, converting their mass back to pure energy.

10^{-32} to 10^{-12}

Quark   **Antiquark**

Quark - antiquark pair

X-boson

Particle soup

If you turn the heat up high enough, everything melts. When the universe was 10^{-32} seconds old, it burned at a magnificent 1,000 trillion trillion degrees Celsius. At this remarkable temperature, the tiniest building blocks of matter – quarks and anti-quarks, leptons and anti-leptons – swirled freely in a particle soup called the quark-gluon plasma. Gluon is the invisible 'glue' that carries the strong force, binding quarks into protons and neutrons.

3 TOP FACTS
EVIDENCE FOR THE BIG BANG

Background radiation

1 Cosmic microwave background radiation – which fills the universe uniformly – is the super-cooled afterglow from the original big bang.

Expanding universe

2 Galaxies outside of the Milky Way move away from us at a rate proportional to their distance from us, pointing to a continual expansion from a single source.

Big bang nucleosynthesis

3 Big bang theory predicts that the earliest atoms to emerge from the dense particle soup were hydrogen and helium in a 3:1 ratio. Using powerful telescopes and spectrometers, cosmologists confirm that the observed universe is 74% hydrogen, 25% helium and 1% heavier elements.

DID YOU KNOW? None of the essential elements of human life (carbon and oxygen) were created during the big bang

Let there be light

The primordial soup of the early universe was composed of pairs of particles and anti-particles (mostly quarks, anti-quarks, leptons and anti-leptons). Picture this ultra-hot, supercharged environment as the original super collider. Particles and anti-particles smashed together in a process called annihilation, producing beams of photons (light radiation). As more particles collided, more light was generated. Some of those photons reformed into particles, but when the universe finally cooled enough to form stable atoms, the spare photons were set free. The net result: the universe contains a billion times more light than matter.

X-bosons

A funny thing happened at 10^{-39} second after the beginning of time. The universe produced huge particles called X-bosons (1,015 times more massive than protons). X-bosons are neither matter nor anti-matter and exist only to carry the Grand Unified Force, a combination of the electromagnetic, weak and strong forces that exist today.

The Grand Unified Force drove the early expansion of the universe, but rapid cooling caused X-bosons to decay into protons and anti-protons. For reasons that aren't clear, a billion and one protons were created for every billion anti-protons, creating a tiny net gain of matter. This imbalance, forged during a short blip in time, is the reason for our matter-dominated universe.

Re-creating the big bang

CERN's Large Hadron Collider (LHC) is the world's largest particle accelerator. At full power, trillions of protons will travel at near light speed through super-cooled vacuum tubes buried 100 metres below the surface. As the protons smash into each other – at a rate of 600 million collisions per second – they will generate energy 100,000 times hotter than the Sun, a faithful recreation of the cosmic conditions milliseconds after the big bang. Using ultra-sensitive detectors, scientists will scour the debris trails for traces of quarks, leptons and even the Higgs boson, a highly theoretical particle believed to give mass to matter.

A computer simulation of the decay path of a Higgs boson after two protons collide in the LHC

Separation of the Electroweak force

During the Planck era, the four forces of nature were briefly unified: gravity, the strong force, electromagnetism and the weak force. As the Planck era ended as the universe cooled, gravity separated out, then the strong force separated during the inflation. But it wasn't until the end of the Quark era that the universe was cool enough to separate the electromagnetic and weak forces, establishing the physical laws we follow today.

110^{-9} to 10^{-62}

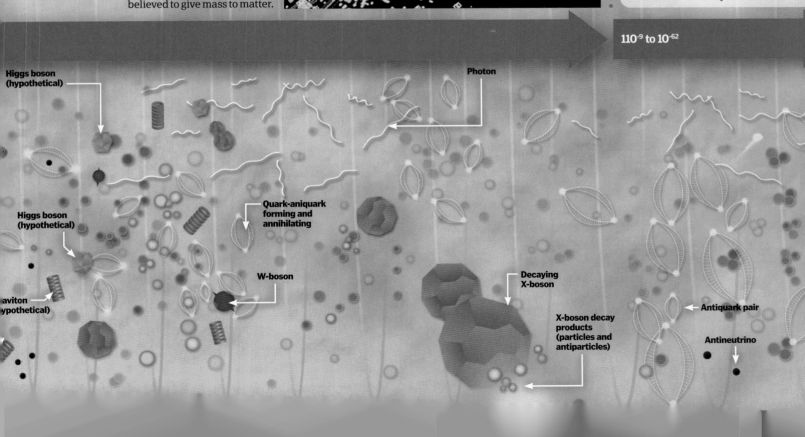

Higgs boson (hypothetical)

Photon

Higgs boson (hypothetical)

Quark-aniquark forming and annihilating

aviton ypothetical)

W-boson

Decaying X-boson

X-boson decay products (particles and antiparticles)

Antiquark pair

Antineutrino

"72 per cent is dark energy, a bizarre form of matter that works in opposition to gravity"

The origins of matter

Everything in the universe – the galaxies, the stars, the planets, even your big toe – is made of matter. In the beginning (roughly 13.7 billion years ago), matter and radiation were bound together in a superheated, super-dense fog. As the universe cooled and expanded, the first elemental particles emerged: quarks and anti-quarks. As things cooled further, the strong force separated, pulling together clumps of quarks into protons and neutrons, building the first atomic nuclei. Half a million years later, conditions were finally cool enough for nuclei to pull in free electrons, forming the first stable atoms. Small fluctuations in the density of matter distribution led to clusters and clouds of matter that coalesced, over hundreds of millions of years, into the stars and galaxies we explore today.

Dark forces

So what is the universe made of? Well, there is more to the universe than meets the eye. Cosmologists have proved that the visible or 'luminous' portions of the cosmos – the stars, galaxies, quasars and planets – are only a small fraction of the total mass and composition of the universe. Using super-accurate measurements of cosmic microwave background radiation fluctuations, scientists estimate that only 4.6 per cent of the universe is composed of atoms (baryonic matter), 23 per cent is dark matter (invisible and undetectable, but with a gravitational effect on baryonic matter), and 72 per cent is dark energy, a bizarre form of matter that works in opposition to gravity. Many cosmologists believe that dark energy is responsible for the accelerating expansion of the universe, which should be contracting under its own gravitational pull.

Hadron era

When the expanding universe cooled to 1,013K (ten quadrillion degrees Celsius), quarks became stable enough to bond together through the strong force. When three quarks clump together in the right formation, they form hadrons, a type of particle that includes protons and neutrons. Miraculously, every single proton and neutron in the known universe was created during this millisecond of time.

Lepton era

During this comparatively 'long' era, the rapidly expanding universe cools to 109K, allowing for the formation of a new kind of particle called a lepton. Leptons, like quarks, are the near mass-less building blocks of matter. Electrons are a 'flavour' of lepton, as are neutrinos.

Nucleosynthesis era

For 17 glorious minutes, the universe reached the ideal temperature to support nuclear fusion, the process by which protons and neutrons bond together to form atomic nuclei. Only the lightest elements have time to form – 75 per cent hydrogen, 25 per cent helium – before fusion winds down.

10^{-6} to 1 second

1 second to 3 minutes

3 minutes to 20 minutes

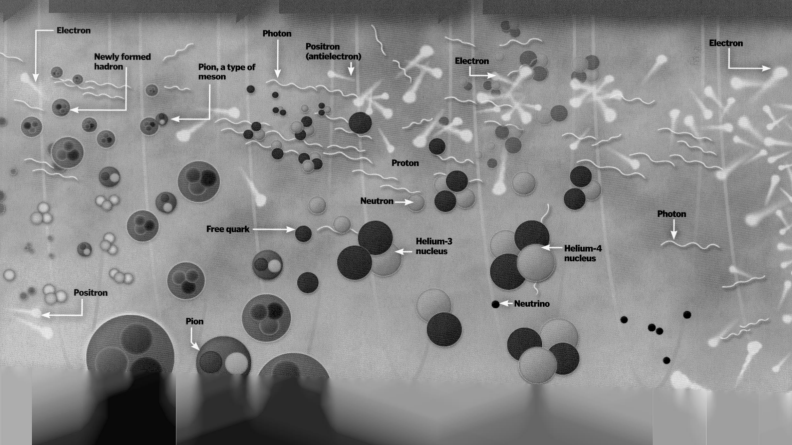

Electron

Newly formed hadron

Pion, a type of meson

Photon

Positron (antielectron)

Electron

Electron

Proton

Neutron

Free quark

Helium-3 nucleus

Helium-4 nucleus

Photon

Positron

Neutrino

Pion

Head to Head
Scientists

MOST FAMOUS
1. Albert Einstein
Einstein's revolutionary Theory of General Relativity paved the way for the idea that all matter in the universe was uniformly distributed from a common source.

LESS FAMOUS
2. Edwin Hubble
Edwin Hubble calculated that galaxies moved away from one another at a rate relative to the distance between them – thereby proving that the universe was expanding.

LEAST FAMOUS
3. Gamow, Alpher & Herman
In the Forties, these three analysed the creation of elements from the big bang's fallout, discovering that only hydrogen and helium could've been produced in large quantities.

DID YOU KNOW? *If there were more matter in the universe, its mass would be too great and it would collapse on itself*

Cosmic microwave background radiation
The residual heat from the big bang can give us a clue to the origin of the universe

As the universe expands, it also cools. The inconceivable heat released during the big bang has been slowly dissipating as the universe continues its 14 billion-year expansion. Using sensitive satellite equipment, cosmologists can measure the residual heat from the big bang, which exists as cosmic microwave background radiation (CMBR). CMBR is everywhere in the known universe and its temperature is nearly constant (a nippy 2.725K over absolute zero), further proof that the radiation emanated from a single, ancient source.

Minute differences in microwave background radiation levels (+/-0.0002K) reveal fluctuations in the density of matter in the primitive universe

Opaque era
These are the 'dark ages' of the universe, when light and matter were intertwined in a dense cosmic fog. Photons of light collided constantly with free protons (hydrogen ions), neutrons, electrons and helium nuclei, trapping the light in a thick plasma of particles. It is impossible for cosmologists to 'see' beyond this era, since there is no visible light.

Balance of elements
When the temperature dropped to 10,000K, electrons slowed down enough to be pulled into orbit around atomic nuclei, forming the first stable, neutral atoms of hydrogen, helium and other trace elements. As atoms started to form, photons were freed from the cosmic fog, creating a transparent universe. All cosmic background radiation originated with this 'last scattering' of photons.

Matter era
During the Opaque era, matter and light were stuck together as plasma. Photons of light applied radiation pressure on matter, preventing it from bonding together to form atoms and larger particles. When light and matter 'decoupled', the radiation pressure was released as light, freeing matter to clump and collect in the first clouds of interstellar gas. From there, the first stars were born around 400 million years after the big bang.

20 minutes to 377,000 years

500,000 to the present

Photon

Helium atom (two protons and two electrons)

Free photon

Proton

Electron

Hydrogen atom (single proton and single electron)

The 'God' particle
We take for granted the idea that if something is made of protons, neutrons and electrons, then it inherently has mass. But cosmologists now believe that no particle has mass simply by merit of its existence. Instead, mass is bestowed on particles as they pass through a Higgs field, a theoretical quantum field named after British physicist Peter Higgs. Imagine the Higgs field as a bowl of honey and quantum particles as a string of pearls. As you drag the pearls through the honey, they are imbued with mass. Every quantum field has a fundamental particle, and the particle associated with Higgs field is the Higgs boson. One of the goals of the Large Hadron Collider at CERN is to prove the existence of the elusive Higgs boson once and for all.

"The largest x-ray generator on Earth"

Inside the Z m

The machine that could offer the solution to the world's energy shortage

The electrifying Z machine is actually an x-ray generator – the largest on Earth. It is operated by Sandia National Laboratories from the company's main site in New Mexico. The machine is designed to test materials in conditions of extreme temperature and pressure.

With its pulsing purple tubes, the machine looks like something from a science-fiction movie. It sends a powerful electrical discharge into thin tungsten wires, which then vaporise and are transformed into a cylindrical plasma curtain. The machine uses a z-pinch process of fusion, a 'pinch' being what happens when you run current through plasma, and Z referring to the direction in cylindrical geometry.

Sandia runs a Z-Pinch Inertial Fusion Energy program (Z-IFE) in an attempt to harness fusion power. The Z machine can run at ultra-high temperatures, opening the theoretical possibilities of achieving fusion of light hydrogen atoms with lithium or boron, which would have no nuclear waste – clean fusion and the potential to create unlimited electrical power from seawater. Its achievements to date include melting diamond, shooting plates faster than the Earth moves through space and reaching the temperature of the Sun. Practically, it has allowed scientists to estimate conditions similar to the core of Jupiter and the surface of Neptune for astronomers to study. It could also enable the simulation of the effects of nuclear weaponry, meaning that they don't need to be physically tested.

Advances in the field back in the late-Nineties meant that the machine was capable of outputting an x-ray power of 290 trillion watts, equivalent to 80 times the world's output of electricity. It began a retrofit programme in 2004 to increase its power further, which was completed in October 2007 and reopened officially in February 2008. This increased the output from 18 million amperes to 26 million amperes (bearing in mind a 120-watt light bulb uses one ampere). ✦

5 TOP FACTS
THE Z MACHINE

Remodelling
1 The task of dismantling the machine in 2004 was undertaken to replace its 20-year-old equipment.

Save on power
2 Its work could stop our dependence on non-renewable fuels such as coal and gas extraction for energy.

In its roots
3 The Z machine was constructed as the Particle Beam Fusion Accelerator II back in 1985.

Book it out
4 The machine was overbooked before its remodelling with requests from labs and researchers.

Small target
5 The massive amount of power focuses entirely on target the size of a spool of thread.

DID YOU KNOW? The Z machine is housed at Sandia's main site in Albuquerque, New Mexico

achine

The centre of this chamber can reach extraordinarily high temperatures

Image courtesy of Sandia National Labs

1. Skin injury
Blood vessels in the dermis become damaged when the skin is broken which results in bleeding at the site of the injury.

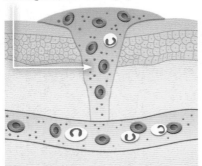

2. Clotting
The body's repair cells, which include fibroblasts, travel towards the injury site and the blood forms a clot.

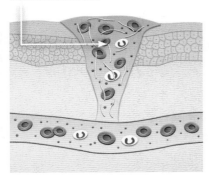

3. Plugging
A plug of fibrous tissue is formed within the clot by the fibroblasts. This allows new tissue to form beneath the protection of the plug.

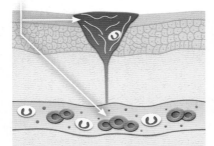

4. Scab
A scab is formed by the fibrous plug hardening. It will eventually fall off but may leave some scarring at the location of the wound.

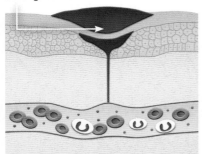

How do we heal?

We always expect our bodies to heal when we injure ourselves, but how does this happen?

Healing can be defined as the restoration of injured tissue back to usual function. There are two main ways in which tissue heals: regeneration and repair. Healing involves the removal and replacement of damaged tissue, and most organs will use both methods to fix damage – although cardiac muscle cells and neurons are examples of cells that cannot use regeneration.

Regeneration is when cells replicate within the same tissue mass that was damaged. These then replace the cells that have been damaged or died. Most cells in the body can repair damage in this manner, but the surrounding collagen network must remain in good condition for this to be able to occur.

Repair takes place when the damaged tissue cannot replicate cells of the same type, and scar tissue is then formed. Repair is made up of three stages; the inflammatory phase, the proliferative phase and the maturation phase. The inflammatory phase is when bacteria is killed off by macrophages and phagocytic cells and growth hormones released encourage cell growth in the area of damage. The following stage is when the wound starts closing up and filling with collagen, which will form the scar tissue. During the final maturation phase, healing tissue is replaced with stronger collagen and unnecessary tissue produced during the earlier phases is removed. ✿

Why do feet smell?

Producing up to a pint of sweat each day, no wonder your feet get a bit whiffy

Sweat actually keeps the skin of our feet moist and flexible to cope with the constantly changing pressure when we walk. Without this moisture the skin would dry and crack, and walking would become extremely painful.

Despite the huge number of glands (250,000 per foot) and amount of sweat that comes from our feet, it's still just salt and water. The odour comes from the bacteria that live on human skin, which, while unsettling, are perfectly natural. Our socks are a dark, moist feast for them as they eat sweat and dead skin. The waste products they excrete are what smells bad. The more the bacteria eat the worse our feet smell. To keep the smell down, make sure you change your socks and let your shoes air for 24 hours if you can. Also, wash your feet and spray them with antiperspirant. ✿

The wonderful smell of freshly cut grass, daisies, and feet...

Head to Head
WORLD'S SMELLIEST

ANIMAL

1. Striped Skunk
SKunks are known for their ability to secrete a liquid with a strong, foul smelling odour, which they can use as a defensive weapon. They can shoot it up to 5 metres.

PLACE

2. Rotorua, New Zealand
Located in the most geologically active area of New Zealand, Rotorua is a stinky place surrounded by mud pools, geysers and steam vents.

PLANT

3. Titan arum
This monstrous, three-metre tall plant smells like a combination of rotten eggs and rotting meat to attract insects.

Head to Head
EGGS

BIGGEST EVER

1. Elephant bird
Elephant birds, native to Madagascar, have been extinct since the 17th Century. The eggs often measured over one metre in circumference.

BIGGEST LIVING

2. Ostrich
Ostrich eggs are the largest of all eggs but the smallest relative to the size of the actual bird. On average they are 15 centimetres long and 13 centimetres wide.

SMALLEST

3. Hummingbird
The smallest bird egg belongs to the little bee hummingbird. You could put 4,700 of these inside one ostrich egg. It's the size of a pea and weighs a measly 5.6 grams

DID YOU KNOW? *In Britain the average person eats 172 eggs a year*

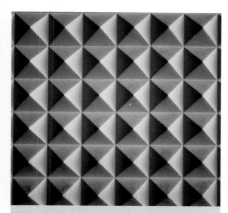

How do you soundproof a room?

With the increased noise of modern society, soundproofing is becoming more and more important for individuals living in urban environments

 Soundproofing works by reducing the amount of external noise received in a set area through the absorption or blocking of incoming sound waves. The most common method utilised in order to achieve this is the installation of insulating panels – made mainly of foam – on the walls and ceiling of a room, which not only decrease the amount of sound waves transmitted through it, but also reduce echo, reverberation and the reflection of sound. This 'dampening' of sound waves also helps restrict their movement while in the room, preventing them from penetrating outwards or reflecting inwards.

Other ways in which a room can be soundproofed include the installation of a 'floating floor', a construction method that further reduces vibration and noise penetration by elevating the floor of a room on joists thereby trapping errant sound waves and reducing their reverberation. Double glazing can also aid soundproofing, as the vacuum created between the two panes of glass prevents sound waves from passing through. Finally, sound waves struggle to pass through liquids, so in certain circumstances the use of water tanks can reduce noise also. ✿

1. Eggshell
If hard, the outer layer is known as the eggshell and will normally be a heavily mineralised protein structure.

2. Outer membrane
Some eggs only have a flexible outer layer and this is a membrane layer. This still serves a similar purpose to the eggshell in protecting the embryo.

3. Chalaza
These support the yolk in the egg, alongside the albumen. They ensure the yolk does not break and lose nutrients.

5. Albumen
The albumen, also known as the 'white' of the egg, provides support for the yolk and further nutrition for the embryo as it grows. This is the cytoplasm of the egg.

6. Yellow yolk
The yolk in particular is rich in fat, cholesterol and protein and will feed the embryo as it grows inside the egg.

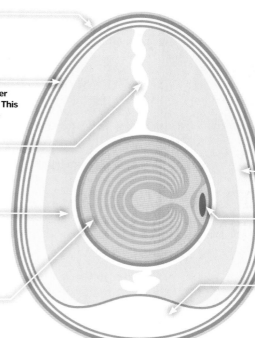

Looks cramped in there

4. Inner membrane
This layer offers further defence against bacterial invasion.

7. Germinal disc
The nucleus of the egg when you consider the egg as a cell. It is also where sperm must enter to fertilise the egg.

8. Air cell
This bubble of air can contract and expand as necessary, serving as a kind of diaphragm to allow for temperature change.

What is an egg?

Eggs are produced by many animals, but what exactly are they and how do they work?

 Eggs are generally the fertilised ovum of an animal, although eggs produced by birds that we eat are actually unfertilised. All oviparous animals use the egg in order to reproduce, and generally this means little or no development of an embryo actually occurs inside the mother. However, eggs often have to be kept at a certain temperature in order for the embryo to grow inside the egg, and ultimately hatch successfully, so individuals involved in fertilising or producing the egg are often still needed after fertilisation.

The main purpose of an egg is to contain all the elements that an embryo needs in order to develop in safety, most crucially an egg offers protection from external elements and also nutrients needed for growth and development before hatching. ✿

Surface tension
How does surface tension work?

 When you think of surface tension, that familiar tried-and-tested science experiment we all performed at school of balancing a paper clip on the surface of a cup of water, slowly filters back into our realm of consciousness – but why doesn't it sink?

Surface tension is caused by the attraction between the liquid's molecules by various intermolecular forces. In the liquid each molecule is pulled equally in all directions by neighbouring molecules, resulting in a net force of zero. At the surface of the liquid the molecules here are pulled inwards but this is balanced by the substance's resistance to compression, meaning there is no net inward force. But there is a driving force to diminish the surface area and as such the liquid squeezes itself together until it has the locally lowest surface area. So in the paper clip experiment the clip is prevented from submerging when the water level is at its maximum without spilling over the rim. ✿

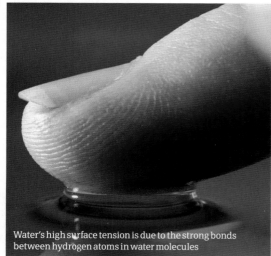
Water's high surface tension is due to the strong bonds between hydrogen atoms in water molecules

"Biofuels are heralded as pure and easily available"

What are biofuels?

Meet the future fuels that could save the planet

Does the future hold fields of fuel for as far as the eye can see?

5 TOP FACTS
BIOFUELS

1 Test of time
Biofuels have been around as long as the automobile, with Henry Ford planning to fuel Model Ts with ethanol.

2 Bioethanol
Bioethanol is an alternative to petrol and can be made from sugar cane, maize or wheat.

3 Detriment
The amount of grain needed to fill a 25-gallon SUV tank with ethanol could feed one person for an entire year.

4 Global issue
Up to 60 million indigenous people are at risk of becoming biofuel refugees.

5 Production
World biofuel production totals about 130 million barrels a year.

 Biofuels are heralded as pure and easily available fuels, derived from biomass and biowaste. These combustible fuels are produced from crops, trees, animal waste and now algae, making them far more renewable energy sources than conventional limited fossil fuels such as liquid petroleum. They also promote greater attitudes towards recycling due to their production from waste products, and are environmentally conscious by helping to reduce the amount of greenhouse gasses.

They come in solid, liquid and gaseous forms and are also know as agrofuels. Specific agricultural products are also used to produce biofuels in regions across the globe. The US is responsible for manufacturing switchgrass, soy beans and corn, with Europe contributing to the stock of sugar beet and wheat while Brazil produces sugar cane, China cassava and sorghum, southeast Asia produces miscanthus and palm oil, while India produces jatropha. They are commonly used to power vehicles, home heating and cooking appliances.

However, there are also some reservations related to biofuels. As well as environmental concerns they raise questions over detrimental effects to global provisions. For example, oil palm – a common agricultural produce – is grown at the expense of clearing biologically rich habitats, such as tropical rainforests. However, this is now giving way to more scientific exploration in biofuels produced from small developed spaces, rather than extensively on crop lands, such as the use of algae mentioned earlier. These can be grown using land and water that is unsuitable for plant or food production, preserving the food-fertile land. Plus they are still highly biodegradable and relatively harmless to the environment, as they consume carbon dioxide, which provides greenhouse gas mitigation benefits. ✿

DID YOU KNOW? Realistic projections share the belief that the production of biofuels will instigate an increase in the share of the world's fertile land to grow the necessary biomass. This increase will see the amount rise to four per cent by 2030. What this means is it will be possible to meet five per cent of road transport fuel demands, due to this first-generation technology and cultivated area. There's also a realistic possibility that these second-generation biofuels could become commercially available.

DID YOU KNOW? Biofuels are a renewable energy source, as we can simply grow as many plants as needed

Types of biofuel

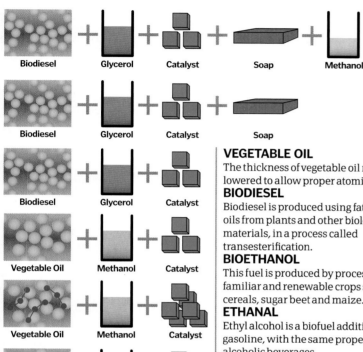

VEGETABLE OIL
The thickness of vegetable oil must be lowered to allow proper atomisation.

BIODIESEL
Biodiesel is produced using fats and oils from plants and other biological materials, in a process called transesterification.

BIOETHANOL
This fuel is produced by processing familiar and renewable crops such as cereals, sugar beet and maize.

ETHANAL
Ethyl alcohol is a biofuel additive for gasoline, with the same property as alcoholic beverages.

BIOGAS
Biogas originates from the gases released from decaying organic matter in the absence of oxygen.

How to make biodiesel

The creative process for producing biodiesel is an elaborate one. It begins with the filtering of waste vegetable oil, removing food particles. This can be achieved through extensive filtering processes. Once this is complete all water still contained within the residual gangue must be expelled. This is achieved by boiling the oil at 100 degrees Celsius, evaporating traces of H2o.

Next the titration processes begin. This determines the concentration of mixable lye and methanol necessary. This process in turn requires an alkaline catalyst to increase the rate of the chemical reaction between the methanol and vegetable oil. Sodium hydroxide is the most commonly used, but potassium hydroxide is also acceptable. This instigates the production of sodium methodixe, creating a residue which is then heated up to as hot as 54 degrees Celcius.

After this, another good mixing is in order with the formula left to rapidly cool. Once the temperature has calmed,

the glycerine produced from this chemical reaction will sink to the bottom due to its density. Biofuels produced will float to the top. The catalyst, glycerol and vegetable oil can then all be easily separated at this stage.

However, the reheating process can cause the fatty acids bonded to the glycerol to break away. This is resolved by increasing the amount of catalyst in the single transesterification process, so that the additional catalyst neutralises the free fatty acids. This creates soap as an additional by-product.

Biodiesel in general should be compatible with diesel engines, but the main obstacle will be the parts attached – namely any rubber ones. This fuel's solvent powers are concerning, so any rubber piping and other parts in contact with fuel should be replaced with modern hard-wearing nylon pipes immediately to prevent any serious problems. Biodiesel is not a suitable fuel for spark ignition engines and considerable damage is likely to occur.

How petrol is made from crude oil

Discover how liquefied dinosaurs create fuel for your car

 Petrol is refined from crude oil or petroleum. This is made up of the semi-fossilised, liquefied remains of prehistoric plants and animals crushed between layers of sediment in the Earth's crust over a period of millions of years. This causes the constituent elements (like us, dinosaurs were primarily made up of hydrogen and carbon at the atomic level) to break down into large, rich molecules known as hydrocarbons, which are packed full of organic goodness. They are basically made up of chains of hydrogen and carbon atoms strung together. The length of the chain controls the properties of the hydrocarbon. We extract crude oil from the depths of the Earth and use a chemical reaction called catalysis to control the length of the molecule chains and turn petroleum from dinosaur stew into petrol and diesel.

A catalyst is an element that when inserted into a chemical reaction makes that reaction happen faster and overall creates a much more effective end product. In the amusingly named cat-cracking process, crude oil is heated in a process called distillation. Different lengths of hydrocarbon chains have different boiling points, when they start to turn into vapour. The vapour is drawn off before being moved on to the next phase, where it's forced into a chamber with the catalyst. In this case, it's different grades of distilled petroleum, including the leftovers from the previous reaction. This makes the big hydrocarbon molecules crack into much smaller ones.

Larger, heavier molecule chains with more carbon break down into heavy oils and have a higher boiling point, while smaller molecule chains with less carbon rise into vapours again and become lighter substances such as naphtha. Standard petrol is manufactured to fall in the middle ground between the two. This is important, as being in this relatively balanced state it can withstand more compression without spontaneously exploding, making it reasonably stable. ✿

The molecular length of hydrocarbons defines their behaviour

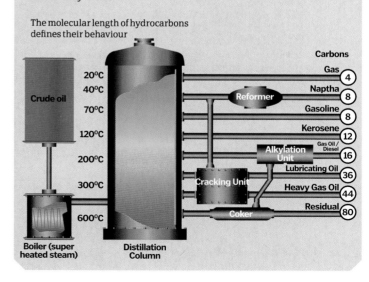

"Some DNA constantly replicates itself"

The building block of all cells

Unravelling the mystery of DNA

In 1953, James Watson and Francis Crick discovered that the DNA molecule resembles a double helix, one of science's most significant revelations

2. Doubling up
Each cell contains 23 chromosome pairs, for a total of 46 chromosomes.

1. DNA
A chromosome contains a coiled mass of DNA and the proteins that control how it works.

3. Coiled
A strand of DNA would be about three metres in length if uncoiled.

4. Base pairs
DNA strands contain about 3 billion of these nucleotide base pairs, comprising either adenine with thymine or guanine with cytosine

5. Sides
Sugar-phosphates form the sides of the DNA 'spiral staircase'

DNA and genetic traits

When a person is conceived, they inherit one copy of each chromosome from each parent for a total of 23 pairs. There are about 200 inherited traits that are determined by these genes, including physical and behavioural. We can also inherit a predisposition towards getting a particular disease or disorder. These genetic variations are called alleles. Some are dominant, while others are recessive.

While some traits are determined by a single gene, others come from multiple genes, the environment or a combination. There are multiple genes for determining eye colour, for example, but there's no known gene for being extraordinarily good at playing a specific sport. The latter is likely a combination of genes, health, nutrition and other environmental factors.

Deoxyribonucleic acid, better known as DNA, is the building block of all cells. DNA not only makes the proteins that determine our biological traits, it also gets copied and passed from generation to generation. Changes in DNA over time result in the evolution of traits in a species. Although scientists had learned about DNA and suspected its genetic function since the 1890s, its exact structure wasn't known until 1953.

Cambridge University scientists James Watson and Francis Crick won the 1962 Nobel Prize in Medicine – along with Maurice Wilkins – for discovering that the molecule was a double helix, two ladder-like strands twisted together that resemble a spiral staircase. These long molecules are twisted, along with various proteins, into a single chromosome. While DNA structure looks complicated, it comprises just four sugars called nucleotide bases: adenine (A), thymine (T), cytosine (C) and guanine (G). These four sugars are strung together to form a sequence, similar to the way that letters of the alphabet form words, and words form sentences. Groups of three nucleotides form 'words' called codons, which form 'sentences' called genes. These genes contain information on how and when to build a protein from a combination of 20 different amino acids.

To build a protein, DNA is copied to a type of RNA (ribonucleic acid) called messenger RNA (mRNA). Two types of special RNA molecules, called transfer RNA (tRNA) and ribosomes (rRNA), use amino acids to build the protein using the pattern described in the mRNA. Sometimes several different proteins are made from the mRNA. This is called protein synthesis.

When a cell needs to reproduce, all of its genetic information must copy over to the new cells. This means that the DNA must copy itself, or replicate. Enzymes, hormones and other chemicals in the body drive this process. Essentially the double helix zips apart and enzymes copy the codons, check the copies for accuracy, and seal up the strands. The frequency with which replication occurs depends on the type of cell in which the DNA resides. Cells in our skin, for example, are constantly dividing, so the DNA in those cells is constantly replicating itself.

Sometimes there are minor changes made in the processes of DNA replication and protein synthesis. Because there are some repeater codons, these variations don't always cause a problem. Often they result in a positive outcome, such as increased survival of certain types of diseases. However, depending on the variation, mutations can occur that can ultimately result in hereditary diseases. ✿

Heart lube
1 Your heart is surrounded by a membrane called the pericardium. It secretes fluid that acts as a lubricant so the heart doesn't suffer wear and tear when it beats.

Tubes of air
2 Artery literally means 'wind pipe'. Anatomists dissected corpses to learn about the body. After death, blood drains from arteries, so they were full of air, hence the name.

Coronary bypass
3 A coronary bypass is a type of surgery in which surgeons shunt a coronary artery around a blockage using blood vessels from other parts of the body.

Veins vs arteries
4 The ultimate difference between veins and arteries lies in whether they actually carry blood towards (veins) or away (arteries) from the heart.

Heart power
5 Your heart runs on just a few watts of power, about the same as a small LED light. Over the course of a long lifetime, it adds up to several billion joules.

DID YOU KNOW? *The heart pumps about 1 million barrels of blood during the average lifetime*

The heart – a vital organ

Your heart is a turbocharged double-pumping muscle that beats more than 40 million times every year

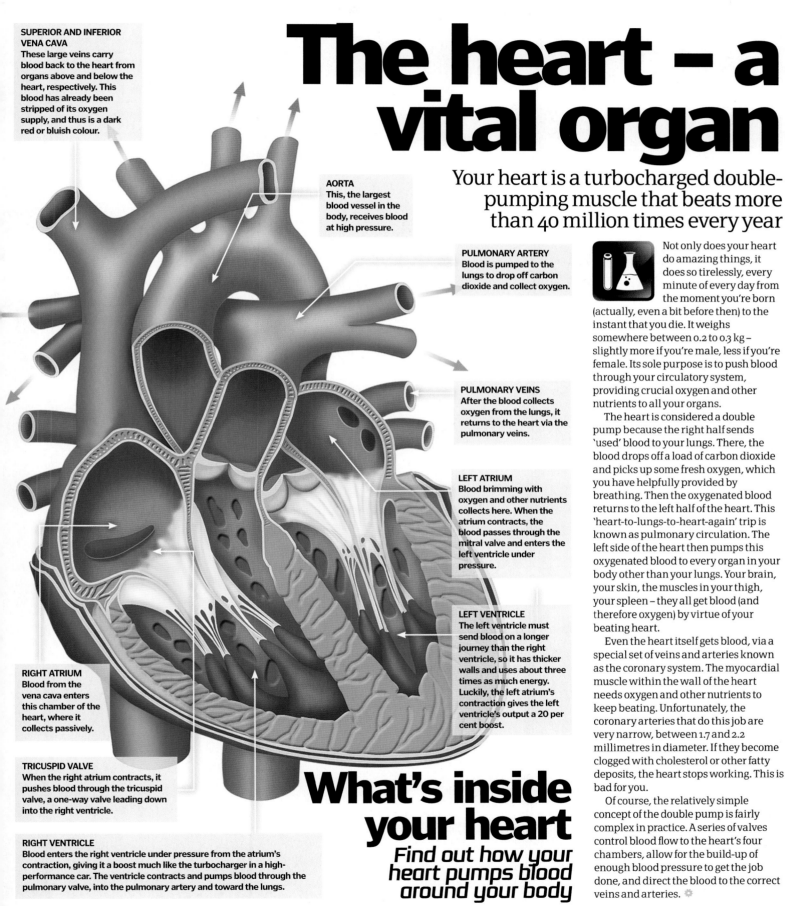

SUPERIOR AND INFERIOR VENA CAVA
These large veins carry blood back to the heart from organs above and below the heart, respectively. This blood has already been stripped of its oxygen supply, and thus is a dark red or bluish colour.

AORTA
This, the largest blood vessel in the body, receives blood at high pressure.

PULMONARY ARTERY
Blood is pumped to the lungs to drop off carbon dioxide and collect oxygen.

PULMONARY VEINS
After the blood collects oxygen from the lungs, it returns to the heart via the pulmonary veins.

LEFT ATRIUM
Blood brimming with oxygen and other nutrients collects here. When the atrium contracts, the blood passes through the mitral valve and enters the left ventricle under pressure.

LEFT VENTRICLE
The left ventricle must send blood on a longer journey than the right ventricle, so it has thicker walls and uses about three times as much energy. Luckily, the left atrium's contraction gives the left ventricle's output a 20 per cent boost.

RIGHT ATRIUM
Blood from the vena cava enters this chamber of the heart, where it collects passively.

TRICUSPID VALVE
When the right atrium contracts, it pushes blood through the tricuspid valve, a one-way valve leading down into the right ventricle.

RIGHT VENTRICLE
Blood enters the right ventricle under pressure from the atrium's contraction, giving it a boost much like the turbocharger in a high-performance car. The ventricle contracts and pumps blood through the pulmonary valve, into the pulmonary artery and toward the lungs.

What's inside your heart
Find out how your heart pumps blood around your body

Not only does your heart do amazing things, it does so tirelessly, every minute of every day from the moment you're born (actually, even a bit before then) to the instant that you die. It weighs somewhere between 0.2 to 0.3 kg – slightly more if you're male, less if you're female. Its sole purpose is to push blood through your circulatory system, providing crucial oxygen and other nutrients to all your organs.

The heart is considered a double pump because the right half sends 'used' blood to your lungs. There, the blood drops off a load of carbon dioxide and picks up some fresh oxygen, which you have helpfully provided by breathing. Then the oxygenated blood returns to the left half of the heart. This 'heart-to-lungs-to-heart-again' trip is known as pulmonary circulation. The left side of the heart then pumps this oxygenated blood to every organ in your body other than your lungs. Your brain, your skin, the muscles in your thigh, your spleen – they all get blood (and therefore oxygen) by virtue of your beating heart.

Even the heart itself gets blood, via a special set of veins and arteries known as the coronary system. The myocardial muscle within the wall of the heart needs oxygen and other nutrients to keep beating. Unfortunately, the coronary arteries that do this job are very narrow, between 1.7 and 2.2 millimetres in diameter. If they become clogged with cholesterol or other fatty deposits, the heart stops working. This is bad for you.

Of course, the relatively simple concept of the double pump is fairly complex in practice. A series of valves control blood flow to the heart's four chambers, allow for the build-up of enough blood pressure to get the job done, and direct the blood to the correct veins and arteries. ✿

Return of the Large Hadron Collider

After nine months of repair work, the biggest machine in the world (and the most expensive science experiment of all time) is once again ready for action

Remember how much fun you used to have hurling toy cars into each other for hours on end? The Large Hadron Collider (LHC) is something like that – except the cars are subatomic particles that race along a 27-kilometre circular track buried 50-170 metres below Switzerland and France, crashing into each other at 99.9999991 per cent the speed of light. The people doing the smashing also have more noble intentions than your average six-year-old. Scientists from all over the world have high hopes that the LHC will unlock revolutionary secrets of the universe.

On 10 September 2008, CERN successfully sent a single particle beam around the LHC. But just nine days later, they had to shut it down following a major malfunction.

Here's the skinny on what the LHC does, how it does it, what went wrong, and what the European Organisation for Nuclear Research (CERN) has been working on since.

Why smash?

The basic idea of the LHC is to accelerate either streams of protons (part of an atom's nucleus) or streams of ions (charged atoms) in opposite directions, so that they collide into each other. The particles – collectively known as hadrons – are so tiny that making any two hit is extremely difficult.

CERN compares this challenge to trying to launch individual needles into each other from two positions ten kilometres apart.

The LHC manages to boost the collision rate by upping the particle count and focusing a huge number of particles into a very small area. Each particle stream includes around 3,000 bunches, and each bunch contains as many as 100 billion particles. The bunches cross each other around 30 million times a second, which means the LHC can produce up to 600 million collisions per second.

As cool as smashing things together is, you can rest assured the 24 countries who funded the LHC didn't drop €2 billion just for the heck of it. They

Lucio Rossi, head of CERN's Magnets, Cryostats and Superconductors group

undertook the project to fill in gaps in our fundamental understanding of what makes the universe tick.

Understanding the universe is something like devising the recipe for a mysterious dish when the chef is long gone. We can never actually witness the moment of creation, so scientists have to piece together theories by examining what exists today. This means, in large part, investigating the smallest particles that make up all matter. The high intensity collisions in the LHC are powerful enough to break ions and protons into smaller secondary particles we've never observed before. A collection of sophisticated detectors will measure the position, mass, energy, charge, trajectory, and speed of the particles from each collision and record the results. Then scientists will pour over the data to figure out what sorts of particles were produced and what they did. The results could prove or disprove various theories. Or it could turn up something completely unexpected.

The big mysteries

So, what could these particles tell us? Over the years, scientists have developed a substantial body of knowledge about subatomic particles, called the Standard Model of particles and forces. But while the Standard Model explains many things well, it doesn't account for a number of known phenomena. Scientists hope LHC experiments will shed light on these perplexing mysteries:

■ What causes gravity?
■ What gives something mass, and why do some particles have mass while others don't?
■ What are dark matter and dark energy? Scientists know it makes up 96 per cent of the universe, but since it's invisible, they don't know much about it.
■ Why is there matter and no antimatter? Scientists believe that the Big Bang created equal amounts of matter and its opposite counterpart, antimatter. Matter and antimatter particles should destroy each other when they meet, yet somehow a certain amount of matter survived, while no antimatter did. Scientists want to know why nature gave matter the edge.
■ What was matter like just after the Big Bang?
■ Are there other dimensions?

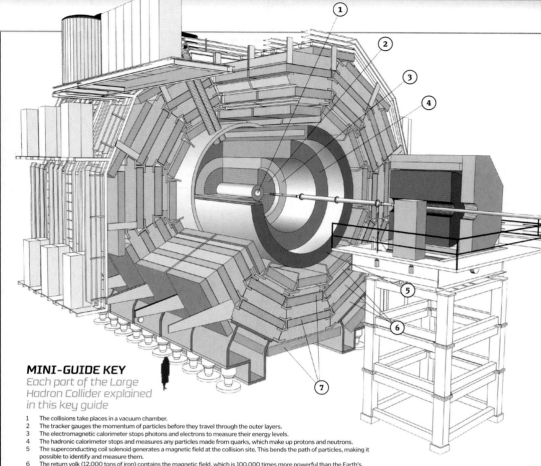

MINI-GUIDE KEY
Each part of the Large Hadron Collider explained in this key guide

1 The collisions take places in a vacuum chamber.
2 The tracker gauges the momentum of particles before they travel through the outer layers.
3 The electromagnetic calorimeter stops photons and electrons to measure their energy levels.
4 The hadronic calorimeter stops and measures any particles made from quarks, which make up protons and neutrons.
5 The superconducting coil solenoid generates a magnetic field at the collision site. This bends the path of particles, making it possible to identify and measure them.
6 The return yolk (12,000 tons of iron) contains the magnetic field, which is 100,000 times more powerful than the Earth's.
7 The muon chambers track the path of (you guessed it) muons. These are charged particles that scientists expect will be produced when unknown particles, like the Higgs boson, decay following collisions.

How does it work?

The collision process begins with either hydrogen or lead. To produce a proton stream, operators strip electrons away from hydrogen atoms. To produce an ion stream, operators heat lead atoms to 550 degrees celsius and then pass the lead vapour through an electric current to ionise it.

Once the particles are ready, the operators pass them through an accelerator chain outside the LHC track itself. This chain applies radio frequency electrical fields to energise the particles (get them up to high speed), before injecting them into the LHC's circular "beam pipe" tracks.

As the beams zip around the pipes, in a ultra-high vacuum, they pass through periodic radio frequency cavities. These cavities produce electrical fields that energise the particles, keeping them moving at top speed. The pipes intersect at various collision points around the LHC ring, and the particles

collide. Detectors at the intersection points register what happens.

The biggest engineering challenge is guiding the particles – that is, steering them along the circular track and focusing them into beams. The LHC does this with powerful electromagnets, which generate magnetic fields to push the particles in the right direction. There are a total of 9,300 magnets in the LHC, including 1,232 15-metre-long dipole magnets that bend the beams so they follow the track, and 392 five to seven-metre magnets that focus the beams.

A conventional electromagnet consists of a coil of wire, hooked up to a power source that produces an electrical current. The current in the wires generates a magnetic field, thanks to the electromagnetic effect. In the massive LHC, the energy consumption for this type of electromagnet would be

prohibitively expensive. Instead, the LHC sports supercooled superconducting electromagnets made from niobium-titanium cable. Niobium-titanium is a superconductive metal, meaning that if you keep it cold enough, it offers no electrical resistance and sustains an electrical current indefinitely. In other words, you can use it to create electromagnets that continually carry a current (13,000 amps, in the case of the LHC), while consuming no power whatsoever.

The catch is that you have to keep the magnets incredibly cold. To do this, engineers first cool the magnets to -193.2 degrees celsius, using liquid nitrogen. Next, they cool the magnets down to a steady -271 degrees celsius, using an advanced refrigeration system. This system, essentially the biggest fridge in the entire world, uses superfluid liquid helium as a coolant.

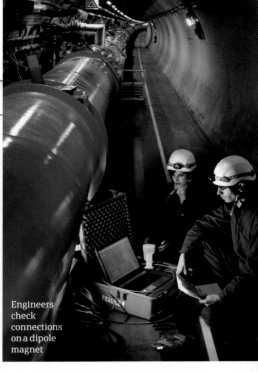

An engineer prepares a replacement magnet to be lowered into the LHC tunnel

Engineers check connections on a dipole magnet

Working on an interconnection between two magnets

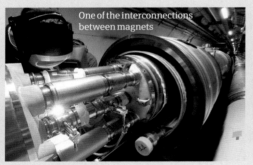

One of the interconnections between magnets

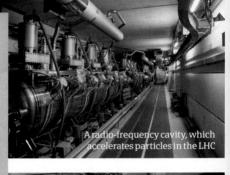

A radio-frequency cavity, which accelerates particles in the LHC

Installing the beam pipe in the middle of the ATLAS magnet doughnut

DID YOU KNOW?

Big fridge

The LHC is also the world's largest fridge. The magnets are first pre-cooled to -193.2°C using liquid nitrogen before nearly 60 tons of liquid helium bring them down to a rather frosty -271.3°C.

Trouble in the tunnel

Given the enormous complexity of the LHC, the malfunction in September of 2008 wasn't a total shock. We talked to the man in charge of the LHC magnets, Lucio Rossi, to find out what happened.

Rossi explained that the engineers were able to test some parts of the LHC ahead of time, but not everything. "To be sure that the magnet works, we tested them between 2002 and 2006," Rossi said. "But what we couldn't test was the connection between the magnets – the assembly of the magnets – the 27-kilometre long ring."

These interconnections turned out to be a weak link, which in turn led to major malfunction. "The 13,000 amp current has to pass from one magnet to another," Rossi explained. "To do this, there is a special joint, or splice. One of these failed and overheated."

The engineers didn't recognise the problem right away, and the connection heated from -270 degrees celsius up to 800 degrees, essentially melting away. Things got even worse when a 9,000-amp electrical arc formed between the magnets. "A lot of power went into the arc," Rossi said, "and so everything melted in this zone between two magnets."

As a result, the super-fluid helium from the cooling system leaked into the vacuum, forming a powerful pressure wave. "Because of this pressure wave, we had magnets that were pushed, literally pushed," Rossi explained. "These weigh 30 metric tons and they were pushed, some of them a half a meter, some of them only two centimetres."

The malfunction ended up being fairly substantial: "We had to remove and repair and substitute a lot of magnets. In total, we removed 53 magnets – a line of magnets more or less 700 metres long. So, 700 metres of the accelerator has been completely repaired. All the magnets have been removed, either repaired and put back again, or completely substituted with brand new magnets," stated Rossi.

The supercooling system added to the repair time. It took about a month just to warm the magnets to the point that the engineers could handle them. Additionally, the engineers had to remove all the damaged magnets from their cryostats – advanced thermos systems that help keep the magnets cool. According to Rossi, the repair work took eight to nine months, and involved around 300 people.

What's next?

The Large Hadron Collider engineers had everything replaced and in working order by early July 2009. However, they still had to cool the magnets down to operating temperature. This took about a month per section, and inevitably delayed the re-launch. However, on 30 November 2009, the LHC broke the world record and accelerated its twin proton beams to 1.18 teraelectron volts.

The collider is currently well on its way to achieving its ultimate operating conditions, and at an international conference held in Paris in July 2010, CERN's director general Rolf Heuer was optimistic for the future: "Rediscovering our 'old friends' in the particle world shows that the LHC experiments are well prepared to enter new territory. It seems that the Standard Model is working as expected. Now it is down to nature to show us what is new."

Know your LHC experiments

There's not much point in smashing particles together if you don't record what happens. This work falls to six advanced detectors, spaced out around the LHC ring. Each detector is part of a different experiment

1 CMS (Compact Muon Solenoid) serves the same basic purpose as ATLAS, but goes about it in a different way. Instead of a magnetic doughnut, it uses a giant solenoid – a coil of superconducting cable. This solenoid can generate a magnetic field 100,000 times more powerful than the Earth's. A massive steel yoke contains the field.

2 ATLAS (A Toroidal LHC ApparatuS), the biggest detector, is like a giant doughnut, made from eight 25-metre superconducting magnetic coils that surround the beam pipe. It's a general detector, designed to dig up clues related to a variety of phenomena, including gravity, mass, dark matter, and extra dimensions.

3 ALICE (A Large Ion Collider Experiment) is designed to create and observe quark-gluon plasma, a state of matter that scientists believe existed soon after the Big Bang. Lead ion collisions will generate energy 100,000 times hotter than the centre of the Sun, essentially melting the protons. This should release the quarks and gluons that make up the protons. As this plasma cools, it should re-form into atoms, in the same way it did when the universe was forming.

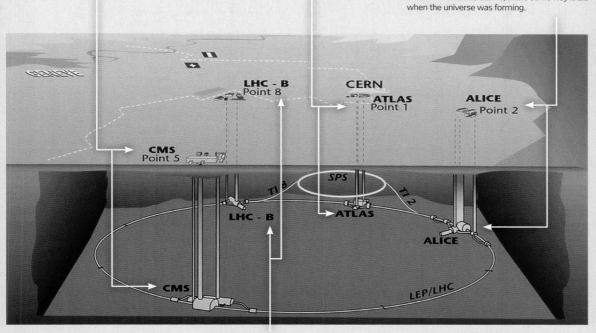

Peter Higgs visits the ATLAS experiment, which may finally find the Higgs boson

4 TOTEM (TOTal Elastic and Diffractive Cross Section Measurement) is designed to measure particles very near the beams, in order to gauge proton size and the LHC's performance, among other things.

5 LHCb (Large Hadron Collider beauty) consists of a series of sub-detectors designed to examine a type of particle called a 'beauty quark'. The hope is observations of these particles will shed light on the relationship between matter and antimatter.

6 LHCf (Large Hadron Collider forward) is the smallest experiment of the bunch. The idea here is to observe cascades of particles caused by LHC collisions to gain a better understanding of cosmic rays, charged particles from space that create similar cascades when they encounter Earth's atmosphere.

The hunt for Higgs

Whether or not scientists find it, one of the biggest stars of the LHC will be the Higgs boson. In 1964, physicists Peter Higgs, Robert Brout, and François Englert proposed this theoretical particle as a possible explanation for one of the biggest mysteries in physics – why some particles have mass and others don't.

The physicists proposed that just after the Big Bang, particles had no mass. But as the universe cooled, a force field formed that had the ability to give particles mass. Whenever a particle encounters this 'Higgs field' it gains mass from a particle called a Higgs boson. This gels well with other theories, but scientists haven't been able to confirm that the Higgs boson exists. If it's real; the LHC should reveal it. And if it doesn't show up, physicists will get a nudge to pursue alternative theories.

Too much information

With 150 million sensors capturing data 40 million times a second, the LHC will produce a phenomenal volume of information for scientists to analyse. Specifically, the four experiments will result in 15 million gigabytes of data per year – that's equivalent to a 20-kilometre stack of CDs. This is too much for any one computer to handle, so CERN will rely on 'The Grid' – thousands of computers from around the world that are networked together via the net.

Your nervous system

Lovely as you may be, you are really just an organisation of not especially talented cells

Like any organisation, your success depends on communication between your individual members. In a sense, you actually are this communication, since it is the magic that makes you a single, clever creature. Your built-in communications network, known as the nervous system, perceives the outside world, keeps all body parts working in harmony, and forms the thoughts and memories that make you unique.

The nervous system comprises hundreds of billions of specialised cells called neurons. A typical neuron consists of a compact cell body, protruding filaments called dendrites, and a long single fibre called an axon. The axon can transmit signals to other neurons and to muscle cells, while the dendrite can receive signals from other neurons and sensory cells. A neuron's axon may extend across the brain or body and branch off hundreds of times.

When something excites a neuron, the cell body will send an electrical charge down the length of an axon, triggering axon terminals to release chemicals called neurotransmitters. These neurotransmitters can travel to receptors on dendrites of an adjoining neuron, across a small gap called a synapse. Depending on the type of neurotransmitter and receptor, the signal may excite the adjoining neuron to fire an electrical charge down its own axon, or the signal may inhibit the neuron from firing. The complex connections and signal patterns among the hundreds of billions of neurons in your brain form thoughts, memories and all other mental activities.

Similarly, axons that extend out from your brain and spinal column into your body can release neurotransmitters to trigger muscle movement and organ activity. This is how your brain controls the rest of your body. Neurons also carry signals from the body back to the brain. You perceive sights, sounds, smells and taste when sensory cells in your eyes, mouth, nose and ears excite nearby neurons. The neurons send an electrical signal up to the brain, which interprets them. Sensory neurons near your skin and other parts of the body fire an electric signal in response to pressure, which your brain perceives as the sense of touch. ✿

1. Cerebellum
Latin for "little brain," the cerebellum co-ordinates and fine-tunes skilled movements, based on incoming sensory information. It's also involved in maintaining balance and posture.

2. Facial nerve
Branching sensory fibres run to the taste buds and the front of the tongue, while motor nerves connected to your salivary glands and muscles form facial expressions.

3. Vagus nerve
A critical nerve running from the brain to the neck, throat, chest and abdomen, the vagus is key to controlling your heart rate, swallowing, digestion and respiration.

4. Ganglion
Bundles of tightly packed neurons that serve as key connection hubs in the body's complex network of nerves.

5. Spinal cord
A bundle of long axons that run from the brain to the lower spinal column, forming the key connection between the brain and body.

6. Radial nerve
A nerve that carries muscle motor commands that move your elbow, wrist and fingers.

7. Ulnar nerve
A key nerve involved in bending your fingers and wrist.

Know your nerves
It would be impossible to give due credit to all the interconnected neurons, nerves, and supporting cells that make up your nervous system, but we can point out some of the most valuable players...

Hitting a nerve: the not so funny bone

Most of the larger nerves in your body are insulated by muscle, bones and tissue. The big exception is the ulnar nerve, which runs down your arm, by way of your elbow. The nerve carries motor commands to your ring and pinkie fingers and relays sensory information back to the central nervous system. If you bang your elbow, the humerus bone bumps the nerve, jarring the axons inside, which your brain interprets as a tingling sensation.

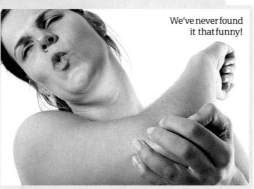

We've never found it that funny!

5 TOP FACTS
NERVOUS SYSTEM

World's largest neuron
1 The giant squid axon, which is almost a metre long and can be up to a millimetre thick, helps propel a squid forward (it propelled early nervous system research too).

No nervous system
2 Sponges are the only multi-cellular animals without neurons. They don't really do much, so they don't actually have much need for a nervous system.

Getting a head
3 Most animals have evolved cephalisation, an efficient clustering of neural structures (usually a brain) near sensors and feeding organs at one end of the body (a head).

Gotta sing!
4 During the spring, a flood of testosterone greatly expands the song areas of a male bird's brain so it is able to handle complex mating calls.

Conscious breathers
5 For whales and dolphins, breathing isn't part of the automatic nervous system. They have to do it consciously, which means they can never go to sleep completely.

DID YOU KNOW? Laid out flat and end-to-end, all the nerves in your body would wrap 2.5 times around the planet

Anatomy of a nerve

Nerves are sturdy enough to protect your sensitive axons from damage, but flexible enough to snake around your body parts...

4. Nerve fascicle
A bundle of axons.

1. Axon
The neural fibre that carries electrical signals representing motor commands and sensory information.

2. Myelin sheath
Fatty insulation that keeps axons from short-circuiting.

5. Blood vessels
Supply of blood that provides neurons with energy.

3. Perineurium
Sheath of connective tissue that protects each fascicle.

6. Epineurium
Outer connective tissue that protects the nerve.

Your built-in autopilot

Your automatic nervous system (ANS) works behind the scenes to keep your body running smoothly. The ANS is part of your peripheral nervous system, made up of sensory nerve fibres that constantly relay information about the state of your body and the motor nerves that relay commands from the brain and spinal cord to various glands, the involuntary smooth muscles in organs and blood vessels, and the cardiac muscles that control your heart.

The ANS's chief function is homeostasis – adjusting bodily processes to maintain internal stability. The ANS does this through two opposing, yet complementary sub-systems: the sympathetic division and parasympathetic division. The sympathetic division is like the accelerator in your car. The motor neurons excite your body, by increasing your heart rate and producing stress hormones, among other things. The parasympathetic division is like the brakes. The motor neurons can relax your body, by doing things like decreasing heart rate, constricting the trachea and bronchial tubes, and relaxing the bladder sphincter.

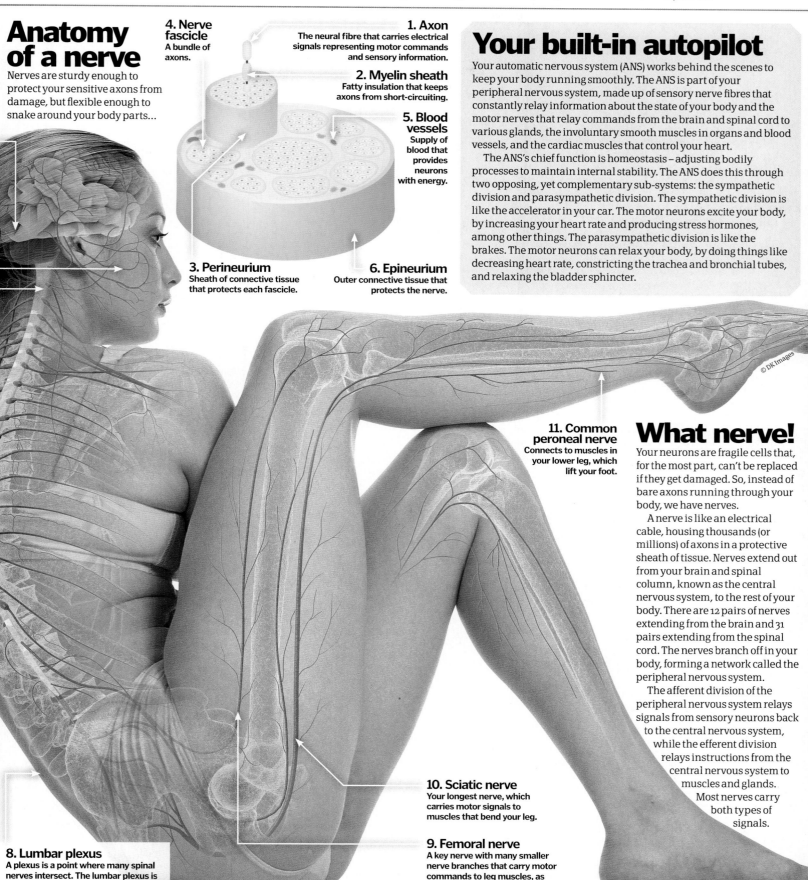

© DK Images

11. Common peroneal nerve
Connects to muscles in your lower leg, which lift your foot.

What nerve!

Your neurons are fragile cells that, for the most part, can't be replaced if they get damaged. So, instead of bare axons running through your body, we have nerves.

A nerve is like an electrical cable, housing thousands (or millions) of axons in a protective sheath of tissue. Nerves extend out from your brain and spinal column, known as the central nervous system, to the rest of your body. There are 12 pairs of nerves extending from the brain and 31 pairs extending from the spinal cord. The nerves branch off in your body, forming a network called the peripheral nervous system.

The afferent division of the peripheral nervous system relays signals from sensory neurons back to the central nervous system, while the efferent division relays instructions from the central nervous system to muscles and glands. Most nerves carry both types of signals.

10. Sciatic nerve
Your longest nerve, which carries motor signals to muscles that bend your leg.

9. Femoral nerve
A key nerve with many smaller nerve branches that carry motor commands to leg muscles, as well as sensory information from the thigh and lower leg.

8. Lumbar plexus
A plexus is a point where many spinal nerves intersect. The lumbar plexus is the meeting point for nerves controlling the abdomen, lower back, and legs.

1. Coronary arteries
These are the arteries that supply the heart with blood. They are crucial to keeping the heart working effectively.

4. Blockage occurs
Either through excess clotting or further deposit build-up, a blockage can occur. This means blood flow cannot get through at all and the lack of oxygen results in heart tissue dying.

How do cats see at night?

Understanding the facts behind this feline phenomenon

 Cats often hunt at night, and consequently they need superior night-time vision to primarily diurnal creatures. The way their eyes have adapted is by the introduction of an extra layer behind the retina, called the tapetum lucidum, which reflects light back through the retina to enhance perception in low-level light. This allows cats to see even when the level of light is seven times lower than a human needs to be able to see.

Many other animals that operate at night also have this layer and it is this that makes nocturnal animals' eyes seem to glow when you look at them at night. This concept has also been used to make 'cat's eyes' road markings. However, although this layer gives nocturnal creatures benefits at night, it can cause issues when there are high levels of light present as too much light travels through the eye. Many cats display a slit-like pupil to control amounts of light entering the eye.

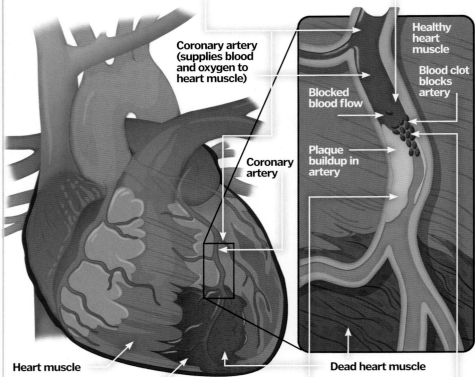

Coronary artery (supplies blood and oxygen to heart muscle)

Coronary artery

Healthy heart muscle

Blood clot blocks artery

Blocked blood flow

Plaque buildup in artery

Heart muscle

Dead heart muscle

Iris
The slit-like shape of the iris is different to what we observe in humans, and this is due to the need for control over the level of light entering the eye at differing times.

Retina
This is the light-sensitive layer of cells located at the back of the eye. In humans, there is a central point which allows an individual clear sight, in cats this is a 'central band'.

5. Dead tissue
Due to a lack of oxygen, some sections of heart muscle can die off. This can reduce effectiveness of the muscle as a whole following recovery.

2. Plaque build-up
Plaque, made up of inflammatory cells, proteins, fatty deposits and calcium, narrows the artery and means that only a reduced blood flow can get through.

3. Plaque rupture
Plaque becomes hardened as it builds up, and it can rupture. If it ruptures, platelets gather to clot around the rupture, which can cause a blockage to occur.

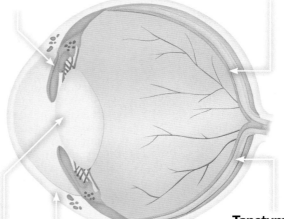

Lens
The lens is a transparent disc in the eye and its primary role is to refract light that enters into the eye so that it is received by the retina.

Cornea
The cornea is a transparent layer covering the pupil, iris and aqueous humour. It helps refract light towards the retina so light is received in the correct area.

Tapetum lucidum
This is the thin, reflective layer located just behind the retina that bounces light back through the retina for improved perception at night.

Heart attacks

Heart attacks are one of the western world's biggest killers, but what causes them and how do they kill?

 A heart attack, also known as a myocardial infarction, occurs when a blockage stops blood oxygenating the heart muscle. If this is not corrected quickly, the muscle tissue that is lacking oxygen can become damaged, or indeed die. The scale of impact on the individual's health after the attack is dependant on how long the blockage occurs for, what artery it affected and what treatment was received. Following the initial attack, heart failure or arrhythmias can occur, both of which may prove fatal. However, given the right treatment many sufferers go on to make good recoveries and can eventually return to their normal activities.

The most common reason for heart attacks is coronary artery disease (CAD). This is where arteries are constricted due to plaque build-ups and this layer then ruptures. Blood platelets make their way to the site of rupture and start to form blood clots. If these clots become too large, the narrowed artery will block and a heart attack occurs. Heart attacks can also be caused by coronary artery spasms, but these are rare.

Although some people will be genetically predisposed to heart attacks, individuals can reduce risk by keeping their weight down, watching what they eat, not smoking, and exercising regularly.

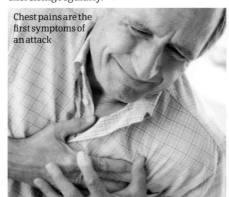

Chest pains are the first symptoms of an attack

Head to Head
ADDICTIVE SUBSTANCES

HARDEST TO QUIT

Nicotine
According to tests by Henningfield and Benowitz, nicotine is the hardest drug to stay off and has the highest number of addicts.

WORST WITHDRAWAL

Alcohol
The same tests found that booze addicts had the most severe withdrawal symptoms produced by stopping use of the drug.

MOST ADDICTIVE

Cocaine
Henningfield and Benowitz found that cocaine was the drug that most induced users and addicts to take it again and again.

Why do we get addicted?

And is it all in our head?

The way we use the word addiction has long been a subject of contention. Many talk of addiction in regards to drugs use, eating or gambling, though not all of these would be classified as an addiction if we used purely physiological addiction definitions. Recently, however, scientists and psychologists have put forward that addiction should also be used to describe psychological dependence as well.

Physiologically, addiction is defined as a chronic condition when an individual becomes biologically and physically dependent upon something, often causing a craving or compulsive behaviour through a chemical change inside the individual. The individual will continue to repeat the behaviour even if it is detrimental to their self. Psychologically, the term addiction is used to describe a recurring compulsion to perform a specific behaviour, again, even if this is detrimental.

While physiological addiction is easier to classify and diagnose due to obvious physical withdrawal symptoms if a substance is removed, psychological dependence is much harder to classify due to the fact individuals can be overly interested, even to near obsessive, about a behaviour, and miss it when removed, but not actually be fully addicted and experience physical withdrawal symptoms when the behaviour is stopped. Often the issues with individuals trying to lose an addiction, such as smokers, is the psychological dependence rather than the physical, in that a smoker will miss the physical smoking of the cigarette and associated behaviour or feelings more than the chemical nicotine rush.

The five basic human tastes

Building a map of the tongue

There is general agreement that humans have five basic tastes, although the fifth taste 'primary' has only been recently officially recognised. Sweetness, bitterness, sourness and saltiness were joined by savouriness in 2002. Several other sensations that the tongue can recognise have been identified but are not classified as tastes.

Sweetness is associated primarily with simple carbohydrates – of which sugar is one of the most common. The way sweetness is detected is complex and only recently has the current model of multiple binding sites between the receptors and sweet substance itself been proposed and accepted. A sweet taste infers that the substance is high in energy and studies have shown that newborns in particular, who need a high calorie intake to grow, demonstrate a preference for sugar concentrations sweeter than lactose, which is found in breast milk.

Bitterness can be detected in very low levels and is generally perceived to be an unpleasant or sharp taste. Many toxic substances in nature are known to be bitter and there is an argument proposed by evolutionary scientists that bitterness sensitivity is an evolutionary defence mechanism. Humans, however, have now developed various techniques to make previous inedible bitter substances edible through reducing their toxicity, often through cooking.

The taste of saltiness is produced by the presence of sodium ions, or other closely related alkali metal ions. Potassium and lithium produce a similar taste as they are most closely related to sodium.

Sourness detects acidity. The way we measure the degree of sourness is through rating sour substances against dilute hydrochloric. The mechanism involved in detecting sourness is similar to saltiness in that taste is caused by a concentration of ions – in this case hydrogen ions. Savouriness is the newest of the recognised basic tastes and the taste is produced by fermented or aged foods. Glutamate is a common compound that can cause this taste and consequently savouriness is considered fundamental to Eastern cuisine.

Taste qualities are found in all areas of the tongue, although some regions are more sensitive than others

Your taste buds have very tiny, sensitive hairs called microvilli which send messages to your brain about how something tastes

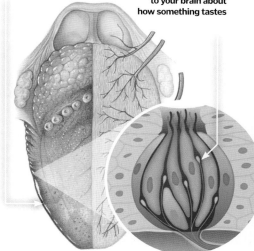

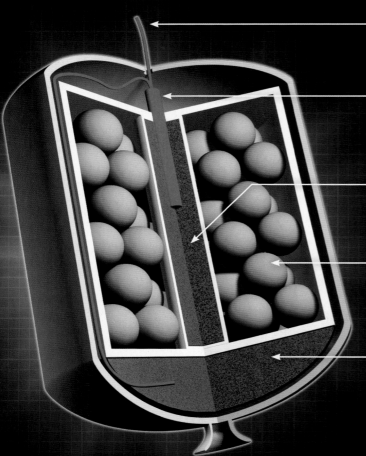

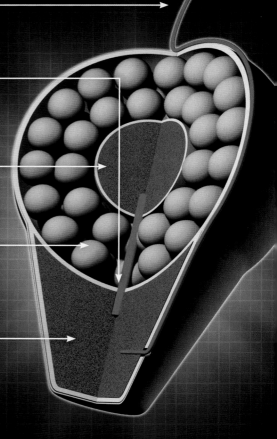

1. Fuse
The first fuse sets everything in motion. After the shell is in the mortar, the fuse is lit and the flame makes its way to the lifting charge.

3. Time-delayed fuse
While the shell soars up into the air, the time-delayed fuse continues to burn, buying enough time to get the shell at its highest point before reaching the bursting charge.

4. Bursting charge
The bursting charge is more black powder, stored higher up the shell. Once the time-delayed fuse reaches the bursting charge, the combustion sets off the stars.

5. Stars
The stars begin their heat-induced chemical reactions. The shell can no longer contain the power of the combustion, and the stars are sent flying, creating the traditional fireworks shapes.

2. Lifting charge
Black powder (also called gunpowder) is ignited by the fuse, and the explosion can send a shell up to 1,000 feet into the air.

Italian-style shell
Creates more elaborate bursts

Oriental-style shell
Produces spherical bursts

Inside fireworks
What makes the firework explode

How fireworks explode

These bright and festive chemistry experiments have been delighting people for hundreds of years

Despite all their different colours, shapes, and sounds, all fireworks have the same basic components. Aerial fireworks consist of a shell made of heavy paper that holds the 'lift charge', the 'bursting charge', and the 'stars'. All of these glittery spectacles come from good old-fashioned combustion. Combustion is a chemical reaction between two substances (a fuel and an oxidant) that produces light and heat. The heat causes gasses to expand rapidly, building pressure. The shells are tightly wrapped cylinders, which provide good resistance to this pressure, giving it a short time to build in intensity. Then, when the reaction overpowers the shell, you get the explosive firework effect.

It all starts when the shell is placed into a mortar (a cylinder the same size as the shell, which holds the firework in place while the fuse burns). The lift charge, at the bottom of the shell, is basically concentrated black powder (charcoal, sulphur, and potassium nitrate). When lit by the dangling fuse, the lift charge sends the shell into the air. Basic firecrackers are just paper-covered black powder: you light the fuse and listen to the popping sound.

The bursting charge is another round of black powder with its own time-delayed fuse higher up in

5 TOP FACTS
FIREWORKS

World's largest display
1 This record was set on 31 December 2006 in Funchal, Madeira, as part of Portugal's new year celebrations. 66,236 fireworks lit up the sky to claim the world record.

Most rockets in 30s
2 The world record for the most rockets fired in 30 seconds is 56,405, achieved on 16 August 2006. An attempt to beat this on Bournemouth seafront in 2009 failed.

Tallest bonfire
3 Hiroshima, Japan was the setting for the world's tallest bonfire – a quite collosal 37metre high, lit on 9 February 2003 as part of the city's Centennial celebrations.

Gunpowder plot
4 Bonfire Night held on 5 November is the celebration of the failed 1605 gunpowder plot in which Guy Fawkes attemped to blow up the British Houses of Parliament.

Huge Catherine wheel
5 We have the Newick Bonfire Society to thank for the monsterous 85-foot world-record-breaking Catherine wheel constructed in the UK on 30 October 1999.

DID YOU KNOW? *A modern sparkler burns at a temperature over 15 times the boiling point of water*

What makes the colours?

Colours are a matter of delicate balance. The wrong combination can mean a wrong colour... or worse

Colours involve different measurements and combinations of oxygen producers, fuels, binders, and colour producers. You can make colour through incandescence – light created through heat (orange, red, white), or luminescence – light created from a chemical reaction without extreme heat (blue, green). It's all about temperature control and balance.

Red – Strontium and lithium
Orange – Calcium
Gold – Incandescence of iron, charcoal or lampblack
Yellow – Sodium
Electric white – Magnesium or aluminium
Green – Barium plus a chlorine producer
Blue – Copper plus a chlorine producer
Purple – Strontium plus copper
Silver – Aluminium, titanium or magnesium powder or flakes

The time-delay fuse continues to burn, reaching the next cluster of stars as the first explosion fades.

Each set of stars is in its own cardboard compartment, allowing for separate explosions. The first bursting charge sets off the first cluster of stars.

The shell rises into the air as the time-delay fuse burns.

The fuse is lit, setting off the lift charge.

The short life of a firework

A lot of careful planning has to go into a multi-break firework. All for about three seconds' worth of entertainment...

the shell. The bursting charge creates the heat to activate the stars that surround it and explode them outward from the shell. The stars are where the magic happens.

Stars are balls made up of fuels, oxidisers, colour-creating combinations of different kinds of metals, and a binder to hold everything together. The stars can be arranged within the firework shell to create shapes. The shapes can be things like hearts, stars, and circles. Hundreds of stars can be used in a single firework shell.

More complex fireworks – for example, ones that produce a shape like a smiley face, have multiple phases of different colours, or make extra sounds like whistles – have shells with a more intricate infrastructure. In these types of fireworks, there are more time-delayed fuses linked to various bursting charges with their own surrounding stars. Each of these may sit in its own individual interior shell. These are called 'multi-break shells'.

While a sight to behold, fireworks are individually wrapped chemistry experiments. Tapping one too hard or creating a static electricity shock with your synthetic-material clothing could be deadly and one exploding near to your face could result in horrific burns and even blindness. They don't have the word 'fire' in them for nothing.

The effects of ageing

What happens to our bodies as we get older?

Many scientists are still baffled by why we age, only knowing that it makes us frail and weak, and eventually causes us to die. Visual effects of ageing are clear to see, skin wrinkles and hair greys, but there are massive changes that occur inside the body as well. Organs start to lose effectiveness, bones start to calcify and brain function decreases.

Although there have been many proposed theories for ageing, there is actually no agreed scientific reason for the process, just two commonly accepted theories. The mutation accumulation theory suggests that traits linked to ageing, which will only affect us after reproductive age, can be passed on to our offspring when we reproduce as they are neither selected for or

against survival as they are neutral at that point. These kinds of mutation then build up in the population.

The other major theory is the antagonistic pleiotropy theory that states that genes which aid reproduction or growth in childhood have a cost later in life, meaning they are actively selected for when we reproduce even though they have a negative cost for the individual later on. These theories are similar, but one assumes mutations are collected without intention, and the other suggests they are selected for a reason.

Understanding ageing is very important as once we understand exactly how we age, we can then better treat problems that are brought about by ageing and then hopefully extend life expectancies across the globe. ✿

Older doesn't necessarily mean wiser, especially after three sherries

"Hold the fries please, I'm on a diet"

Why do we get fat?

As the obesity epidemic grows, it is important to understand just what causes us to gain weight

Daily calorie intake for an average adult is set between 2,000 and 2,500 kcals and recommended fat intake is between 70 and 90 grams. The body needs this level of calories in order to function at maximum efficiency. However, if we consume more than is needed to run our body, it stores these extra calories as fat. These fat stores can serve as a reserve if we don't eat enough, but if someone consistently over-eats, they'll become overweight as the body continues to store the excess calories.

Obesity is becoming more prevalent across the world, within developed and developing countries. Highly calorific food and snacks, with generally poor nutritional value, have become more widely and cheaply available and the amount of saturated fat being consumed by an average adult is much higher than 20 years ago. Changes in behavioural

patterns of societies have also contributed to the problem as average levels of physical activity have reduced. Eating patterns have also changed due to lifestyle changes. Busy lives and more focus being placed on careers has led to the advent of the 'ready meal' and an increase in the number of takeaways eaten – which are often very high in saturated fat and calories. Genes can also have an impact on weight gain, but most cases of obesity that we see are actually due to average calorie intake increasing, with actual need reducing.

Over the last 20 years, child obesity levels have also been increasing dramatically, again primarily due to physical exertion decreasing and calorific intake increasing. This is of particular concern because of the many health problems associated with obesity such as type two diabetes, cardiovascular disease, strokes and certain forms of cancer among others. ✿

Working out your body mass index (BMI)

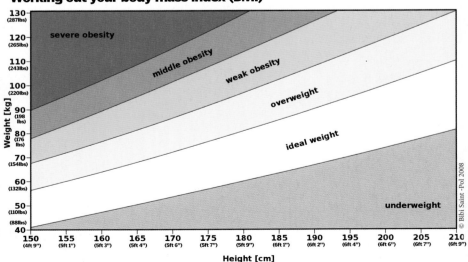

© Bibi Saint -Pol 2008

5 TOP FACTS
SKIN

Bacteria thrive on human skin
1 Every square inch of skin has an average of 32 million bacteria on it... no matter how many baths or showers you have a day.

You shed your skin every day
2 Every 24 hours, you will lose your uppermost layer of dead skin cells, helping to keep your skin fresh and clean and able to breath.

Skin varies drastically in thickness
3 Skin is around 1 mm thick on your eyelids, but on your feet this thickness increases to 3 mm, giving you much more protection where needed.

As we age, our skin thins
4 Skin thins over time and begins to loosen, which is where wrinkles come from... it's also why some people opt for plastic surgery in later life.

We have billions of sweat glands
5 Each square inch of healthy skin contains close to 650 sweat glands, which are essential for keeping you cool.

DID YOU KNOW? *All mammals have hair on their skin, including marine mammals which appear hairless*

Under the skin

Find out more about the largest organ in your body...

Our skin is the largest organ in our bodies with an average individual skin's surface area measuring around two square metres and accounting for up to 16 per cent of total body weight. It is made up of three distinct layers. These are the epidermis, the dermis and the hypodermis and they all have differing functions. Humans are rare in that we can see these layers distinctly.

The epidermis is the top, waterproofing layer. Alongside helping to regulate temperature of the body, the epidermis also protects against infection as it stops pathogens entering the body. Although generally referred to as one layer, it is actually made up of five. The top layers are actually dead keratin-filled cells which prevent water loss and provide protection against the environment, but the lower levels, where new skin cells are produced, are nourished by the dermis. In other species, such as amphibians, the epidermis consists of only live skin cells. In these cases, the skin is generally permeable and actually may be a major respiratory organ.

The dermis has the connective tissue and nerve endings, contains hair follicles, sweat glands, lymphatic and blood vessels. The top layer of the dermis is ridged and interconnects securely with the epidermis.

Although the hypodermis is not actually considered part of the skin, its purpose is to connect the upper layers of skin to the body's underlying bone and muscle. Blood vessels and nerves pass through this layer to the dermis. This layer is also crucial for temperature regulation, as it contains 50 per cent of a healthy adult's body fat in subcutaneous tissue. These kinds of layers are not often seen in other species, humans being one of few that you can see the distinct layers within the skin. Not only does the skin offer protection for muscle, bone and internal organs, but it is our protective barrier against the environment. Temperature regulation, insulation, excretion of sweat and sensation are just a few more functions of skin. ✿

1. Epidermis
This is the top, protective layer. It is waterproof and protects the body against UV light, disease and dehydration among other things.

2. Dermis
The layer that nourishes and helps maintain the epidermis, the dermis houses hair roots, nerve endings and sweat glands.

3. Nerve ending
Situated within the dermis, nerve endings allow us to sense temperature, pain and pressure. This gives us information on our environment and stops us hurting ourselves.

5. Subcutaneous tissue
The layer of fat found in the hypodermis that is present to prevent heat loss and protect bone and muscle from damage. It is also a reserve energy source.

4. Pore
Used for temperature regulation, this is where sweat is secreted to cool the body down when it is becoming too hot.

© DK Images

Baby-soft or old and wrinkly, skin is the largest organ in the body

How your skin works
The skin is made of many more elements than most people imagine

"The eye is often compared to a basic camera. The first camera was designed with the concept of the eye in mind"

How vision and sight works

An eye-opening look at how we see...

1. Retina
The retina is the light-sensitive area that processes light admitted into the eye and converts it into electrical impulses, which are transmitted to the brain via the optic nerve.

2. Optic nerve
After the retina has processed light into electrical impulses, the optic nerve transports this information to the brain.

The biology of the eye is extremely complex, especially when you consider the human eye only has the rough diameter of 2.54 cm and weighs approximately 7.5 grams. It is made up of around 15 distinct parts, all with different roles to play in receiving light into the eye and transmitting the electrical impulses, which ultimately relay image information to our brains so that we can perceive the world we live in.

The eye is often compared to a basic camera, and indeed the very first camera was designed with the concept of the eye in mind. We can reduce the complex process that occurs to process light into vision within the eye to a relatively basic sequence of events. First, light passes through the cornea, which refracts the light so that it enters the eye in the right direction, and aqueous humour, into the

main body of the eye through the pupil. The iris contracts to control pupil size and this limits the amount of light that is let through into the eye so that light-sensitive parts of the eye are not damaged.

The pupil can vary in size between 2 mm and 8 mm, increasing to allow up to 30 times more light in than the minimum. The light is then passed through the lens, which further refracts the light, which then travels through the vitreous humour to the back of the eye and is reflected onto the retina, the centre point of which is the macula.

The retina is where the rods and cones are situated, rods being responsible for vision when low levels of light are present and cones being responsible for colour vision and specific detail. Rods are far more numerous as more cells are needed to react in low levels of light and are situated

around the focal point of cones. This focal gathering of cones is collectively called the fovea, which is situated within the macula. All the light information that has been received by the eye is then converted into electrical impulses by a chemical in the retina called rhodopsin, also known as purple visual, and the impulses are then transmitted through the optic nerve to the brain where they are perceived as 'vision'. The eye moves to allow a range of vision of approximately 180 degrees and to do this it has four primary muscles which control the movement of the eyeball. These allow the eye to move up and down and across, while restricting movement so that the eye does not rotate back into the socket. ✿

Independent evolution across species

1 Convergent evolution has produced a very similar eye across species – mammals and cephalopods' common ancestor had a photoreceptive spot.

8 per cent of males can't see green...

2 ...or red. X chromosome-inherited mutations can lead to colour blindness, the most common of which is red/green colour blindness.

Hawks have 20/2 vision

3 Hawks have up to eight times better vision than the average human due to increased levels of cones and rods in the eye.

Your eyes don't get tired

4 The eye is the only organ of the body that doesn't actually need to rest. Your eyes can operate at 100 per cent all the time.

Over half the brain involved in seeing

5 The eye uses 65 per cent of the nerve pathways the human brain. We a very much visually dependent beings.

DID YOU KNOW? *The study of the iris of the eye is called iridology*

Inside the human eye
How an eye sees

4. Lens
The lens is a transparent disc in the eye which, with the cornea, refracts light that enters the eye so that it is received by the retina.

3. Sclera
This is the fibrous, white exterior of the eye that is an important protective layer for the more delicate insides of the eye.

6. Cornea
The cornea is a transparent layer, covering the pupil, iris and aqueous humour. It helps refract the light towards the retina so that light is received in the correct area.

5. Iris
The Iris is the coloured part of the eye which contracts to control the level of light admitted into the eye. The hole though which light enters is called the pupil.

Rods and cones

Rods are the light-sensitive cells in our eyes that aid our vision in low levels of light. Rods are blind to colour and only transmit information mainly in black and white to the brain. They are far more numerous with around 120 million rods present in every human eye compared to around 7 million cones. Cones are responsible for perceiving colour and specific detail. Cones are primarily focused in the fovea, the central area of the macula whereas rods mainly surround the outside of the retina. Cones work much better in daylight as light is needed to perceive colour and detail.

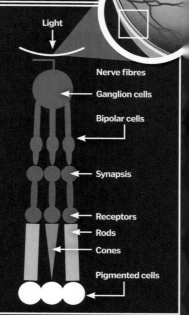

Light

- Nerve fibres
- Ganglion cells
- Bipolar cells
- Synapsis
- Receptors
- Rods
- Cones
- Pigmented cells

How do we see in colour?

Colour is not actually inherent in any object. We only see colour because objects absorb some colour from light, and reflect others. It is the reflected ones that we see and that give an object a set 'colour'. Therefore, for example, grass is not green, it purely absorbs all other colours in light and reflects back green. I an object reflects all colours we will see it as white, if it absorbs all colours we see it as black. We use cones to perceive colour as rods are blind to colour.

"The pupil can vary in size between 2 mm and 8 mm, increasing to allow up to 30 times more light in than the minimum"

If this doesn't make you want a beer, nothing will...

The process of fermentation

Humans have used fermentation for centuries to produce alcohol and preserve many different types of food, but how does the process occur?

5 TOP FACTS
FERMENTED PRODUCTS

1 Beer
Ales and lagers are produced through the fermentation of several various cereal grains. However, malted barley is most commonly used.

2 Vinegar
Vinegar's key ingredient is acetic acid, and this is formed through the fermentation of ethanol. Vinegar is an excellent preservative.

3 Cheese
Many cheeses, such as brie, camembert and blue cheese are produced through the process of fermentation.

4 Salami
Salami is actually dried, cured, fermented meat. This treatment stops meat ruining for extended periods of time, even when stored at room temperature.

5 Vodka
While most commonly made from fermented grain, vodka can also be made from rye, wheat or potatoes.

Fermentation is actually a means of deriving energy from organic compounds through oxidation of these materials. More specifically, the term fermentation often refers to the conversion of a carbohydrate into either an alcohol or an acid using enzymes that are released by micro-organisms.

Bacteria or yeast enzymes are used to break down the natural sugars present in carbohydrates into simpler acids or alcohols. Whether acid or alcohol is produced is dependant on whether oxygen is available or not, the type of agent used (bacteria or yeast) and also the type of carbohydrate fermenting. In aerobic environments, the process normally converts carbohydrates into alcohols and carbon dioxide, while in anaerobic environments organic acids, such as lactic acid, are often produced. ✿

Newton's cradle
A popular desk toy, but just how does it work?

Invented in 1967 by actor Simon Prebble and named after the distinguished scientist and mathematician Sir Isaac Newton, Newton's cradle is a device that visually demonstrates the Laws of Conservation of Momentum and Energy, as well as the effects of friction and dampening.

The cradle is constructed from a series of odd-numbered metal balls (usually five or seven) each of which are suspended from a fixed rack by two wires or rods in order to keep them on a single plane. The device, when operated by lifting one of the outward end balls, acts akin to a simple pendulum. However, thanks to the inclusion of other balls in its swing arch, it transfers its kinetic energy through them to its polar opposite outward ball, swinging it up on the same plane and arch.

This effect is produced in accordance with Newton's aforementioned laws that state that the amount of momentum that an object has depends on its mass and velocity, and that the total momentum of any group of objects remains the same unless outside forces act upon them. This directly translates to the activity of the cradle as, considering the momentum and energy produced by releasing the outward ball must be maintained in the system, the opposite ball will have the same velocity and total mass as the instigator. Vis-à-vis, if two balls are initially released, two balls will replicate the arch on the other end of the cradle, as the total velocity and mass must be maintained.

Of course, while these laws would seem to indicate that the cradle's movement must therefore be perpetual, this is not the case, as friction caused between the balls' collisions as well as their natural elasticity and material dampening effects, means that the arch of any moving balls will decrease over time, eventually coming to a standstill. The longevity and conservation of momentum is therefore directly proportional to the material used in the balls, with metal often used thanks to its low elasticity. ✿

1 x ball
A single ball will transfer its energy proportionally
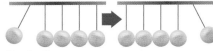

2 x ball
Twice the energy is passed along the plane

3 x ball
Fewer balls remain static as momentum is maintained
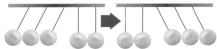

4 x ball
Friction is increased and duration of movement slowed

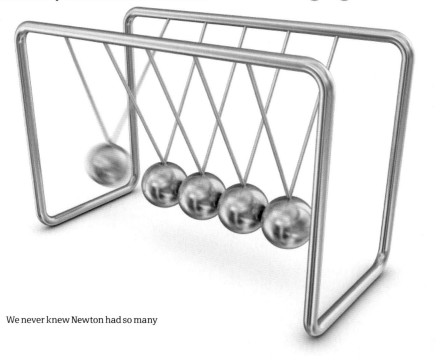

We never knew Newton had so many

5 TOP FACTS
CIRCADIAN RHYTHMS

Jet lag
1 Time zone changes can often disrupt circadian rhythms. Your body clock may be out of sync with your wristwatch, but it will reset itself after a few days.

Mental state
2 Health conditions such as depression, bipolar disorder and seasonal affective disorder (SAD) are all associated with abnormalities in circadian rhythms.

Latin name
3 With these rhythms known to occur approximately every 24 hours, the phrase 'circadian' stems from Latin for 'circa', which means 'about', and 'diem', which means 'day'.

The living clock
4 In the 18th Century, a botanist called Carolus Linnaeus is said to have invented a living clock. His garden could help him tell the time based on the flowers he planted.

Time to take your pills
5 Doctors tell you to take medicine at a prescribed time because the body clock can affect their effectiveness. Aspirins function better when taken in the morning.

DID YOU KNOW? The pineal gland, located near the centre of the brain, is about 8 mm long and shaped like a pine cone

Circadian rhythms
How does our internal body clock tell us when to sleep?

The sleep-wake cycle

The variations in the amount of melatonin secreted by the body create a daily rhythm of rising and falling hormone levels. These hormones, along with the SNC, affect appetite, body temperature and a lot else.

NOON 12.00

09.00 Highest testosterone secretion

10.00 High alertness

14.30 Best co-ordination

08.30 Bowel movement likely

15.30 Fastest reaction time

07.30 Melatonin secretion ends

06.45 Steep rise in blood pressure. Heart attacks are more likely to occur in the morning than any other time due to this rise in blood pressure

06.00

17.00 Highest cardio-vascular efficiency and muscle strength

18.00

18.30 Highest blood pressure

04.30 To conserve energy during sleep, body temperature drops. It is at its lowest just before waking

19.00 Body temperature is highest during late afternoon

LARKS VS OWLS
We all know that our genes make us different, and this also affects our individual natural rhythms. Some people have a body clock that lasts longer than 24 hours, which means they tend to stay up later: these people are referred to as owls. Other people with shorter body clocks, meanwhile, tend to rise earlier in the morning: people like this are larks.

02.00 Deepest sleep

00.00 MIDNIGHT

22.30 Bowel movements suppressed

21.00 With the fading of sunlight into the evening, melatonin secretion begins – and increases tenfold – making us sleepy

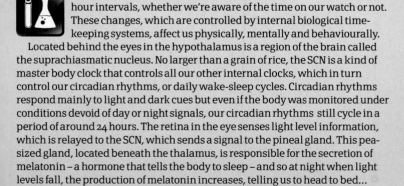

Circadian rhythms are biological changes that occur at roughly 24-hour intervals, whether we're aware of the time on our watch or not. These changes, which are controlled by internal biological time-keeping systems, affect us physically, mentally and behaviourally.

Located behind the eyes in the hypothalamus is a region of the brain called the suprachiasmatic nucleus. No larger than a grain of rice, the SCN is a kind of master body clock that controls all our other internal clocks, which in turn control our circadian rhythms, or daily wake-sleep cycles. Circadian rhythms respond mainly to light and dark cues but even if the body was monitored under conditions devoid of day or night signals, our circadian rhythms still cycle in a period of around 24 hours. The retina in the eye senses light level information, which is relayed to the SCN, which sends a signal to the pineal gland. This pea-sized gland, located beneath the thalamus, is responsible for the secretion of melatonin – a hormone that tells the body to sleep – and so at night when light levels fall, the production of melatonin increases, telling us to head to bed...

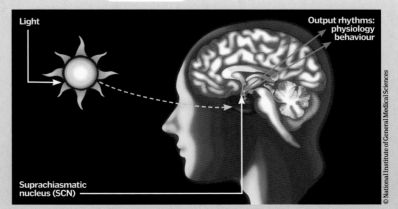

Light

Output rhythms: physiology behaviour

Suprachiasmatic nucleus (SCN)

© National Institute of General Medical Sciences

135

"Materials like wood, glass, ceramics and cotton all have electrons"

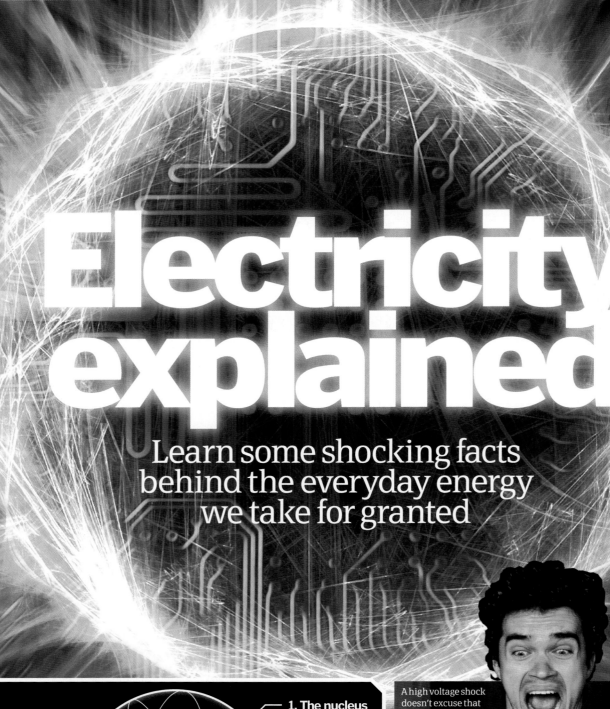

Electricity explained

Learn some shocking facts behind the everyday energy we take for granted

Many people think of electricity as something you buy from the power companies, but as well as coming out of the wall socket, electricity is one of the many ingredients that make up the universe. Read on to find out what electricity is, how it behaves and how electrical energy reaches your home.

All matter in the universe consists of molecules and atoms. Every atom consists of a nucleus orbited by one or more electrons. These electrons carry a negative charge whereas the nucleus is positively charged.

We're all familiar with the effects of static electricity. We are not often aware of electricity around us as the positive and negative charges usually balance. When certain objects touch, however, electrons can jump between them. For instance, when you rub a balloon against your hair electrons will jump across to the balloon giving the balloon stationary negative charge or static electricity. Static electricity relies on electrons not being able to move around easily. Materials like wood, glass, ceramics and cotton all have electrons that like to stick with their atoms and because the electrons don't move, the materials can't conduct electricity very well.

In most metals, electrons can move freely to form an electric current. When charges move, the electrical current flows, and this is the power that drives much of the contemporary world. Current can be measured by the amount of charge passing through a fixed point each second. ✿

Inside an atom

Atoms are held together by electrical forces. The positive nucleus attracts the negative electron. The two cancel each other out so the atom has no electric charge

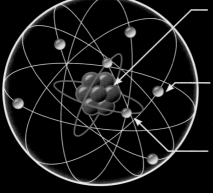

1. The nucleus
The nucleus is at the centre of the atom and is positively charged

2. Negative charge
Each electron is negatively charged

3. Electrons
Electrons orbit the nucleus

A high voltage shock doesn't excuse that hair cut

Head to Head
ELECTRIC INVENTORS

THE WORD
1. William Gilbert 1544-1603
Scientist and physician to Queen Elizabeth I, he invented the term and was the first to describe the Earth's magnetic field.

THE LIGHTNING ROD
2. Benjamin Franklin 1706-1790
Flew a kite with a metal key attached into a thunderstorm to prove that lightning is an electrical phenomenon.

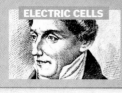

ELECTRIC CELLS
3. Alessandro Volta 1745-1827
This Italian scientist's experiment using soaked paper in salt water, zinc and copper created the first electric cell.

DID YOU KNOW? *The word 'electricity' is derived from the Greek word for amber, elektron*

Plasma balls – static incarnate

They went out of fashion in the Eighties but still demonstrate electricity really well

1. Full of gas
The glass ball is filled with a mixture of gases, usually helium and neon, at low pressure.

4. Touch the power
Placing your hand on the glass alters the electric field and causes a single beam to migrate from the inner ball to the point of contact, the glass does not block the electromagnetic field created by the current flowing through the gas.

3. Lights
Current moves across the gas-filled globe from the electrode to the outer glass insulator.

2. Charged up
The metal ball at the centre is electrically charged, serving as an electrode.

Conductors

Very simply, a conductor is a material that allows electric charge to pass along it as a current. As stated, metals make good conductors as the electrons of their atoms are loosely bound and free to move through the material. For instance, in copper a lot of the electrons are free to move around and strongly repel each other. Any external influence that moves one of them will be replicated through the material.

A superconductor is a material that has no resistance at all to the flow of current when kept below a certain temperature. For most superconducting materials, the critical temperature is below about 30K (that's -243°C).

No current flowing

These free electrons can move in any direction | The copper atoms retain their electrons | Wire surface

Current flowing

The free electrons move towards the positive terminal | The copper atom remains in place

Insulators

Insulators are materials that have the exact opposite effect on the flow of electrons. Their atoms have tightly bound electrons which are not free to roam around. That said, insulators can still play an important role in the flow of electricity by protecting us from the dangerous effects of a current flowing through conductors. If the voltage is high enough an electric current can be made to flow through a material that is not a good conductor, like the human body. The function of our hearts can be affected by an electric shock and the heat generated by the current can cause burns.

The ceramic insulators on this pylon are there to prevent this worker becoming toast

Conductors and insulators at work

Conductors and insulators are put to good use in a household cable

1. Rubber to be safe
The whole cable is encased in rubber or plastic to protect against electric shocks.

2. Plastic for protection
There is a further plastic insulator around each copper cable to stop current flowing between them.

3. Copper conductor
The copper wire provides an excellent conductor due to its low resistance.

4. Colour coded
Each wire is colour coded to ensure correct connection.

Vive la resistance

Resistance is a very important property, it's the factor behind many domestic appliances including old-school light bulbs, kettles, toasters, heaters and irons to name a few. All these rely on the generation of heat energy. Resistance is the ability of a substance to prevent or resist the flow of electrical current. Materials resist electric current because of a collision between electrons and atoms. This slows the electrons down and converts some of their energy into heat energy.

An electric current passes through a thin filament, heating it so that it produces light

"Electricity requires circuits, which provide a path through which the electrical current can flow"

Circuits

Putting electricity to work all over the world

Now you know where electrical energy comes from it's time to look at some of the work it can do for us. Electricity requires circuits, which provide a path through which the electrical current can flow. Circuits include devices such as resistors, which control the flow of electrical charg (or difference in electrical charge), and capacitors, which store electrical charge and come in one of two types, series and parallel.

Parallel circuits

In a parallel circuit there is more than one pathway between its beginning and end. Since the electrical current has more than one route to take, the circuit can still function should one component fail. This means that parallel circuits are much less prone to failure than the series variety. For this reason parallel circuits are the kind you will find in most everyday items such as domestic appliances and other household wiring.

Series circuits

A series circuit has more than one resistor and only one path through which the charges can move. A resistor is anything that uses electrical energy to do work (in this example, light bulbs) and the electric charge must move in series from one resistor to the next. If just one component in the circuit is broken, no charge can move through it. An example of a series circuit is old-style Christmas lights, if one bulb breaks the whole string goes out.

Laws of circuits

Ohm's triangle – not as exciting as the Bermuda triangle but more useful

Many laws are applied to electrical circuits, but Ohm's law is one of the most important. Ohm's law states that, as long as the temperature remains constant, an electrical circuit's current is directly proportional to its voltage and inversely proportional to its resistance. So, if voltage increases, so too will the current, and if resistance increases, current decreases. The formula for Ohm's law is $V = I \times R$, where V = voltage in volts, I = current in amperes, and R = resistance in ohms.

Circuit control

The simplest electrical control is a switch. This breaks the circuit to stop the current flowing and is most notably seen in domestic light switches. They may seem simple, but the most complex computers are made from millions of electronically controlled switches.

CIRCUIT JARGON

Voltage
The flow of an electric charge. Unit: volt, symbol: V.

Current
Or electrical potential difference, the force that drives the current in one direction. Unit: ampere, symbol: A.

Resistance
The opposition of an object to having current pass through it. Unit: ohm, symbol: Ω.

How electricity reaches your home

It's taken for granted that the light will come on when you hit the switch, here's how the power gets to your house

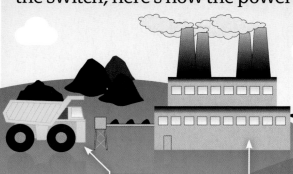

1. Coal or nuclear
Coal is burned at the electricity plant to generate steam. Nuclear power stations use a different method and so too do hydroelectric plants.

2. Generation X
Be it nuclear, coal-fired or hydro, a turbine spins a huge magnet inside a copper wire. Heat energy is converted to mechanical energy, which is then converted to electrical energy in the generator.

3. High voltage!
The electrical charge then flows though heavily insulated wires to a step-up transformer. This raises the pressure so it can travel long distances over the grid. Depending on the country, it can be raised as high as 756,000 volts.

4. Transform it
The electricity then runs along the power lines until it reaches a substation. This lowers the pressure to around 2,000-13,000 volts.

5. Pylon it up
The current continues along the lines to another transformer, either a pole transformer or an underground box, and pressure is lowered again to between 120 and 240 volts.

6. Service with a spark
The next stop is the service box at your home. Here your meter will measure how much elecrtical energy you use. Wires then take the electrical energy around your home powering your lights and everything else.

Head to Head
ELECTRIC INVENTORS

ELECTRIC MOTORS

1. Michael Faraday 1791-1867
Faraday discovered that when a magnet is moved inside a coil of copper wire, a tiny electric current flows through the wire.

DC GENERATOR

2. Thomas Edison 1847-1931
Edison built a DC (direct current) electric generator in America. He later provided all of New York City's electricity.

AC GENERATOR

3. Nikola Tesla 1856-1943
Developed an AC motor and a system of AC power generation. This became the established power supply in the States.

DID YOU KNOW? Edison saw Tesla's system as a threat to his DC supply and spread stories that it wasn't safe

Electricity in your home

Once electricity reaches your home, how does it get around?

2. Electricity meter
Electricity meters are typically calibrated in billing units, the most common being the kilowatt hour. Periodic readings of electric meters establishes billing cycles and energy used during a cycle.

3. Distribution box
This contains the main switch and fuses for each circuit.

4. Appliances of science
Domestic appliances are connected in parallel. In a parallel circuit even if there is a fault or short-circuiting in any one line, the corresponding fuse blows off, leaving the other circuits and appliances intact and prevents damage to the entire house.

1. Entry point
Electrical power enters the home via the live wire – one of three wires that enter, the others being the neutral and earth wires.

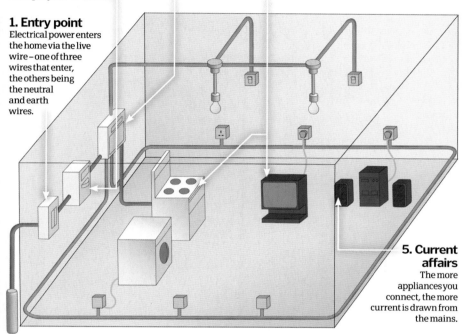

5. Current affairs
The more appliances you connect, the more current is drawn from the mains.

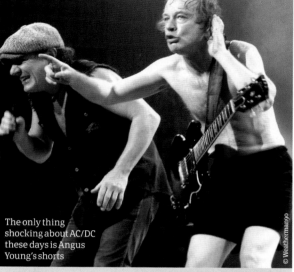

The only thing shocking about AC/DC these days is Angus Young's shorts

All about AC/DC

The word 'electricity' is derived from the fact that current is electrons moving along a conductor, which have been harnessed for energy. The difference between alternating current (AC) and direct current (DC) relates to the direction in which the electrons flow. In DC the electrons flow steadily in a single 'forward' direction. In AC electrons keep switching directions. The power supplied by electricity companies is usually AC because it's more efficient to transmit – the reason being that it's easier to step up to a higher voltage (with a transformer). It's also more efficient to send along power lines before being stepped down by another transformer at the customer's end.

Why are British plugs so big?

We owe our plugs to World War II

Visitors to, and natives of the British Isles get to use one of the weirdest plugs in the world. Unlike many other plugs it has a built-in fuse. After being bombed heavily by the Germans during WWII, much of the country had to be rebuilt. Building supplies were short so rather than wiring each socket to a fuseboard they were linked together on one wire and the fuses put in each plug, saving a great deal of copper in the process.

1. Ground to Earth
The Earth wire is there to prevent electric shock and is secured by a screw terminal.

2. Fused
The fuse is designed to blow and break the circuit if the appliance gets too much current.

Inside a British plug

Why do all countries have different plugs?

"Dammit, all I wanted was a shave!"

Even more than baggage handling and passport control, one of the biggest problems faced by the frequent traveller is the fact that every country in the world has different plugs. In the US, shortly after the AC/DC battle had been resolved (AC won) a man named Harvey Hubbell invented the two-pin plug "so that electrical power in buildings may be utilised by persons having no electrical knowledge or skill" (his words). This was later developed into a three-pin plug by Philip Labre in 1928 with the third pin for grounding. At the same time, developments like this were occurring all over the world with no global-standardisation. There was some effort made by the International Electrotechnical Commission shortly before the Second World War occurred and spoiled it all.

Two pin or three pin? It depends where you are!

142
Journey through the solar system

148
The Shuttle orbiter

160
How the seasons work

156
On board the International Space Station

164
Inside the Sun

168
Space junk

172 Titan: Saturn's largest moon

167
Types of galaxy

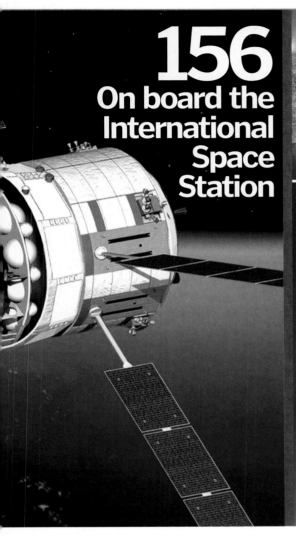

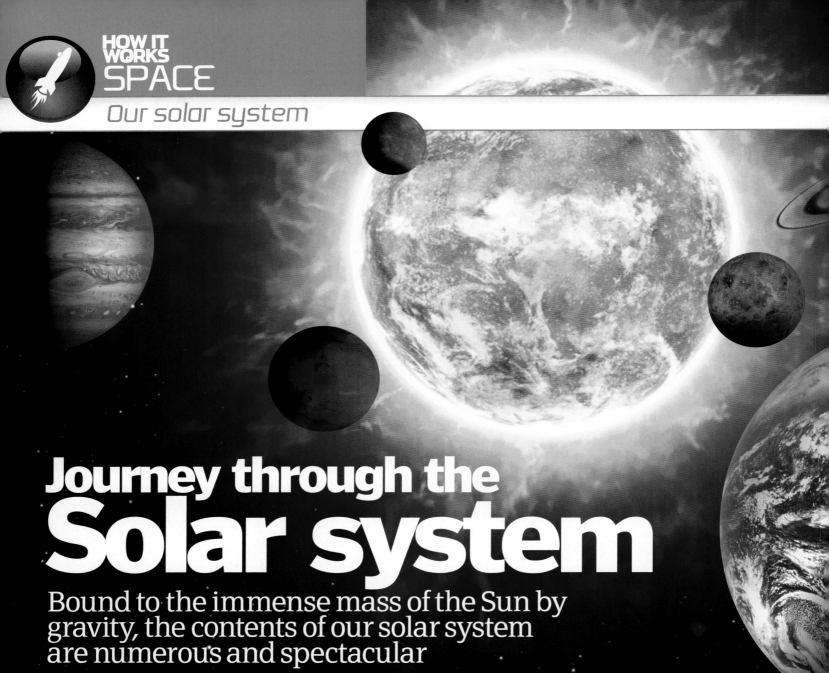

Journey through the
Solar system

Bound to the immense mass of the Sun by gravity, the contents of our solar system are numerous and spectacular

 The solar system formed about 4.6 billion years ago, when part of a giant molecular cloud experienced a gravitational collapse. The centre became the Sun, which comprises more than 99 per cent of the solar system's total mass. The rest of the cloud became a dense, flat rotating disk of gas from which planets formed, called a protoplanetary disk. In our solar system, most of that disk became the eight planets, each of which orbits the Sun.

There are two different categories of planet: gas giants and terrestrials. The gas giants are the four outer planets: Jupiter, Saturn, Uranus and Neptune. They are much bigger than the terrestrial planets and are mostly made of helium and hydrogen, although Uranus and Neptune also contain ice. All of the outer planets have ring systems made of cosmic dust. These planets comprise more than 90 per cent of the rest of the solar system's mass.

The four inner planets are very close to the Sun. To grant perspective, for example, the distance between Jupiter and Saturn is larger than the radius of all the inner planets put together. These terrestrials are made up from rocks and metals, have no ring systems and have a low number of satellites (moons). They include Mercury, Venus, Earth and Mars. Except for Mercury, the inner planets also have recognisable weather systems operating in their atmospheres.

In addition to the eight main planets, there are also dwarf planets such as Pluto. The five dwarf planets are Ceres, Pluto, Haumea, Makemake and Eris. In addition, the solar system is home to numerous small solar system bodies, which include all minor planets, asteroids and comets.

Earth to Saturn in a Mini Metro!
How long would it take to reach the planets in a moderately priced car?

Can't afford that ticket on the next spaceship out of town? Well, fear not, for if you are the patient type and hold an interplanetary driving licence then you can drive to that Earth colony orbiting Saturn in next to no time… well, relatively speaking. In our souped-up Mini Metro, travelling at an average speed of 120mph, any traveller can reach Saturn in only 842 years. Better stock up on travel sweets then…

Head to Head
LARGEST PLANETS

1. Uranus
BIG
Diameter at equator: 25,559km
Average distance from Sun:
2.88 billion km (19 AU)
Orbital period: 84.02 years
Mass (Earth=1): 14.37 Earth masses
Number of moons: 27

2. Saturn
BIGGER
Diameter at equator: 60,260km
Average distance from Sun:
1.4 billion km (9.4 AU)
Orbital period: 29.5 years
Mass (Earth=1): 95 Earth masses
Number of moons: 34

3. Jupiter
BIGGEST
Diameter at equator: 142,985km
Average distance from Sun:
778 million km (5.2 AU)
Orbital period: 11.86 years
Mass (Earth=1): 318 Earth masses
Number of moons: 63

DID YOU KNOW? Astronomers estimate there may be billions of solar systems in our galaxy. About 70 have been discovered

What and where are the asteroid belts?

There are a few asteroid belts in our solar system, but none can compare to the main belt, a massive ring between the orbits of Mars and Jupiter. Here the dwarf planet Ceres, the large asteroids 2 Pallas, 10 Hygiea and 4 Vesta, and millions of small asteroids and dust particles orbit the Sun. Most of the larger asteroids have elliptical orbits and an orbital period of a few years. Some astronomers believe that the main belt's contents are left over from a planetary collision or from a planet that never formed due to the strong gravitational pull of Jupiter.

Bound together by gravity

When the International Astronomical Union (IAU) defined planets in 2006, part of that definition included the requirement that a planet has enough mass that its self-gravity causes it to reach hydrostatic equilibrium. The planet is able to resist compressive forces in space to hold together and stay rounded in shape.

Planets also "clear the neighbourhood" around their orbits. This means that there are no other bodies of the same size in its orbit. The Sun has a strong enough pull to keep the planets and other bodies orbiting around it.

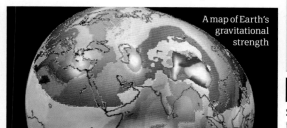

A map of Earth's gravitational strength

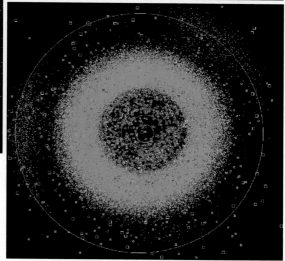

Below shows the placement of inner solar system objects on 20 July 2002. Light blue lines are planet orbits. Green dots show asteroids. Red dots are asteroids that come within 1.3AU of the Sun. Comets are dark blue squares, and dark blue points are Jupiter Trojans.

Measuring our solar system

Understanding the size of planets and where they are

Before the development of radar, astronomers measured the distance between planets through trigonometry, a process where distance to an object is derived from the measurements of angles and distances taken between two known positions. Today, radar is the predominant method of measuring distance and allows for more accurate measurements to be attained. This process works by astronomers timing how long it takes the radar beam, which is travelling at the speed of light, to travel the distance to an object and back. By multiplying the speed of light by time taken, then dividing that by two, scientists can derive the distance to the object.

Once distance has been derived, the mass of the object can be ascertained by monitoring the orbital periods of circling satellites. To do this astronomers measure the angular separation between the satellite and the object and then use trigonometry to convert that angular separation into distance. Astronomers can then use Kepler's third law to determine total mass.

1 AU (astronomical unit) = 92,960,000 miles, the mean distance between the Sun and the Earth

THE SOLAR SYSTEM IN AU

MERCURY 0.39AU
VENUS 0.72AU
EARTH 1AU
MARS 1.52AU
JUPITER 5.20AU
SATURN 9.54AU
URANUS 19.2AU
NEPTUNE 30.1AU
PLUTO 39.5AU

Pluto the dwarf

Since its discovery in 1930, Pluto had been considered the ninth planet in our solar system. However, more recent discoveries of dwarf planets larger in size and mass than Pluto have made some astronomers question its status. In 2006, the International Astronomical Union (IAU) decided upon a conclusive definition of what constituted a planet. Pluto's low mass – not even a fifth the mass of the moon – excluded it from that definition. Now Pluto is considered a dwarf planet,

Size compared to Earth
Pluto is a dwarf-planet, smaller than our own moon

Jupiter – 459 years
Mars a little too dusty? Then why not visit Jupiter, only 459 years of 120mph driving away.

Mars – 134 years
At 120mph you could drive to the planet named after the Roman god of war in only 134 years.

Neptune – 2,497 years
One for colder climates? Then Neptune should be top of your list. At 2,497 years distance, though, it is a long drive, so make sure you take regular breaks and keep at 120mph!

"Saturn is so light that if it could be hypothetically placed in a galactic-sized ocean of water it would float"

8. Neptune

Neptune was imaged for the first time in 1989, discovering an encircling set of rings and six of its 13 moons. Neptune's structure is very similar to that of Uranus, with no solid surface and central layers of water, methane and ammonia ices as well as a possible rock/ice-based core.

The Statistics
Neptune

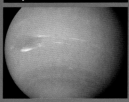

Type: Gas giant
Rotation (Equatorial): 60,179 days
Rotation (Polar): 16.11 hours
Volume: (Earth = 1) 57.74
Average distance from Sun: 2.8 billion miles
Number of moons: 13
Speed: 5.43km/s
Surface temp: -220°C

7. Uranus

The first planet to be discovered by telescope, Uranus appears to the eye as a pale blue, characterless disk, encircled by a thin system of 11 rings and 27 tiny moons. Its blue colour is a result of the absorption of the sunlight's red wavelengths by methane-ice clouds within the planet's cold atmosphere – a process which also renders its atmosphere calm and inert thanks to the creation of haze particles. In reality, however, Uranus's atmosphere is active and consistently changing with huge winds driving systems of ammonia and water over its surface.

The Statistics
Uranus

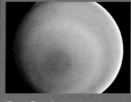

Type: Gas giant
Rotation (Equatorial): 30,799 days
Rotation (Polar): 17.24 hours
Volume: (Earth = 1) 63.1
Average distance from Sun: 1.78 billion miles
Number of moons: 27
Speed: 6.81km/s
Surface temp: -214°C

Comets

Comets are small, fragile, irregularly shaped bodies composed of a mixture of non-volatile grains and frozen gases

9. Pluto

Often mistaken as the last planet in our solar system, Pluto is actually not one but instead a dwarf planet. Dwarf planets are bodies that orbit the Sun and have enough mass and gravity to be spherical, but ones that have not cleared the region around its orbit. Pluto is such a dwarf planet and is one of the furthest circling bodies of our solar system. Pluto's atmosphere is 99.97 per cent nitrogen and it is astronomically cold, with an average temperature of -230 degrees Celsius.

The Statistics
Pluto

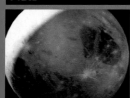

Type: Dwarf
Rotation (Equatorial): 90,613 days
Rotation (Polar): N/A
Volume: (Earth = 1) 0.0059
Average distance from Sun: 3.7 billion miles
Number of moons: 3
Speed: 4.666km/s
Surface temp: -230°C

5. Jupiter

The largest and most massive of all planets in the solar system, Jupiter has almost 2.5 times the mass of the other eight planets combined and over 1,300 Earths could fit inside it. Jupiter is also the first of the gas giants and is largely not solid in composition, consisting of an outer layer of gaseous hydrogen and helium, an outer layer of liquid hydrogen and helium and an inner layer of metallic hydrogen. However, deep in its body (roughly 37,000 miles in) there is a solid core made up of rock, metal and hydrogen compounds.

6. Saturn

A massive ball of gas and liquid, Saturn is the least dense of all the planets in the solar system. Circled by a spectacular system of rings, which are composed of stellar dust, boulders and gases, Saturn has a hazy appearance and due to its rapid spin is a massive ten per cent larger at its equator than at its pole. Interestingly, Saturn is so light – thanks to its composition from the lightest elements – that if it could be hypothetically placed in a galactic-sized ocean of water it would float. As with Jupiter, Saturn is a gas giant with a tiny solid core composed of rock and ice.

The Statistics
Saturn

Type: Gas giant
Rotation (Equatorial): 10,759 days
Rotation (Polar): 10.66 hours
Volume: (Earth = 1) 763.59
Average distance from Sun: 888 million miles
Number of moons: 34
Speed: 9.69km/s
Surface temp: -140°C

The Sun

4.6 billions years old and currently in its main-sequence stage, our Sun is a huge sphere of exceedingly hot plasma containing 750 times the mass of all the solar system's planets put together. Deep in its core nuclear fusion of hydrogen produces massive energy that is gradually carried outwards through convection before escaping into space.

The Statistics
The Sun

Type: Star
Rotation (Equatorial): 25 days
Rotation (Polar): 34 days
Mass: (Earth = 1) 333,000
Surface temperature: 5,500°C
Core temperature: 15 million °C
Diameter (Equatorial): 864,900 miles

Main belt

Often referred to as the asteroid belt, the Main belt is an encircling ring of meteors, asteroids, dwarf planets and dust particles that sits between the terrestrial planets and the gas giants

5 TOP FACTS
SOLAR SYSTEM

Lightweight
1 Hypothetically speaking, Saturn is so light that if it were placed in a galactic sized swimming pool it would float. Hard experiment to carry out though!

Binary
2 Due to the size and short orbital distance between Pluto and its largest moon Charon, it is often treated as a binary system as its centre of mass lies with neither.

Dust bowl
3 Mars, often referred to as the 'red planet', is actually red thanks to its coating of iron dust, which prevails in its carbon dioxide-rich atmosphere.

Big boy
4 Jupiter is so large that over 1,300 Earths could fit inside it and it has a mass which is 2.5 times larger than the total of all other eight planets combined.

Tantastic
5 During the day on Mercury the closest planet to our Sun in the solar system, the temperature reaches up positively scorching 430 degrees Celsius.

DID YOU KNOW? Our solar system is nearly 5 billion years old and is made up of eight planets and 170 moons

The Statistics
Jupiter

Type: Gas giant
Rotation (Equatorial): 4,331 days
Rotation (Polar): 9.93 hours
Volume: (Earth = 1) 1,321
Average distance from Sun: 483.6 million miles
Number of moons: 63
Speed: 13.07km/s
Surface temp: -110°C

The Statistics
Earth

Type: Terrestrial
Rotation (Equatorial): 365.26 days
Rotation (Polar): 23.93 hours
Mass: (Earth = 1) 1
Average distance from Sun: 93 million miles
Number of moons: 1
Speed: 29.783km/s
Surface temp: 15°C

3. Earth
While similar in internal composition to its neighbouring planets – composed of three distinct layers made up mainly of iron, magnesium and silicates respectively – Earth differs on its surface thanks to an abundance of liquid water and an oxygen-rich atmosphere. Due to Earth's rotation the planet bulges at its equator by 13 miles when compared to both its poles and its spin axis is tilted at an angle of 23.5 degrees, one of the factors that gives rise to its seasons.

4. Mars
Known as the red planet thanks to its rust-red colouring, and named after the Roman god of war, Mars is home to the highest volcanoes (albeit dry and inactive) of any planet in the solar system. Current research and evidence suggests that while Mars is an inert planet now, in the past it was very much active, with volcanic activity and water existing over large parts of it. Mars is the outermost of the four terrestrial 'rocky' planets and its internal structure is rich in sulphur, iron sulphide and silicate rock

The Statistics
Mars

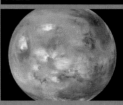

Type: Terrestrial
Rotation (Equatorial): 687 days
Rotation (Polar): 24.63 days
Mass: (Earth = 1) 0.15
Average distance from Sun: 141.6 million miles
Number of moons: 2
Speed: 24.007km/s
Surface temp: -125°C – 25°C

Map of the solar system
Discover the star, planets and space phenomena that make up our solar system

The Statistics
Mercury

Type: Terrestrial
Rotation (Equatorial): 88 days
Rotation (Polar): 59 days
Mass: (Earth = 1) 0.056
Average distance from Sun: 36 million miles
Number of moons: 0
Speed: 47.87km/s
Surface temp: -187°C – 427°C

1. Mercury
Iron-rich Mercury is the second smallest planet in the solar system and the closest to the Sun. There is almost no protective atmosphere surrounding Mercury and, because of this, temperatures on the planet fluctuate massively from 427 degrees Celsius during the day to -187 degrees Celsius during the night. Worryingly, if an observer were able to stand on the planet they would experience a period of 176 Earth days between one sunrise and the next. Better stock up on suntan lotion and woolly socks then

2. Venus
The hottest of all planets, Venus – thanks to its permanent atmospheric blanket of dense gaseous clouds – has an average temperature of 464 degrees Celsius. The surface is dry, lifeless, scorching hot and littered with volcanoes and dust storms. Named after the Roman goddess of love and beauty due to its beautiful, sun-reflecting, cloud-based atmosphere, in reality Venus holds one of the most hostile environments of any planet. Interestingly, Venus spins in the opposite direction from most other planets

The Statistics
Venus

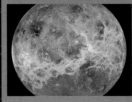

Type: Terrestrial
Rotation (Equatorial): 224.7 days
Rotation (Polar): 243 days
Mass: (Earth = 1) 0.86
Average distance from Sun: 67.2 million miles
Number of moons: 0
Speed: 35.02km/s
Surface temp: 464°C

"In essence, any orbit is maintained by the direction of its motion and acceleration, both of which alter constantly"

How orbits work

Why does the Moon not crash into Earth?

Orbits work because two bodies of mass are attracted to each other with force and that for every action there is an equal and opposite reaction, as explained in Newton's Third Law of Motion. In terms of orbits, this means that when one object rotates around another of a higher mass it experiences continuous free fall towards the larger body, undertaking a constant gravitational acceleration towards the greater object that deflects what would otherwise be its straight-line motion into a curved trajectory. In essence, any orbit is maintained by the direction of its motion and acceleration, both of which alter constantly, thereby producing its curved orbit.

All closed orbits are elliptical in shape, the degree of which varies from a perfect circle to a stretched egg form, and is referred to as an orbit's eccentricity. Many of our solar system's orbits – such as our moon's around Earth – are pretty circular with a low eccentricity. Here, both bodies rotate around the joint centre of mass – which in the Earth/moon relationship is deep inside the Earth – and the lesser body remains relatively circular throughout its orbit. Others, such as Pluto's orbit around the Sun, are highly elliptical and elongated, with a large gap between its perigee (its closest point of approach) and its apogee (the point where it is farthest from the orbit's focus). In the case of Pluto and its own moon Charon, while Charon follows a largely circular orbit due to its large size and close proximity (it is roughly half Pluto's size), the mass centre of the two objects is not within Pluto but out in space between the two.

An easy way to understand orbits is to imagine a cannonball fired out of a cannon from the top of an impossibly high mountain – a visual image first used by Isaac Newton in the 18th Century. Once fired the cannonball moves sideways and falls towards the Earth (the central body), however it has so much tangential velocity that it misses the central object as it curves away beneath it due to its circular shape and continues to fall indefinitely, caught in an equilibrium sustained by its velocity and the pull of gravity. ✿

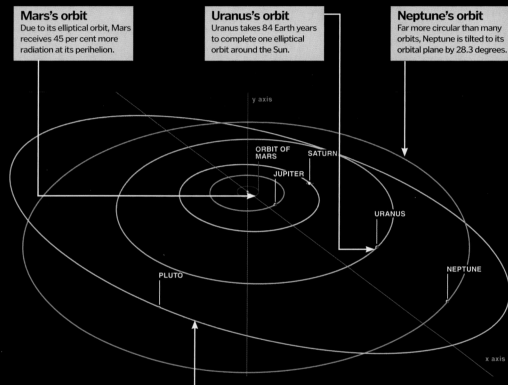

Mars's orbit
Due to its elliptical orbit, Mars receives 45 per cent more radiation at its perihelion.

Uranus's orbit
Uranus takes 84 Earth years to complete one elliptical orbit around the Sun.

Neptune's orbit
Far more circular than many orbits, Neptune is tilted to its orbital plane by 28.3 degrees.

y axis

ORBIT OF MARS   SATURN

JUPITER

URANUS

PLUTO

NEPTUNE

x axis

Pluto's orbit
Pluto's orbit is far from circular and it lasts 248 years. It is inclined by 17.1 degrees.

A view of our moon on its elliptical orbit

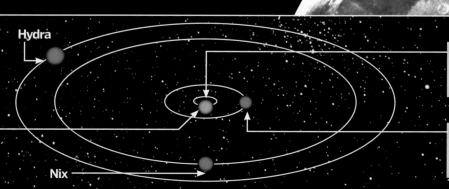

The Pluto system
The orbits around Pluto

Hydra

Nix

Barycentre
The barycentre is a system's mass centre. Pluto's is out of the planet in space.

Pluto's orbit
Pluto orbits around its mass centre and around the Sun – the latter is highly eccentric.

Charon's orbit
Charon is a large moon compared to Pluto and orbits it every 6.38 Earth days.

5 TOP FACTS
WONDERS OF THE SOLAR SYSTEM

Largest canyon
1 The largest known canyon in the solar system is also found on Mars. The Valles Marineris spans about 25 per cent of Mars's circumference at over 4,000 kilometres long.

Largest desert
2 The planet Venus is likely the solar system's largest desert, with a mean surface temperature of 460°C and less than 0.002 per cent water vapour in its atmosphere.

Largest crater
3 Mars has the largest impact crater of any planet in the entire solar system, the Borealis Basin, measuring in at approximately 8,500 kilometres wide.

Largest lake (on Earth)
4 The largest lake (by surface area) is either the Caspian Sea – often referred to as a lake – with 371,000km² or Lake Michigan-Huron with a total of 117,600km².

Largest Lake (not on Earth)
5 Titan, one of Saturn's moons, is believed to have several large methane lakes, including one that is approximately 100,000km² – not really ideal for a swim though...

DID YOU KNOW? *Before photos from Mariner 9 confirmed its mountain status, Olympus Mons was called Nix Olympica*

Olympus Mons

The tallest mountain and the largest volcano in the solar system

Olympus Rupes

Caldera complex

Karzok Crater

Olympus Rupes

Pangboche Crater

© NASA

Olympic-sized mountain

Rising more than 27 kilometres above the surface, Olympus Mons is three times the height of Earth's tallest mountain, Mount Everest. It is about 550 kilometres wide, surrounded at its edges by escarpments called Olympus Rupes that are about six kilometres high. If a person were to stand on the surface of Mars, they would not be able to see the top of Olympus Mons due to its height, size and shallow slope. Olympus Mons likely grew to such an impressive height due to Mars's lack of plate tectonics. Without a shifting crust, lava piled up in one place. Mars's low surface gravity, only about 40 per cent that of Earth's, also accounts for the long lava flows that made Olympus Mons so wide.

Olympus Mons versus Mauna Loa

On Earth, the largest volcano is Mauna Loa, found in Hawaii. Another shield volcano, Mauna Loa stands just ten kilometres high above sea level and 75 kilometres wide. It's about 100 times smaller than Olympus Mons, and the entire chain of Hawaiian volcanoes could fit inside the Martian volcano. Mauna Loa is also dwarfed by Mount Everest, which is 8,848 metres high.

Mars has many interesting features, but none so striking as Olympus Mons. Astronomers believe the mountain formed fairly recently in the planet's geologic history, with the 'youngest' areas around 2 million years old. This shield volcano has a shallow slope and is wider than it is tall. It formed from very low viscosity lava that flowed over a long period of time. The peak of Olympus Mons contains a large caldera, a cavity that formed when the roof of the volcano's magma chamber collapsed and the ground above collapsed into it. More lava activity caused additional, smaller calderas that overlap the larger one, creating a caldera complex.

The volcano also has two named craters; the Karzok Crater is 15.6 kilometres wide and the Pangboche Crater is 10.4 kilometres wide. Olympus Mons lies in Tharsis, a bulging volcanic region on Mars. The area is also home to three smaller volcanoes known as the Tharsis Montes. ✿

An overhead view of the caldera, taken from the Mars Express

© NASA

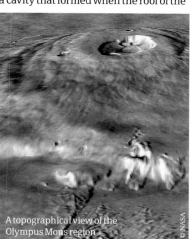

A topographical view of the Olympus Mons region

© NASA

Size comparison of Olympus Mons, Everest and the island of Hawaii

22,500m

10,200m

8,848m

Olympus Mons

Everest

Hawaii

Olympus Mons diameter: 550km

The Martian mammoth dwarfs the mountains found on Earth

HOW IT WORKS
SPACE

"The first was the Columbia, launched on 12 April 1981, followed by the Challenger, Discovery, Atlantis and Endeavour orbiters"

Inside the Space Shuttle orbiter

The Shuttle orbiter

14. Hydrazine and nitrogen tetroxide tanks

8. Vertical stabiliser
Much like on an aeroplane, the vertical stabiliser is designed to reduce side slip. It also holds a rudder and speed brake to assist with deceleration during re-entry.

5. Payload Bay
The payload bay contains the Canadarm, a robotic arm used to retrieve and deploy payloads. The bay's doors contain heat radiators and remain open when in orbit to help with thermal control.

11. Space radiators

6. Space Shuttle main engines (SSMEs)
These engines are fuelled by liquid hydrogen and liquid oxygen from the external fuel tank. They are used solely to propel the orbiter during its ascent.

7. Orbital manoeuvring engines (OMEs)
The OMEs are located in the aft fuselage near the SSMEs. These engines are used to help send the orbiter into orbit and adjust the orbit as necessary.

Endeavour after launch for mission STS-118

9. Elevons
The elevons are located on the edges of the wings. They are used for both roll control and pitch control during landing.

10. Main gear
Upon re-entry, the crew manually deploys the orbiter's landing gear in the form of three sets of wheels through the heat shield.

Inside the Shuttle
Under the skin of the Shuttle's surface

5 TOP FACTS
SPACE SHUTTLE MISSIONS

STS-7: Space Shuttle Challenger
1 Launched on 18 June 1983, this marked the first time that an American female astronaut entered space with the inclusion of Sally K Ride.

STS-31: Space Shuttle Discovery
2 Launching on 24 April 1990, the crew of the Space Shuttle Discovery deployed the Hubble Space Telescope during STS-31.

STS-71: Space Shuttle Atlantis
3 On 27 June 1995, the Atlantis launched STS-71. This mission marked the first time that the Space Shuttle docked with the Russian space station Mir.

STS-88: Space Shuttle Endeavour
4 Launched on 4 December 1998, STS-88 was the first mission to the ISS. As its payload, it carried the first US node for the ISS, Unity.

STS-95: Space Shuttle Discovery
5 Discovery's 25th flight launched on 29 October 1998. It is also well-known as John Glenn's return to space at the age of 77.

DID YOU KNOW? *Upon re-entry, the external Shuttle skin withstands temperatures as high as 1,648° Celsius*

With NASA's main spacecraft scheduled to retire, find out what goes on inside this craft

What we think of as the 'Space Shuttle', NASA calls the Space Shuttle transport orbital vehicle or orbiter (STS-OV, or just OV). It's a reusable winged plane-like spacecraft. In addition to its engines and thrusters, it also has a three-level crew cabin and a payload bay.

The orbiter fleet has had five different craft. The first was the Columbia, launched on 12 April 1981, followed by the Challenger, Discovery, Atlantis and Endeavour orbiters (the latter built to replace Challenger). Although all of the orbiters are similar, rotating maintenance means that each is somewhat unique. The Endeavour is the youngest orbiter, first launched on 7 May 1992.

Three of the orbiters – the Discovery, Atlantis, and Endeavour – are still in use. On 28 January 1986, the Challenger was destroyed a little more than a minute into its tenth mission. A seal on one of the SRBs failed, which caused it to leak flames onto the external fuel tank. The orbiter veered and was torn apart by as much as 20 Gs of aerodynamic force, which resulted in the death of its seven-member crew.

On 1 February 2003, the Columbia was destroyed upon re-entry into the atmosphere, killing its seven crew members. This occurred when gases entered one of the orbiter's wings through a hole made by a piece of foam during launch and caused a structural failure. ⚙

Discovery approaches the ISS for docking

12. Manipulation arm

4. Crew cabin
The crew cabin includes the flight deck with controls. The mid-deck has areas for work, sleeping and hygiene. An airlock contains spacesuits and allows for the crew to perform spacewalks.

A simulation of handling large objects in space

2. RCS thrusters
The reaction control system (RCS) comprises 44 small thrusters located around the orbiter. They are used for close manoeuvring such as docking, orientation and altitude control.

1. Nose cap
The orbiter's nose is made of a carbon fibre and graphic composite known as reinforced carbon-carbon (RCC), which protects the orbiter from the 1,650° Celsius heat during re-entry.

3. Surface tiles
The orbiter's thermal protection system (TPS) includes black high-temperature reusable surface insulation (HRSI) tiles on its underside. They are made of silica ceramic and vary in thickness depending on their location.

13. Electrical system fuel cells

Where the action is
Crew on the flight deck perform duties ranging from piloting the Shuttle to satellite launches

The orbiter's flight deck seats the mission's commander, pilot and two mission specialists. It looks much like the cockpit of an aeroplane, but with more controls – over 2,000 buttons, switches, dials and displays in total. In addition to forward controls in front of the commander and pilot, the flight deck also has displays and controls on its aft side. These are used to operate payloads.

The duties of the commander, pilot and specialists while on the flight deck depends on the details of the mission. In addition to firing the orbital manoeuvring engines (OMEs) to take the Shuttle in and out of orbit, the pilot also steers the Shuttle to rendezvous with the ISS or other crafts. Mission specialists may conduct experiments or retrieve and release satellites from the payload bay.

All images © NASA

How do you weigh planets?

It seems like an impossible task, but how can scientists use an orbiting moon to work out the weight of a planet?

 Newton's Law of Gravitation states that every planetary body has its own gravitational field that pulls on nearby objects – such as moons or spacecraft – with a force proportional to its mass and inversely proportional to the square of the distance between the two objects. Newton also discovered that an object – a moon, for instance – will move at a constant speed and in a straight line unless acted upon by a force such as gravity that will keep the moon in orbit.

By observing the effect of a planet's gravitational attraction on an orbiting moon, scientists can measure the planet's mass. The gravitational attraction between the moon and the planet depends on their mass and the distance between their centres. The heavier the planet, the stronger its attraction to the moon and the faster the moon will travel. Measuring the distance from the planet to the moon and calculating how long it takes to orbit enables astronomers to calculate the weight of a planet. ✿

How hot is it on other worlds?

How infrared telescopes enable us to 'see' the temperatures of planets

A global temperature map, showing the white-hot heat of the equator

 Heat energy is emitted by all objects, including planets. The hotter the planet, the more radiation it gives off. Objects in space emit radiation across the electromagnetic (EM) spectrum – really hot objects, like stars and galaxies for instance, emit much of their energy in the visible, ultraviolet and x-ray range of the EM spectrum. However, celestial objects – such as planets and moons in particular – emit (or glow with) infrared radiation, which is outside the visible wavelength range. This means we cannot see this infrared light with our own eyes; we can only detect the visible light coming from the object. However, just because infrared rays are invisible, it doesn't mean they're not there.

Astronomers have put devices – such as the Spitzer Space Telescope – into orbit that collect and focus the infrared information from distant planets and display it as light we can see. The hotter the planet, the brighter the infrared light information it will produce. If you could see in infrared you would be able to 'see' variations in temperature across the surface of a planet. ✿

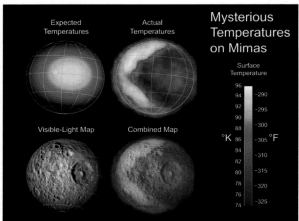

Expected Temperatures   Actual Temperatures   Mysterious Temperatures on Mimas

Visible-Light Map   Combined Map

Surface Temperature

The infrared information of Saturn's moon Mimas here was collected by a composite infrared spectrometer (CIRS) on the Cassini spacecraft on 13 February 2010

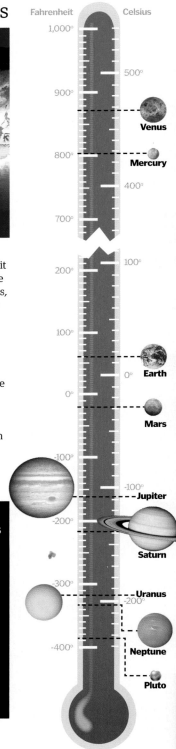

Head to Head
Hubble images

MOST FAMOUS

1. Horsehead
The most impressive image of the Horsehead Nebula which is part of M42, located just below the star Alnitak.

MOST IMPRESSIVE

2. M42
M42, otherwise known as the Orion Nebula is one of the most beautiful and most famous nebulae known to man.

MOST AMAZING

3. Eagle Nebula
Often described as the pillars of creation since it depicts a large region of star formation. This image was created from Hubble images in 1995.

DID YOU KNOW? The Hubble Space Telescope can be seen with the naked eye on a clear, dark night

The Hubble telescope

After a false start and 20 years of faithful service it's a wonder the Hubble space telescope works at all...

Lyman Spitzer Jr was one of the 20th Century's leading scientists. He was also the first person to consider the idea of putting a giant telescope in space and not only lived to see the launch of the Hubble Space Telescope (HST) in 1990, but witness seven years of its incredible contribution to modern science.

Buy why space? Compared to many of the world's most powerful Earth-bound telescopes the HST's optics are actually quite small. Bar obvious payload limitations, in space the required optics of a telescope are smaller since the 'seeing' is always perfect. Looking through Earth's atmosphere is not unlike trying to watch TV through a desert mirage – the seeing is hindered by a constant shimmer produced by the atmosphere. In space the HST's resolution is so great that it's the equivalent of us being able to distinguish a car's two separate headlights from 6,000 km away.

Hubble didn't have the smoothest of starts however, and for the first three years of its life was partially sighted due to an error in the manufacture of its 2.4-metre primary mirror. Thankfully, upon its first servicing mission in 1993 its optics were corrected.

With 19 years service already under its belt, you may wonder how much longer Hubble is due to be with us. It's most recent scheduled servicing mission took place in May 2009 and should allow Hubble to continue its work into 2014, when its successor – the James Webb Space Telescope – is due to launch.

Instrument housing
The rear of Hubble is where the real magic happens. Fine guidance sensors, cameras and spectrograph work together to give us the remarkable view of the universe some of us take for granted today.

Communication antennae
Astronomers and technicians use these antennae to send Hubble orders. Data is bounced off tracking and data relay satellites, then to ground stations and then to the Goddard Space Flight Center before reaching its destination.

© DK Images

Primary mirror
The main light-collecting mirror is positioned at the rear of the assembly, just in front of its main systems and scientific instruments. The original flaw in the design of this mirror was just two microns off – a fiftieth of a human hair.

Secondary mirror
Light is bounced off the primary mirror on to this smaller, secondary mirror before it passes through a small hole in the centre of the larger mirror on its way towards Hubble's various scientific instruments.

Solar panels
Hubble requires some 2,800 watts of electricity to remain operational. It uses its large solar cells to produce all of its power and surplus energy is stored in on-board batteries so it can operate from inside the Earth's shadow (around a third of its complete orbit time).

Hubble's control system

To accurately point this bus-sized piece of technology properly requires gyroscopes. They sense its motion and help it to find its target by acting as a reference point. Next come the reaction wheels that steer it towards its next target. Finally come the fine guidance sensors of which there are three. They pinpoint the aim by using star trackers to lock onto bright guide stars.

Hubble's Pointing Control System

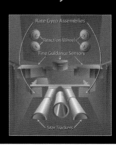

Rate Gyro Assemblies

Reaction Wheels

Fine Guidance Sensors

Star Trackers

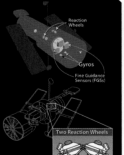

Reaction Wheels

Gyros

Fine Guidance Sensors (FGSs)

Two Reaction Wheels

The Statistics
Hubble telescope

Service: 20 years
Mass: 11,110 kg
Orbital velocity: 7,500 metres per second
Orbit period: 97 minutes
Diameter: 2.4 metres
Telescope focal length: 57.6 metres
Due to be de-orbited: >2021

All images © NASA

Hubble service record
The Hubble telescope was designed to be serviced by astronauts, here's its service history

DEC 1993
The most important part of the first servicing mission (SM1) was to correct the lens abortion. New systems were also installed including the Wide Field Planetary Camera 2.

FEB 1997
Besides important maintenance routines, Hubble's abilities were again upgraded with a new spectrograph able to collect 30 times more data than its predecessor.

DEC 1999
After the forth of six gyroscopes failed in 1999 Hubble was effectively put offline. Luckily, what was planned as a simple servicing mission turned into a successful rescue.

MAR 2002
Much of the work planned for 1999 was carried out in this mission. A new solar panel array was fitted, and despite being a third of the size of the original provided 30 per cent more power.

MAY 2009
The fifth and final servicing mission. Two new scientific instruments were installed and two previously failed instruments were fixed. Hubble is in the best shape it's ever been in.

"The Sun, a type G yellow-white star with a radius of 700,000 kilometres and a temperature of 6,000 kelvin"

A star is b

There may be as many as 10 billion trillion stars in the 100 billion galaxies throughout the universe, but "only" about 100 billion in our galaxy, the Milky Way. Most stars comprise plasma, helium and hydrogen. They form when giant molecular clouds (GMCs), also known as star nurseries, experience a gravitational collapse. This increase in pressure and temperature forces fragments into a body known as a protostar. Over the course of its life, a typical star goes through continuous nuclear fusion in its core. The energy released by this fusion makes the star glow.

Stars are classified according to the Hertzsprung-Russell Diagram, which lists their colour, temperature, mass, radius, luminosity and spectra (which elements they absorb). There are three main types of star: those above, below and on the main sequence. Within these types, there are seven different classifications. We're most familiar with the main sequence star that we call the Sun, a type G yellow-white star with a radius of 700,000 kilometres and a temperature of 6,000 kelvin. However, some stars above the main sequence are more than a thousand times larger than the Sun, while those below the main sequence can have a radius of just a few kilometres. ✿

LOW-MASS STARS

Red dwarf

The cool star
Red dwarfs are small and relatively cool stars, which while being large in number tend to have a mass of less than one-half that of our Sun. The heat generated by a red dwarf occurs at a slow rate through the nuclear fusion of hydrogen into helium within its core, before being transported via convection to its surface. In addition, due to their low mass red dwarfs tend to have elongated life spans, exceeding that of stars like our Sun by billions of years.

Giant molecular cloud

Proto-stars

SUN-LIKE STARS

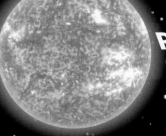

Red giant

A star explodes
If a star has enough mass to become a supergiant, it will supernova instead of becoming a white dwarf. As nuclear fusion ends in the core of a supergiant, the loss of energy can trigger a sudden gravitational collapse. Dust and gas from the star's outer layers hurtle through space at up to 30,000 kilometres per second

Almost a star
A protostar is a ball-shaped mass in the early stages of becoming a star. It's irregularly shaped and contains dust as well as gas, formed during the collapse of a giant molecular cloud. The protostar stage in a star's life cycle can last for a hundred thousand years as it continues to heat and become denser.

Star or planet?
A brown dwarf is sometimes not even considered a star at all, but instead a sub-stellar body. They are incredibly small in relation to other types of stars, and never attained a high enough temperature, mass or enough pressure at its core for nuclear fusion to actually occur. It is below the main sequence on the Hertzsprung-Russell Diagram. Brown dwarfs have a radius about the size of Jupiter, and are sometimes difficult to distinguish from gaseous planets because of their size and make-up (helium and hydrogen).

Brown dwarf

HIGH-MASS STARS

The rarest star
Supergiants are among the rarest types of stars, and can be as large as our entire solar system. Supergiants can also be tens of thousands of times brighter than the Sun and have radii of up to a thousand times that of the Sun. Supergiants are above the main sequence on the Hertzsprung-Russell Diagram, occurring when the hydrogen of main sequence stars like the Sun has been depleted.

NEAREST

1. Proxima Centauri
Other than our Sun, the closest star to Earth is Proxima Centauri. It is about four light-years from the Sun.

LARGEST

2. VY Canis Majoris
The largest known star, VY Canis Majoris, has a radius of between 1,800 and 2,100 times that of the Sun.

OLDEST

3. HE0107-5240
HE0107-5240, a giant star in the Milky Way, may be nearly as old as our universe at about 13.2 billion years old. It could've once been part of a binary star system.

DID YOU KNOW? A star may have a life cycle of millions to trillions of years. The larger the star is, the shorter its life cycle

om

Compared to other stars, the Sun is in the middle of the pack when it comes to size and temperature

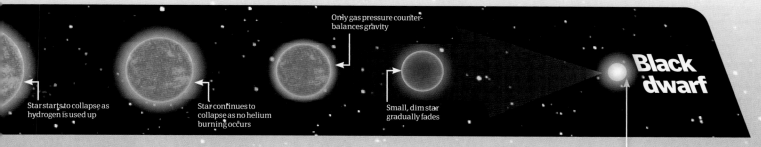

Only gas pressure counter-balances gravity

Star starts to collapse as hydrogen is used up

Star continues to collapse as no helium burning occurs

Small, dim star gradually fades

Black dwarf

Catch a dying star
White dwarfs are considered the final phase in a star's life cycle unless it attained enough mass to supernova (and more than 95 per cent of stars don't). The cores of white dwarfs typically comprise carbon and oxygen, left over after the gas is used up during nuclear fusion and occurring after a main sequence star has gone through its giant phase. A white dwarf is small, with a volume comparable to that of Earth's, but incredibly dense, with a mass about that of the Sun's. With no energy left, a white dwarf is dim and cool in comparison to larger types of stars.

The stellar remnant
Black dwarfs are the hypothetical next stage of star degeneration after the white dwarf stage, when they become sufficiently cool to no longer emit any heat or light. Because the time required for a white dwarf to reach this state is postulated to be longer than the current age of the universe, none are expected to exist yet. If one were to exist it would be, by its own definition, difficult to locate and image due to the lack of emitted radiation.

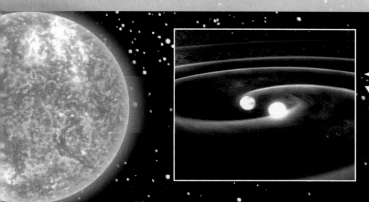

White dwarf

Black dwarf

Beyond the supernova
A hypernova is a supernova taken to an even larger degree. Supergiant stars with masses that are more than 100 times that of the Sun are thought to have these massive explosions. If a supergiant were close to Earth and exploded into a hypernova, the resulting radiation could lead to a mass extinction.

Neutron star

All Images © NASA

The neutron dance
Neutron stars are a potential next stage in the life cycle of a star. If the mass that remains after a supernova is up to three times that of the Sun, it becomes a neutron star. This means that the star only consists of neutrons, particles that don't carry an electrical charge.

Super giant

Super-novae

The absence of light
Stellar black holes are thought to be the end of the life cycle for supergiant stars with masses more than three times that of our Sun. After supernova, some of these stars leave remnants so heavy that they continue to remain gravitationally unstable.

Hypernovae

Black hole

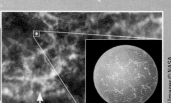

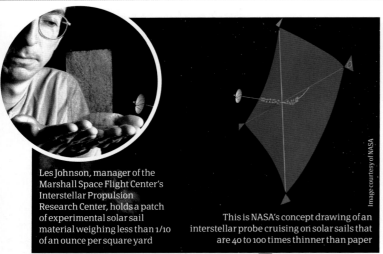

Les Johnson, manager of the Marshall Space Flight Center's Interstellar Propulsion Research Center, holds a patch of experimental solar sail material weighing less than 1/10 of an ounce per square yard

This is NASA's concept drawing of an interstellar probe cruising on solar sails that are 40 to 100 times thinner than paper

Image courtesy of NASA

How solar sails work

A cosmic kite blown by photons is our greatest hope for interstellar travel

When the Space Shuttle fuels up for a short commute to the International Space Station, 95 per cent of its weight is in the gas tank. The sheer weight of rocket fuel is one of the greatest obstacles to interstellar space travel. That's why space futurists are so excited about solar sails, a 'fuel free' craft powered by beams of sunlight.

Sunlight travels in packets of energy called photons. When a photon reflects off a mirrored surface, it imparts two minuscule taps of energy: once during the initial impact and once as it's reflected. For decades, scientists theorised that if you could make a reflective surface big enough and light enough, it could be nudged through space by a constant barrage of photons.

In 2010, that theory will be tested when the Planetary Society, co-founded by the late Carl Sagan, will launch a 350-square-foot solar sail made of aluminised Mylar (1/5,000 of an inch thick) into space.

Solar sails don't have dramatic blast-offs, but rely on a more patient form of power: constant acceleration. A massive solar sail of 600,000 square metres would accelerate at an underwhelming one millimetre per second. After a day, however, the sail would be moving at a rate of 310 kmps. After 12 days, it would reach 3,700 kmph.

Imagine its velocity after six months – enough, scientists hope, to sail out of our solar system into the great beyond. ✻

Inside a 30-metre diameter vacuum chamber, NASA researchers successfully deploy ten-metre solar sails along delicate, but rigid extendible booms

Image courtesy of NASA

Earth's magnetic field explained

Without our invisible shield, the Earth would be incinerated

When a child draws a picture of the Sun, they will scribble a yellow circle emitting spiky rays. Apparently, kids know a thing or two about astrophysics. The Sun doesn't just shine its beneficent light on the Earth, it also bombards us with deadly gusts of solar wind, a plasma of charged particles (electrons and protons) that speeds towards us at a great speed.

The Earth's magnetic field is the only thing standing between these radioactive winds and the fragile planetary surface. The magnetic field deflects solar wind safely around the planet, creating a comet-shaped protective shield called the magnetosphere. Without this protection, life on Earth could not exist.

The Earth's magnetic field doesn't follow the simplistic north-south orientation of your compass. Magnetic north and magnetic south, for example, are 11 degrees different from Cartesian north and south. And if you were to map the magnetic field, you'd see complex contours of field lines that vary slightly with every location on the planet. Most incredibly, every 250,000 years or so, the magnetic poles reverse.

Where does the magnetic field come from? The leading theory is that the Earth's core is a perpetual electric generator or dynamo. Currents of liquid iron pass through a weak magnetic field generating electromagnetic energy that produces a much larger and stronger magnetic field. ✻

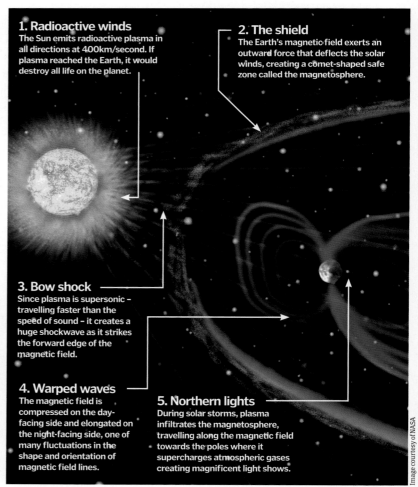

1. Radioactive winds
The Sun emits radioactive plasma in all directions at 400km/second. If plasma reached the Earth, it would destroy all life on the planet.

2. The shield
The Earth's magnetic field exerts an outward force that deflects the solar winds, creating a comet-shaped safe zone called the magnetosphere.

3. Bow shock
Since plasma is supersonic – travelling faster than the speed of sound – it creates a huge shockwave as it strikes the forward edge of the magnetic field.

4. Warped waves
The magnetic field is compressed on the day-facing side and elongated on the night-facing side, one of many fluctuations in the shape and orientation of magnetic field lines.

5. Northern lights
During solar storms, plasma infiltrates the magnetosphere, travelling along the magnetic field towards the poles where it supercharges atmospheric gases creating magnificent light shows.

Image courtesy of NASA

BAD
1. Armageddon
An asteroid is making a beeline for Earth in this blockbuster that sees Bruce Willis make the ultimate sacrifice for mankind. Hollywood at its cheesiest.

BADDER
2. Deep Impact
Okay, so technically *Deep Impact* is about a comet, not an asteroid, but it's still a lump of rock and it's still heading for Earth as Téa Leoni and Morgan Freeman discover.

BADDEST
3. Asteroid
Maybe not the baddest but certainly the most unimaginatively titled. First aired as a mini-series for US TV in 1995, the asteroid of note is heading for Dallas.

DID YOU KNOW? *For half a century Ceres was classified as the eighth planet*

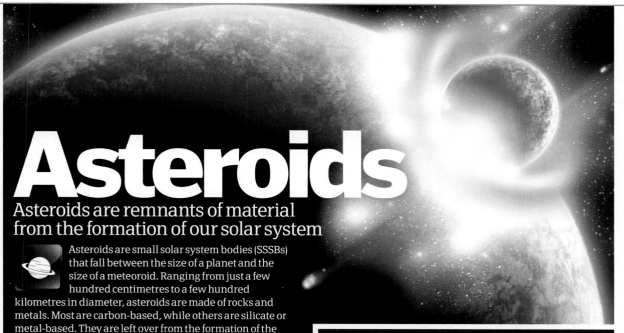

Asteroids

Asteroids are remnants of material from the formation of our solar system

Asteroids are small solar system bodies (SSSBs) that fall between the size of a planet and the size of a meteoroid. Ranging from just a few hundred centimetres to a few hundred kilometres in diameter, asteroids are made of rocks and metals. Most are carbon-based, while others are silicate or metal-based. They are left over from the formation of the solar system more than 4 billion years ago.

Millions of asteroids orbit the Sun in the Main Asteroid Belt, a massive ring between 300 and 600 million kilometres in diameter between the orbits of Mars and Jupiter. Most asteroids have elliptical orbits and take a few years to orbit the Sun. Some astronomers think the Asteroid Belt comprises remnants from a planet that was destroyed during a collision, while others believe that they are material left over from a planet that never formed due to Jupiter's strong gravitational pull. ✿

1. Ceres
Diameter (miles): 605
Orbital period (years): 4.6
Distance from the Sun (AU): 2.767
Date discovered: 1 January 1801
Facts: Ceres is the largest object in the Main Asteroid Belt, and the smallest dwarf planet in our solar system. It is spheroid with clay and icy crust, an icy mantle and a rocky core.

2. Ida
Diameter (miles): 33.3 x 15 x 9
Orbital period (years): 4.84
Distance from the Sun (AU): 2.86
Date discovered: 29 September 1884
Facts: Ida was the first asteroid found to have its own moon, Dactyl. It has an elongated crescent shape covered in craters, and is likely made of silicate rocks like iron, feldspar and olivine.

3. Gaspra
Diameter (miles): 12 x 7.45 x 6.83
Orbital period (years): 3.29
Distance from the Sun (AU): 2.209
Date discovered: 30 July 1916
Facts: The very first asteroid to be closely approached by the Galileo spacecraft, Gaspra is an irregularly shaped asteroid covered in small craters. It is likely made of metal silicates because it has a reflective surface.

Rocky inner core
Lies beneath the ice mantle

Water-ice layer
100km thick provides 50 per cent of Ceres's mass

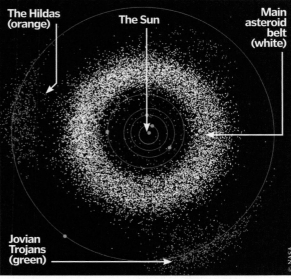

The Hildas (orange)

The Sun

Main asteroid belt (white)

Jovian Trojans (green)

Thin, dusty outer crust
The surface temperature is estimated at -38°C

Inside Ceres
The largest body in the asteroid belt explained

Where to find them

The Asteroid Belt isn't the only group of asteroids. The Hildas have orbits just inside Jupiter's orbit. Another group, called the Jovian Trojans, share Jupiter's orbit at areas called the Lagrangian points. The group 60° ahead of Jupiter's orbit are the Greeks, while the group trailing by 60° are the Trojans.

Will one ever hit Earth?

Some asteroids do break free from their normal orbit, either due to Jupiter's gravity or collisions with other asteroids. When they come within 1.3 AU (195 million kilometres) of the Sun, they are known as near-Earth asteroids (NEAs). Astronomers theorise that an asteroid impact 65 million years ago could be responsible for the extinction of the dinosaurs. The possibility of an asteroid hitting Earth and causing catastrophic damage is very low, although close calls happen on a regular basis. In March 2009, a small asteroid (about 60 metres wide) passed within 66,000 kilometres of Earth.

On board the International Space Station

What's it like to live in space?

Man has had a continuous presence in space since 1998 on the International Space Station. 11 years ago, the Zarya was launched into orbit by the Russian Federal Space Agency. This was the first piece of the ISS. Now that it is more than 80 per cent complete, the ISS is the largest satellite to ever orbit the Earth. When completed in 2011, it also promises to be the most expensive object ever constructed.

The ISS wasn't the first space station; in 1971 the Soviet Union launched the Salyut, which was the first in a series of space stations. Two years later, NASA launched Skylab. However, both of these programmes were single modules with limited life spans. In 1986, the Soviet Union launched the Mir, which was intended to be built upon and added to over time. The United States planned to launch its own space station, Freedom, just a few years later, but budgetary restraints ended the project. After the fall of the Soviet Union, the United States

began negotiating with Russia, along with several other countries, to build a multinational space station.

Until Expedition 20 in May 2009, crews on the International Space Station consisted of two to three astronauts and cosmonauts, who stayed for six months. Now the ISS is large enough to support a six-man crew, the stay has been reduced to three months. The current ISS crew is a crew of five: ESA commander Frank De Winne, NASA flight engineer Jeffrey N Williams, CSA flight engineer Robert Thirsk and cosmonauts Maxim Suraev and Roman Romanenko.

The crew typically works for ten hours a day during the week and five hours on Saturdays. During their eight scheduled night hours, the crew sleeps in cabins while attached to bunk beds, or in sleeping bags secured to the wall. They also wear sleep masks, as it would be difficult to sleep otherwise with a sunrise occurring every 90 minutes. All food is processed so it is easy to reheat in a special oven, usually with the addition

of water. This includes beverages, which the crew drinks with straws from plastic bags. Exercise is a very important part of daily life for the crew of the ISS because of microgravity's adverse effects on the body. The astronauts and cosmonauts may experience muscle atrophy, bone loss, a weakened immune system and a slowed cardiovascular system, among other problems. To help counteract this, the crew exercises while strapped to treadmills and exercise bicycles.

Research is the main reason for the station's existence in low Earth orbit (about 330 kilometres above the planet's surface). Several scientific experiments spanning fields including astronomy, physics, materials science, earth science and biology take place on the station simultaneously. For example, US astronauts are currently conducting about ten different experiments, with an additional five automated experiments. They are also partnering on more than 20 manned and automated experiments with astronauts and cosmonauts from

ATV Dock

The Automated Transfer Vehicle (ATV) is an expendable unmanned resupply vehicle developed by the ESA

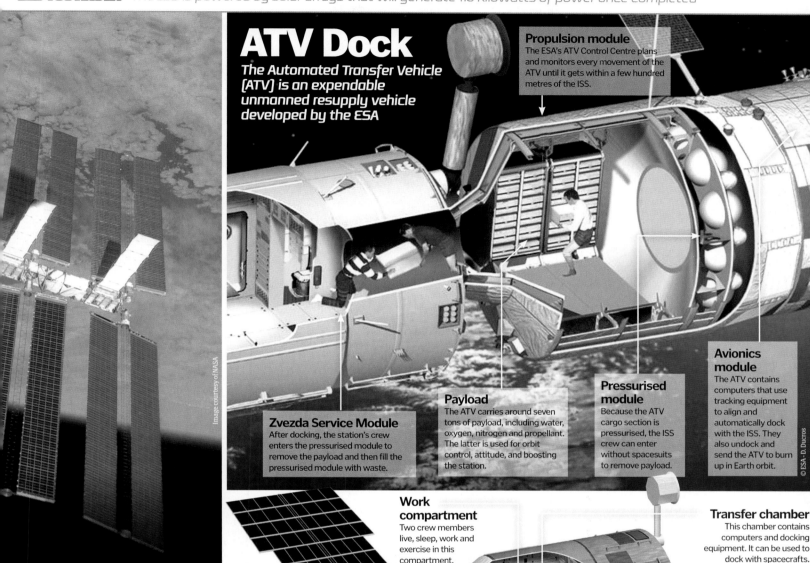

Image courtesy of NASA

Propulsion module
The ESA's ATV Control Centre plans and monitors every movement of the ATV until it gets within a few hundred metres of the ISS.

Zvezda Service Module
After docking, the station's crew enters the pressurised module to remove the payload and then fill the pressurised module with waste.

Payload
The ATV carries around seven tons of payload, including water, oxygen, nitrogen and propellant. The latter is used for orbit control, attitude, and boosting the station.

Pressurised module
Because the ATV cargo section is pressurised, the ISS crew can enter without spacesuits to remove payload.

Avionics module
The ATV contains computers that use tracking equipment to align and automatically dock with the ISS. They also undock and send the ATV to burn up in Earth orbit.

© ESA – D. Ducros

Work compartment
Two crew members live, sleep, work and exercise in this compartment.

Transfer chamber
This chamber contains computers and docking equipment. It can be used to dock with spacecrafts.

Facilities
The Zvezda contains a toilet and hygiene facilities, as well as a kitchen with freezer and refrigerator.

External handrails
The handrails are used during spacewalks, or extra-vehicular activity (EVA).

Transfer compartment
The transfer compartment contains three docking ports. Currently it is docked with the Pirs and the Poisk.

© ESA – D. Ducros

other countries. Since 1998, more than 130 experiments have been conducted on the ISS, and each month brings more published research.

One of the overarching research goals for the station is to learn about the long-term effects of space on the human body. Many of the experiments also study the different ways things react in a low gravity, low temperature environment. There is also an experiment involving the use of ultrasounds so that remote doctors can diagnose medical problems (there is no doctor on the ISS), with the hopes that the technology can also be used on Earth.

The current plan shows the ISS de-orbiting in 2016, and international funding is scheduled to run out in that year. However, a US committee named the Augustine Commission is exploring the possibilities of keeping the programme going until at least 2020. NASA is also conducting studies on whether the station's components could be viable until 2028. ✿

Zvezda Service Module

The Zvezda was the third module to dock and provides life support systems for the ISS

A spacewalk during the ISS's construction

> "A series of complex treaties and agreements govern the ownership, use and maintenance of the station"

The Columbus Module

The Columbus is a research laboratory designed by the ESA – its largest contribution to the ISS

External payload
An external payload facility houses three sets of instruments and experiments, with room for three more.

In the Space Station Processing Facility at NASA's Kennedy Space Center in Florida, a crane lowers the Multi-Purpose Logistics Module Leonardo towards the payload canister

■ United States
■ Russia
■ Japan
■ Europe
■ Canada
■ Italy
■ Brazil

Science Power Platform

Zvezda (Star) Service Module

Docking Compartment

Universal Docking Module

Research Module

Soyuz

Research Module

Soyuz

Zarya (Sunrise) Control Module

Pressurized Mating Adaptor 1

Docking and Stowage Module

Express Pallet

Thermal Control Panels

S0 Truss Segment

Mobile Servicing System

S3 Truss Segment

S6 Truss Segment

S5 Truss Segment

S1 Truss Segment

Unity (Node 1)

Z1 Truss Segment

P3 Truss Segment

P5 Truss Segment

Solar Alpha Rotary Joint

P6 Truss Segment

Port Photovoltaic Arrays

CSA Remote Manipulator System

P1 Truss Segment

P4 Truss Segment

Centrifuge Accommodation Module

Cupola

Airlock

U.S. Lab Destiny

Starboard Photovoltaic Arrays

S4 Truss Segment

Solar Alpha Rotary Joint

Node 3

Habitation Module

Node 2

Crew Return Vehicle

Pressurized Mating Adaptor 3

European Lab — Columbus Orbital Facility

Pressurized Mating Adapter 2

Multi-Purpose Logistics Module

Kibo (Hope) JEM Experiment Logistics Module-Pressurized Section

Kibo (Hope) JEM Remote Manipulator System

Kibo (Hope) JEM Experiment Logistics Module-Exposed Section

Kibo (Hope) JEM Exposed Facility

Kibo (Hope) JEM Pressurized Module

Who built the ISS?

The ISS currently comprises ten different modules and an Integrated Truss Structure. The modules are contributions from the Russian Federal Space Agency (RKA), NASA, the Japanese Aerospace Exploration Agency (JAXA), the Canadian Space Agency (CSA) and the European Space Agency (ESA), which includes 18 member countries. A series of complex treaties and agreements govern the ownership, use and maintenance of the station. When completed, there will be 16 different modules.

DID YOU KNOW? Over 50 missions will be required to transport and assemble all the ISS components

Payload racks
These racks hold science equipment and experiments. Half of the space is allotted to NASA.

Harmony
The Columbus is attached to the NASA Harmony node module.

© ESA- D. Ducros

Creating water in space

For the crew of the ISS, it's better not to think where their next glass of water is coming from

The ECLSS (Environmental Control and Life Support System) provides water with the Water Recovery System (WRS). Water from crew member waste, condensation and other waste water is distilled, filtered and processed. This water is then used for drinking, cooking, cleaning and other functions. An Oxygen Generation System (OGS) separates water into oxygen and hydrogen. An experimental Carbon Dioxide Reduction Assembly (CReA) uses the leftover hydrogen with carbon dioxide filtered from the crew cabins to produce usable water and methane. In addition, the ECLSS filters the cabin air, maintains cabin pressure and can detect and suppress fires.

Anatomy of the Space Station

The ISS is a configuration of modules, trusses and solar arrays

© ESA- D. Ducros

1. Zarya
The Zarya, launched in 1998 and built by the RKA, is now a storage component. As the first module it provided storage, power and propulsion.

2. Unity
Built by NASA and launched in 1998, Unity was the first node module to connect to the Zarya. It provides a docking station for other modules.

3. Zvezda
The RKA-built Zvezda launched in 2000. It made the ISS habitable by providing crew cabins and environmental control as well as other systems.

4. Destiny
The Destiny is a NASA laboratory. Launched back in 2001, it also contains environmental controls and works as a mounting point for the Integrated Truss Structure.

5. Quest
The 2001 NASA-built Quest is an airlock used to host spacewalks. The equipment lock is used for storing the spacesuits, while the crew lock allows exit to space.

6. Pirs
A mini-research module called Pirs was launched in 2001 by the RKA. It can dock spacecraft and also host spacewalks by cosmonauts.

7. Harmony
Harmony, built by NASA in 2007, is a node module. It serves as a berthing point and docking station for modules and spacecraft.

8. Columbus
The Columbus, launched in 2008, is an ESA laboratory specifically designed for experiments in biology and physics. It provides power to experiments mounted to its exterior.

9. Kibo Experiment Logistics Module
This JAXA module (also known as JEM-ELM) is part of the Japanese Experiment Module laboratory and was launched in 2008. It contains transportation and storage.

10. Kibo Pressurised Module
Also launched in 2008, the JEM-PM is a research facility and the largest module on the ISS. It has an external platform and robotic arm for experiments.

11. Poisk
The RKA-built Poisk (MRM2) launched in November 2009. In addition to housing components for experiments, it serves as a dock for spacecraft and a spacewalk airlock.

12. Integrated Truss Structure
The ISS's solar arrays and thermal radiators are mounted to this structure, which is more than 100 metres long and has ten separate parts.

13. Mobile Servicing System
Also known as the Canadarm2, this CSA-built robotic system used to move supplies, service equipment and assist astronauts on spacewalks.

14. Special Purpose Dexterous Manipulator
The SPDM, or Dextre, is a robot built by the CSA and is extremely dextrous. It can perform functions outside the ISS previously requiring spacewalks.

15. Tranquillity
NASA's third nodemodule is Tranquillity, which was launched in February 2010. It contains the Environmental Control and Life Support System as well as berthing stations for other modules.

16. Cupola
Also launched with the Tranquility module in February 2010, this observatory module also contains robotic workstations to operate the Mobile Service System.

17. Rassvet
Connected to the ISS in May 2010, this second RKA mini-research module also serves as storage.

18. Leonardo
A pressurised multipurpose module, the Leonardo launched in September 2010 to serve as a storage unit and free up space in the Columbus.

19. Nauka (MLM)
Scheduled to be launched by the RKA in December 2011, this multipurpose research module will be a rest area for the crew as well as doubling up as a research laboratory.

20. Solar Arrays
These arrays convert sunlight into electricity. There are four pairs on the ISS.

21. Thermal Radiators
The Active Thermal Control System (ATCS) removes excess heat from the ISS and vents it out into space via these radiators.

The ISS in early construction while in orbit in 1999

© NASA

The Statistics
The ISS

© NASA

Mass: 303,663 kilograms
Volume of habitable space: 358 cubic metres
Supplies: 27,222 kilograms per expedition
Orbit: 278 to 460 kilometres high at an angle of 51.6 degrees, travelling at 27,724 kilometres per hour, completing 15.7 orbits per day
Gravity: 88 per cent that of Earth sea level
Cost: US Government Accountability Office estimates a total of $100 billion (£60 billion). ESA estimates a total of 100 billion euros (£90 billion)
Crew support: 100, 000 ground personal, 500 contracting facilities in 37 states and 16 countries
Spacewalks: 28 shuttle-based, 105 ISS-based for more than 830 hours
Meals: About 19,000 consumed aboard
Flights: 30 NASA space shuttle, 2 RKA Proton, 22 RKA Soyuz, 1 ESA Automated Transfer Vehicle, 1 JAXA H-II Transfer Vehicle
Mission control monitoring centres: 2 NASA centres, 1 RKA centre, 1 ESA in Germany, 1 ESA in France, 1 JAXA centre, 1 CSA centre

How the seaso

Get out your flashlight and a beach ball, it's time to talk about tilt

The Earth is a wonky planet. Every year we make a complete near-circular revolution around the Sun, but every day our planet spins around a lopsided axis. This imaginary line that runs through the centre of the planet from the North Pole to the South Pole is tilted at a 23.5-degree angle, and this wonky tilt is the reason for the seasons.

During June and July in the northern hemisphere, the North Pole is tilted towards the Sun and South Pole tilted away. This means that solar radiation hits the northern hemisphere "head on" and is absorbed in a more concentrated area. Because the southern hemisphere is angled away from the Sun, the same amount of solar radiation is spread across a much larger surface area.

But differences in solar intensity aren't enough to create summer and winter. The tilt of the axis also creates radical differences in the length of solar exposure, what we define as daylight. If we go back to our June and July example, the northern hemisphere is directly facing the Sun, which means the Sun carves a high path across the sky, creating longer daylight hours. In the southern hemisphere, the Sun travels much closer to the horizon, which limits daylight hours significantly.

The combination of longer days and concentrated sunlight gives us summer. Shorter days and dispersed solar energy gives us winter. Autumn and spring mark the transitional periods when days are getting longer or shorter and

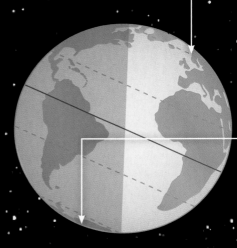

3. Summer solstice
On roughly 21 June, the North Pole tilts the closest to the Sun, bathing the northern hemisphere in summer and the southern hemisphere in winter.

2. Tilted axis
The seasons are powered by the angle of the Earth's axis, which tilts 23.5 degrees away from being perfectly perpendicular with its orbital plane.

1. Revolution
The Earth travels in an elliptical orbit around the Sun, but the path is nearly circular, meaning our distance from the Sun is relatively constant year-round.

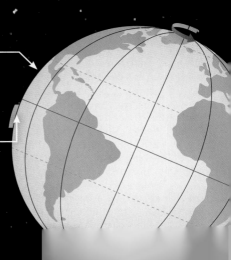

1. The tropics
All year long, the region within the tropics of Cancer and Capricorn receives the most direct and intense sunlight.

2. Concentrated surface area
Since the Sun's rays strike the region around the equator at nearly a 90° angle, the intensity of the radiation is concentrated on a relatively small surface area.

3. Scattered surface area
Near the poles, the Sun's angle of incidence is much lower, meaning solar radiation scatters across a much larger surface area, losing its intensity.

5 TOP FACTS
SEASONS ON OTHER PLANETS

Long summer
1 Because Neptune is so far away from the Sun, it takes over 164 Earth years to complete a revolution. That makes its summer around 40 years long.

"Tropical" Venus
2 Since Venus's axis only tilts at a 3-degree angle, all of its seasons are roughly the same, which results in a rather steamy 750K all year round.

Serious tilt
3 Uranus spins on an axis tilted at 98 degrees, and much of the planet is bathed in continuous darkness or continuous light for 20 years at a time.

Springtime on Uranus
4 There are no April showers on Uranus. When spring arrives after 20 years of darkness, the warming atmosphere generates violent storms.

Long days
5 Due to its slow rotation on its axis and rapid movement around the Sun, a day on Mercury is the equivalent of 176 Earth days.

DID YOU KNOW? *Contrary to common sense, the Earth is closest to the Sun (147,300,000 km) on or around 3 January*

ns work

– 5. Vernal equinox
At this point in the orbit, the Sun shines evenly across the entire face of the Earth, neutralising the effect of the tilted axis.

4. Winter solstice
At the opposite end of the Earth's orbit, it's the southern hemisphere's turn to receive the most direct sunlight while Europe and the United States enter winter.

The cycle of seasons
The seasons correspond not only to Earth's position in orbit around the Sun, but also your physical location on the Earth. At different times of the year, different parts of the planet receive more direct sunlight and longer days (spring and summer), while others receive less direct sunlight and shorter days (autumn and winter).

6. Autumnal equinox
As with the vernal equinox, the first day of autumn has exactly 12 hours of daylight and 12 hours of darkness.

The Sun's intensity varies depending on where you are on the planet

Solar intensity

It gets hotter as you move closer to the equator because the region between the tropic of Cancer and the tropic of Capricorn receives more direct and concentrated solar radiation.

The reason for this is not that the tropics are 'closer' to the Sun than other parts of the planet. It has to do

with something called the 'angle of incidence'. During the vernal and autumnal equinoxes, the Sun's rays strike the equator at a precise 90-degree angle. Since the solar radiation rains down on the Earth so directly, its intensity is concentrated in a relatively small area. Compare this with the

solar exposure of Iceland, which sits right on the Arctic circle at roughly 66 degrees north of the equator. During the autumnal equinox, the Sun's rays hit Iceland on a much shallower angle of 70 degrees, spreading their radiation across a much larger surface area, thereby decreasing their intensity.

Solstice vs equinox
The winter solstice is commonly referred to as the shortest day of the year. Although 21 December is still 24 hours long, it has the fewest hours of sunlight. On this day, the North Pole is tilted the furthest from the Sun, causing the Sun to trace a low path in the sky. As the months pass, the Sun's course drifts upwards until we reach the vernal equinox, a day with exactly 12 hours of light and 12 hours of darkness. Around 21 June, the North Pole tilts closest to the Sun, the Sun rides high in the sky and we have the summer solstice, the longest day of the year. As the Sun's path sinks back towards the horizon, we reach the autumnal equinox, the second time all year when day and night are perfectly equal.

Here comes the Sun... flower

Seasons at the top of the world
For people living at the equator, seasons are virtually meaningless. The closer you are to the equator, the less your weather is affected by the tilt of the Earth. If you tilt a globe back and forth, the top and bottom appear to move further away from you, while the middle will remain relatively central.

In high-latitude regions the differences between seasons are extreme. In the dead of winter in northern Norway, the northern hemisphere is tilted so far away from the Sun that it doesn't peak over the horizon for two months. In the middle of summer, the Sun travels directly overhead, tracing a loop through the sky that holds back the night for 2.5 months.

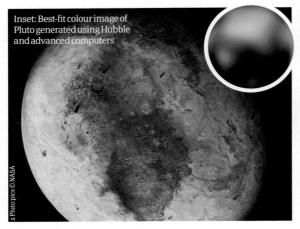
Inset: Best-fit colour image of Pluto generated using Hubble and advanced computers

2 Pluto pics © NASA

Pluto's orbit explained

While Pluto itself is still shrouded in mystery, its orbit – odd as it is – is understood…

Pluto is the largest celestial body in the solar system yet to be probed by man. At the furthest point of its odd orbit, Pluto is nearly 50 times further from the Sun than the Earth (49 astronomical units, or AU). Unlike the Earth or its seven planetary neighbours, the path Pluto takes around our Sun isn't circular, but elliptical. This means its 248 Earth-year orbit brings it within 29 AU at its nearest point and, remarkably, inside the orbit of Neptune. Moreover Pluto's orbit is also inclined by 17 degrees compared to the rest of the solar system, which otherwise sits along a very flat plane called the ecliptic.

Taking the chaotic path-crossing interactions with Neptune into account, it's amazing that Pluto and Neptune can never collide. This is thanks to its inclined orbit and the fact they're locked in a 3:2 orbital resonance, meaning Pluto's orbit takes 1.5 times longer than Neptune's. ✿

Unlocking Pluto's secrets
Ironically, in the same year it was decided that Pluto was no longer a planet, a NASA mission designed to visit Pluto and the outer solar system was launched. New Horizons will reach its destination in 2015.

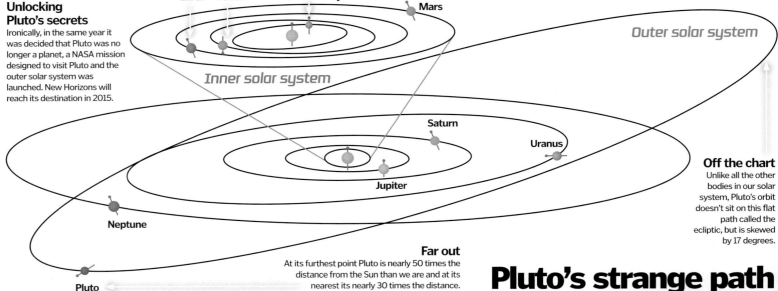

Earth Venus Mercury Mars

Outer solar system

Inner solar system

Saturn

Uranus

Jupiter

Off the chart
Unlike all the other bodies in our solar system, Pluto's orbit doesn't sit on this flat path called the ecliptic, but is skewed by 17 degrees.

Neptune

Far out
At its furthest point Pluto is nearly 50 times the distance from the Sun than we are and at its nearest its nearly 30 times the distance.

Pluto

Pluto's strange path

Jupiter's Great Red Spot

Understanding the biggest storm currently known to exist in the solar system

Jupiter's Great Red Spot has been one of astronomy's great mysteries since its discovery back in 1664 by scientist Robert Hooke. While no one knows quite how long its 350 mph winds have been raging, we do know that its size, shape and intensity aren't constant. It's thought that in its formative years it was more akin to a cigar than a spot, and has been slowly shrinking – some 15 per cent in the last decade alone. However, it would still be possible to fit two Earths standing side-by-side inside the storm and have room left over for the Moon.

The remarkable life span of the storm is largely accredited to the fact there are no landmasses on Jupiter, so unlike hurricanes here, there's nothing to slow its progress. While it's still yet to be proven, with the help of a smaller storm that's appeared over the last decade – Oval BA – NASA scientists are confident the red colour is a chemical reaction of material being dredged up from deep within the atmosphere being exposed to the ultraviolet radiation of the Sun. Oval BA has only recently taken on a red hue in its vortex, demonstrating that the storm is currently gaining in intensity. ✿

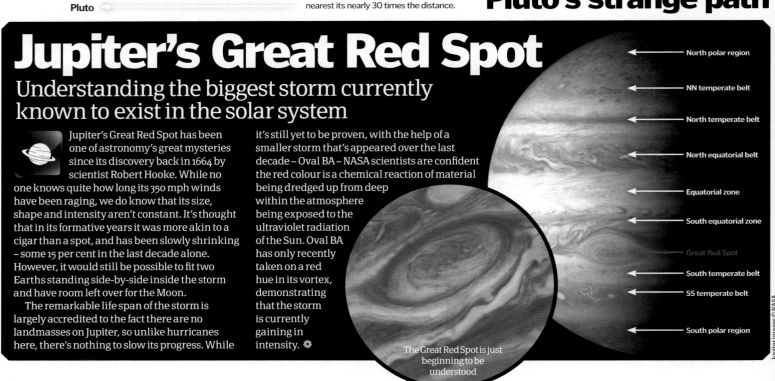

North polar region

NN temperate belt

North temperate belt

North equatorial belt

Equatorial zone

South equatorial zone

Great Red Spot

South temperate belt

SS temperate belt

South polar region

Jupiter images © NASA

The Great Red Spot is just beginning to be understood

Head to Head
IO'S VOLCANOES

LONGEST LASTING PLUME

1. Prometheus
The nearly 100-kilometre dust plume emanating from the Prometheus volcano is thought to have been continuously erupting since at least 1979.

LONGEST LAVA FLOW

2. Masubi Fluctus
Originating from the volcano Masubi, the Masubi Fluctus is an active lava flow more than 500 kilometres long.

BIGGEST VOLCANO

3. Loki Patera
Loki Patera is t biggest volcan depression on a diameter of r than 200 kilon

DID YOU KNOW? Io's volcanic activity was unknown until images were taken by the Voyager spacecraft in 1979

Inside Io
Why is Io so volcanic?

2. Under pressure
The huge gravitational forces expelled upon Io from Jupiter's other moons cause its interior to expand and contract.

3. Mountainous
Io's surface is covered with over 400 volcanoes and 100 mountains.

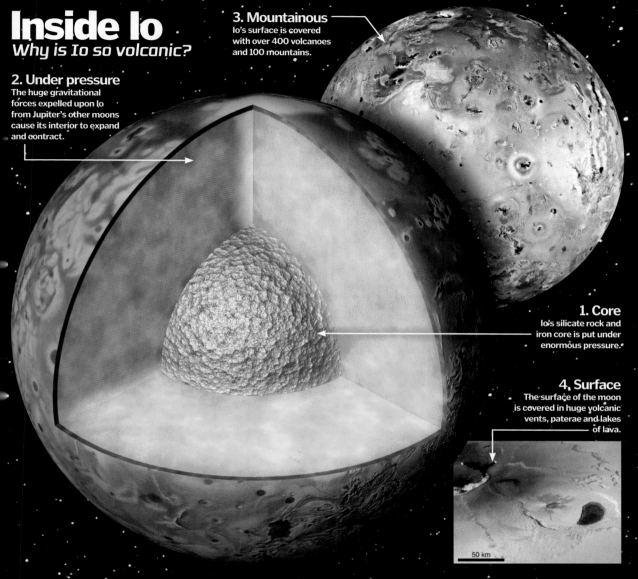

1. Core
Io's silicate rock and iron core is put under enormous pressure.

4. Surface
The surface of the moon is covered in huge volcanic vents, paterae and lakes of lava.

50 km

Jupiter's Galilean moons

Jupiter has 63 known moons, but its Galilean moons – Io, Europa, Ganymede and Callisto – are the four largest. Discovered by Galileo in 1620, the Galilean moons also rank among the biggest moons in the solar system. Io is known for its extreme volcanic activity as well as its unusual silicate rock and iron composition. Europa is the smallest of these moons, with a smooth surface of ice and water. It's thought to potentially harbour extraterrestrial life. Ganymede is the biggest moon in the solar system, with a diameter wider than Mercury's. With a surface that is very old and covered in craters, Callisto is the second-largest Galilean moon. Its largest crater, Valhalla, is 3,000 kilometres wide.

Io: The volcanic moon

When it comes to the landscape on Jupiter's moon Io, the only real constant is change

We often think of moons in the context of Earth's moon – cold, quiet and devoid of activity. While Jupiter's moon Io is roughly the same size as Earth's moon, it couldn't be more different. Io's main feature is its volcanic activity. The moon is covered with more than 400 volcanoes, which constantly spew plumes of sulphur, sulphur dioxide and ash as high as 500 kilometres above its surface. Io is also covered with hundreds of kilometres of lava flows and lakes, massive volcanic depressions called paterae, and openings in its crust called volcanic vents. This non-stop activity

gives Io a colourful surface that looks a lot like a pizza.

So what makes Io so unique? The answer is tides, but these tides are much stronger than those in Earth's oceans. Io experiences tidal heating thanks to the gravitational forces exerted upon it by Jupiter and three of its other moons: Europa, Ganymede and Callisto. Io is the innermost of these moons, so it's constantly in the centre of a tug-of-war between the planet and the other moons. These gravitational forces are so strong that they alternately compress and expand Io's interior, causing the surface to bulge in and out by as much as 100

kilometres. All of this force causes pressure and heat to build in Io's silicate rock and iron core, ultimately sending molten material spewing up through cracks in the crust.

In addition to its numerous volcanic features, Io has more than 100 mountains, some of which are taller than Mount Everest's 8.84 kilometres. These mountains may be the result of the constant resurfacing of the moon's crust due to all of the volcanic activity. A build-up of volcanic material could cause the crust to fall into the mantle, pushing chunks of it up through faults and forming a mountain. ⚙

The Statistics
Io

Diameter: 3,636 kilometres
Mass: 8.93×10^{22} kilograms
Density: 3.5 grams per cubic centimetre
Average surface temperature: -143°C (130 Kelvin)
Core temperature: Estimated at up to 1,726°C (2,000 Kelvin)
Equatorial surface gravity: 0.183 g

"A huge star formed from a massive gravitational collapse when space dust and nebula gas collided"

Inside the Sun

The giant star that keeps us all alive...

A celestial wonder, the Sun is a huge star formed from a massive gravitational collapse when space dust and gas from a nebula collided. It became an orb 100 times bigger and weighing over 300,000 times that of Earth. Made up of 70 per cent hydrogen and about 28 per cent helium (plus other gases), the Sun is the centre of our solar system and the largest celestial body anywhere near us.

"The surface of the Sun is a dense layer of plasma at a temperature of 5,800 degrees kelvin that is continually moving due to the action of convective motions driven by heating from below," says David Alexander, a professor of physics and astronomy at Rice University. "These convective motions show up as a distribution of what are called granulation cells about 1,000 kilometers across and which appear across the whole solar surface."

At its core, the Sun's temperature and pressure are so high and the hydrogen atoms are moving so fast that it causes fusion, turning hydrogen atoms into helium. Electromagetic radiation travels out from the Sun's core to its surface, escaping into space as electromagnetic radiation, a blinding light, and incredible levels of solar heat. In fact, the core of the Sun is actually hotter than the surface, but when heat escapes from the surface, the temperature rises to over 1-2 million degrees. Alexander explained that astronomers do not fully understand why the Sun's atmosphere is so hot, but think it has something to do with magnetic fields. ✿

Beneath the surface of the Sun
What is the Sun made of?

Radiative zone
The first 500,000 k of the Sun is a radioactive layer that transfers energy from the core, mostly towards the outer layers, passed from atom to atom.

Sun's core
The core of a Sun is a dense, extremely hot region – about 15 million degrees Celsius – that produces a nuclear fusion and emits heat through the layers of the Sun to the surface.

Convective zone
The top 30 per cent of the Sun is a layer of hot plasma that is constantly in motion, heated from below.

Right conditions
The core of the Sun, which acts like a nuclear reactor, is just the right size and temperature to produce light.

Engine room
The centre of a star is like an engine room that produces the nuclear fusion required for radiation and light.

All images courtesy of NASA

The Statistics
The Sun

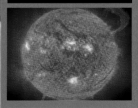

Diameter: 100 times Earth
Mass: 300,000 times Earth
Average surface temp: 1-2 million °C
Core temp: 15 million °C

Magnetic influence
How the Sun affects the Earth's magnetic field

Solar wind
Solar wind shapes the Earth's magnetosphere and magnetic storms are illustrated here as approaching Earth.

Plasma release
The Sun's magnetic field and plasma releases directly affect Earth and the rest of the solar system.

Bow shock line
The purple line is the bow shock line and the blue lines surrounding the Earth represent its protective magnetosphere.

What is a solar flare?

A massive explosion, but one that happens to be several million degrees Celsius in temperature...

"A solar flare is a rapid release of energy in the solar atmosphere (mostly the chromosphere and corona) resulting in localised heating of plasma to tens of millions of degrees, acceleration of electrons and protons to high energies, some to near the speed of light, and expulsion of material into space," says Alexander. "These electromagnetic disturbances here on Earth pose potential dangers for Earth-orbiting satellites, space-walking astronauts, crews on high-altitude spacecraft, and power grids on Earth."

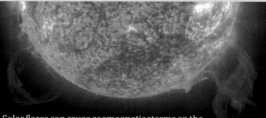

Solar flares can cause geomagnetic storms on the Sun, including shock waves and plasma expulsions

Solar eclipses

When the Moon blocks out the Sun

A solar eclipse is a unique phenomena where the Moon passes directly into a line between the Earth and the Sun, partially or completely blocking our view of the Sun. The Sun is blocked according to the relative orbits of each celestial body. There are two kinds of eclipse: one where the Moon orbit shows the outer edge of the Sun, or where the Moon lines up perfectly and the Sun is blocked completely from view.

Sometimes, the orbits of the Earth and Sun line up perfectly so that the Sun is blocked (eclipsed) by the Moon, shown here with a shadow cast from the eclipse, taken from the ISS

How big is the Sun?
Our Sun has a diameter of 1.4 million km and Earth a diameter of almost 13,000 km

What is a sunspot?

Signifying cooler areas, sunspots show up as dark dots on the photosphere (the visible layer of plasma across the Sun's surface). These 'cool' regions – about 1,000 degrees cooler than the surface temperature – are associated with strong magnetic fields. Criss-crossing magnetic-field lines can disturb the flow of heat from the core, creating pockets of intense activity. The build up of heat around a sunspot can be released as a solar flare or coronal mass ejection (CME), which is separate to but often accompanies larger flares. Plasma from a CME ejects from the Sun at over 1 million miles per hour.

If the Sun were the size of a basketball, Earth would be a little dot no more than 2.2 mm

"As it comes closer, it heats up and spews out dust and gas to form a glowing cloud – the coma"

The Statistics
Halley's Comet

© NASA

Closest approach to Sun: 88 million km
Furthest distance from Sun: 5.3 billion km
Orbital period: About 76 years
First recorded: 240 BC
Last recorded: 1986
Next appearance: 2061
Diameter: 16 x 8 x 7 (km)
Mass: 2.2 x 10^{14} kilograms

Halley's comet
What is this fiery ball and why does it return to the night sky?

Comets are dirty snowballs made of dust and ice left behind when our solar system formed. Halley's comet is the best-known short period comet – a comet that has orbited around the Sun more than once in recorded history.

Comets' orbits can be tilted at a large angle relative to the orbits of the planets. Halley's comet's orbit is so tilted it looks to orbit backwards compared to the planets. The orbit is also very elongated so the distance between Halley's comet and the Sun changes dramatically as it travels.

When the comet is far from the Sun, it's a frozen ball called a nucleus. As it comes closer, it heats up and spews out dust and gas to form a glowing cloud – the coma – and long tail. Each time Halley's comet returns towards the Sun, it loses more ice until, eventually, there will be too little to form a tail.

We'll have to wait until 2061 to see this sight again, by which time we'll be celebrating our 670th issue.

DID YOU KNOW?
Over the centuries, Halley's comet has been blamed for earthquakes, the births of two-headed animals and even the Black Death.

5 TOP FACTS
COMETS

1 Dinosaur extinction
A comet hitting the Earth 200 million years ago could have cleared the way for dinosaurs to rule the world until another comet wiped them out 135 million years later.

2 Lightweight
A person weighing 45 kg on Earth would weigh 0.005 kg on a comet and could jump off into space. A comet's small size gives it little gravity to hold objects down.

3 Gushing gas
Comet Hale-Bopp could have lost 250 tons of dust and gas every second as it swung by the Sun in early 1997 – more than 50 times greater than most comets.

4 Time capsule
Comets could hold a deep-frozen record of the early solar system. Scientists think they formed 5 billion years ago and have remained almost perpetually frozen since.

5 Seeding life
Dust collected from comet Wild 2 in 2004 contained a chemical, glycine, used by living organisms. Scientists think some building blocks for life could have arrived from space on comets.

What is the Kármán line?
Want to turn from an aeronaut into an astronaut? Just cross the Kármán line

The Kármán line is an official boundary between the Earth's atmosphere and space, lying 100 kilometres above sea level. The governing body for air sports and aeronautical world records, Fédération Aéronautique Internationale (FAI), recognises it as the line where aeronautics ends and astronautics begins.

The line is named after aeronautical scientist Theodore von Kármán. He calculated that approximately 100 km above sea level it was more efficient for vehicles to orbit than fly. The air thins with increasing altitude and aircraft rely on air flowing over their wings to keep them aloft so must move faster with increasing height. Above 100 km they would have to move faster than the velocity at which satellites orbit the Earth.

Thin air also explains why the Earth's sky looks blue and space is black. Atmospheric gases scatter blue light more than other colours, turning the sky blue. At higher altitudes, less air exists to scatter light.

The layers in Earth's atmosphere

Exosphere
Many satellites orbit in the exosphere – the highest atmospheric layer. It extends to 10,000 km above sea level and gets thinner and thinner until it becomes outer space.

Thermosphere
'Thermos' means hot. Air molecules in this layer can be heated to over 1,000°C by the Sun's incoming energy, but we would feel cold because there is so little air.

Mesosphere
Meteorites entering the Earth's atmosphere normally burn up in the mesosphere, the coldest layer in the atmosphere that lies 50 to 80 km above sea level.

Stratosphere
The stratosphere stretches from around 12 km to 50 km above sea level. This layer contains the ozone layer, which shields us from the Sun's potentially harmful ultraviolet radiation.

Troposphere
The atmosphere's lowest layer contains 75 per cent of its mass and almost all its weather. It varies from around eight km high at the poles to 20 km over the equator.

DID YOU KNOW?
The first man-made object to cross the Kármán line was a German V-2 rocket during a 1944 test flight.

DID YOU KNOW? *Galaxy classification is notoriously difficult due to its highly subjective nature*

Types of galaxy

They might be grouped like a galactic tuning fork, but galaxy types don't always sing from the same hymn sheet

There are several galaxy classification systems, but the most widely used is the Hubble Sequence, devised by the great Edwin Hubble in 1926 and later expanded upon by Allan Sandage among others. It's more commonly known as the Hubble tuning fork due to the shape the system represents in diagrammatic form.

Hubble's system was designed to demonstrate the various classifications of three main classes of galaxy broken down into elliptical, spiral and lenticular shapes. The latter is essentially an intermediate of the other two types. It was erroneously thought that each galaxy type represented snapshots of the entire life span of galaxies, but it has since been demonstrated that this is not the case.

The most recent version of Hubble's tuning fork comes courtesy of the Spitzer Space Telescope's infrared galaxy survey made up of 75 colour images of different galaxies and includes a new sub-section of irregular galaxy types. You can find a full resolution image of this remarkable accomplishment at http://sings.stsci.edu/Publications/sings_poster.html. Thanks to the internet, anyone can try their hand at galaxy classification and further the science – simply go to www.galaxyzoo.org and join in alongside 150,000 other volunteers. ❖

Types of galaxies

Galaxies can be categorised into these types...

Elliptical galaxies
On the far left of the Hubble Sequence lies the elliptical galaxy types. They show no defined features like the intricate dust lanes seen in classic spiral galaxy types, besides a bright core. Ellipticals are represented by the letter E, followed by a number that represents the ellipticity of its shape.

Spiral types
Appearing flatter on the sky than an elliptical galaxy, spiral galaxies feature two or more spiral 'arms' that wrap around the galaxy core and are made up of vast lanes of stars. The upper half is populated with the standard spiral type, while the lower half contains 'bar' spirals. The twist of the spiral begins at the end of an extended bar.

Lenticular galaxies
Where the handle of the tuning fork and the two spiral arms meet lie the lenticular galaxies. These galaxies feature aspects of both spiral and elliptical galaxies and didn't actually feature on Hubble's original sequence. They have a bright central bulge like an elliptical galaxy, but are surrounded by a structure not unlike a disc.

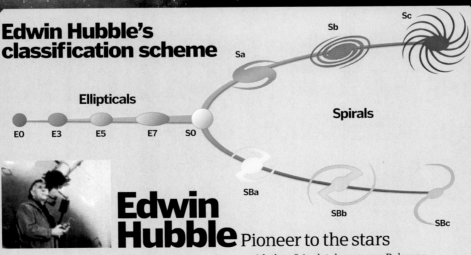

Edwin Hubble's classification scheme

Ellipticals: E0   E3   E5   E7   S0

Spirals: Sa   Sb   Sc

SBa   SBb   SBc

Edwin Hubble
Pioneer to the stars

No person in history has had a greater impact in determining the extent of our universe than Edwin Hubble. From proving that other galaxies existed to giving evidence that galaxies move apart from one another, Hubble's work defined our place in the cosmos. Shown above posing with the 48-inch telescope on Palomar Mountain, the Orbiting Space Telescope was named in memory of his great work.

Today a great controversy rages on about the rate of the universe's expansion, parameterised by a quantity known as Hubble's constant.

All images © NASA

Space junk

The space age junk that pollutes our planet

Since the launch of Sputnik I, which was the first man-made satellite to orbit the Earth in 1957, a vast amount of space debris has accumulated in its wake. This consists of anything from flecks of paint to discarded rocket boosters, 'dead' satellites that no longer function and equipment lost by astronauts during space walks.

The scale of the problem can be grasped by the fact that there are estimated to be several hundred million items of space junk less than 1 cm in size,

several hundred thousand items between 1 cm to 10 cm and at least 19,000 objects larger than 10 cm.

In low Earth orbit (LEO) this junk travels at an average speed of 7.5 kmps, which is ten times faster than a bullet. This means that even the smallest objects can damage the subsystems of a satellite. Objects from 1 cm to 10 cm are part of a 'lethal population' because they are big enough to do considerable damage to a satellite, but are too small to be tracked. Larger debris is tracked and can be avoided; in the case of the

International Space Station, it makes at least one manoeuvre a year to divert it from potentially lethal collisions.

Last year there were 13,000 near misses and by 2059 it is predicted that there will be as many as 50,000. The increased need to use rocket fuel to avoid these hazards shortens the life of satellites, and increases the cost of launching satellites that need to carry extra fuel.

1,400 items of space junk were created when the first ever collision between two satellites occurred on 11 February 2009.

DID YOU KNOW?

Is there junk on Mars?
Space junk is littered over Mars. In 2004, NASA deliberately crashed a heat shield protecting a Mars rover vehicle into the planet. The rover vehicle was then sent to examine the type of impact crater the shield created.

DID YOU KNOW? Villagers near the Plesetsk spaceport are allowed to collect, use or sell the junk metal of spent rocket boosters

A propellant tank from the Delta II launch vehicle that landed in Texas in 1997

"**Last year there were 13,000 near misses and by 2059 it is predicted that there will be as many as 50,000**"

This was between the Iridium 33 US communications satellite and a defunct Kosmos 2251 Russian satellite, 790 km over Northern Siberia.

Even worse, 150,000 pieces of junk were deliberately created when China destroyed an inactive Fengyun-1C weather satellite with a missile, as part of an anti-satellite test.

Radar systems are used to track LEO junk, and telescopes are employed to track objects from 2,000 km to 36,000 km in medium Earth orbit (MEO) and geostationary orbit (GEO) at 36,000 km. Telescopes, however, are only capable of tracking objects that are one metre or more in size. Radio frequency technology can also be used to discover if satellites are operating or not.

Tracking helps warn of possible collisions, but measures that are more drastic are being employed, before it is impossible to launch manned flights, or operate the satellites that provide us with TV signals, weather forecasts, mobile phone networks and global positioning systems.

LOST IN SPACE
What's floating around in the LEO?

Glove
Lost by Ed White, the first American astronaut to take a spacewalk on 3 June 1965, during the Gemini 4 mission

Ed White's first space walk

Cameras
Lost during the Gemini 10 and a Discovery space shuttle mission in December 2006

200 rubbish bags
Ejected from the Russian Mir space station from 1986 to 2001

Metallic spherical drinking water spheres
Started a UFO scare when they crashed in Western Australia in 1965, but were identified as coming from the Gemini spacecraft

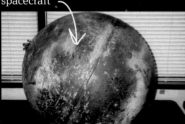

300,000 fragments
Produced when the upper stage of a Pegasus rocket exploded in 1996

Tool bag
Worth $100,000 containing grease guns lost by Heide Stefanyshyn-Piper during a shuttle spacewalk in 2008. It re-entered the atmosphere in August 2009

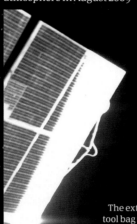

The extravehicular activity tool bag floats away from the International Space Station

128 kg of nuclear reactor coolant
Leaked from inactive Soviet Radar Ocean Reconnaissance Satellites

480 million copper needles
Launched in 1963 as part of Project West Ford to create an artificial ionosphere, it encircled Earth at 3,700 km. Most re-entered the atmosphere in the Seventies

Gene Roddenberry
The *Star Trek* creator's ashes were released in a small capsule by a Pegasus XL rocket in 1997

Gene Roddenberry and the cast of *Star Trek* attending the roll out of the Space Shuttle Enterprise in 1976

Breakdown of space junk

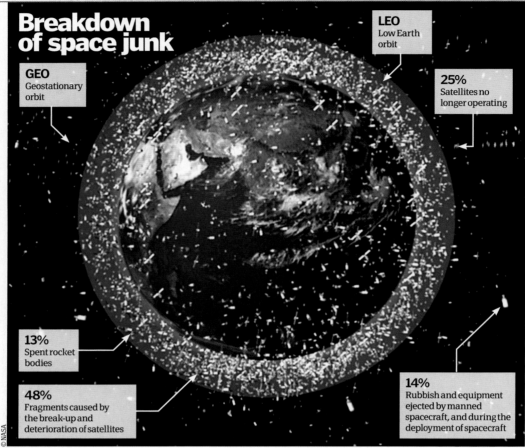

LEO Low Earth orbit

25% Satellites no longer operating

GEO Geostationary orbit

13% Spent rocket bodies

48% Fragments caused by the break-up and deterioration of satellites

14% Rubbish and equipment ejected by manned spacecraft, and during the deployment of spacecraft

© NASA

How the ISS dodges the debris

Orbiting at 350 km in low Earth orbit, the ISS is particularly vulnerable to damage from space debris. Manned modules and other vulnerable areas have been fitted with protective aluminium shields – both during and since construction.

The ISS also carries out Debris Avoidance Manoeuvres (DAMs) to dodge space junk or micrometeorites. When warned of such dangers, the ISS is sent a few kilometres higher or lower, using a short engine thrust from a docked Automated Transfer Vehicle (ATV) or Progress spacecraft. The ATV is fitted with an automatic system that during docking procedure will abort the procedure if it detects any danger from debris.

If any debris comes within 0.75 km above or below, or within 25km around it that cannot be avoided, the ISS is put into unmanned mode and the astronauts have to seek protection in a spacecraft docked with the station. In 2008 and 2009, astronauts had to seek refuge in a Soyuz craft, due to such warnings.

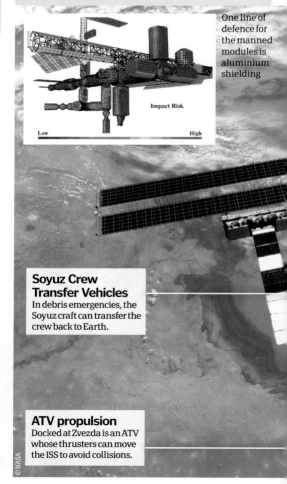

One line of defence for the manned modules is aluminium shielding

Impact Risk — Low ... High

Soyuz Crew Transfer Vehicles In debris emergencies, the Soyuz craft can transfer the crew back to Earth.

ATV propulsion Docked at Zvezda is an ATV whose thrusters can move the ISS to avoid collisions.

Debris in low Earth orbit
A snapshot of the junk orbiting Earth

Objects in low Earth orbit (LEO) are between 160 km and 2,000 km above the Earth. Military satellites, Earth monitoring satellites and communications satellites operate at these orbital altitudes.

LEO satellites pose a problem because they orbit the Earth at least 15 times a day along different orbital planes to provide global coverage. This gives them more chance of hitting other satellites in contrast to those that keep to the elliptical plane of the Sun. In addition, they have shorter battery lives and are more vulnerable to the gravitational pull of the Earth than higher satellites.

The so-called Kessler Syndrome proposes that as collisions multiply they create even greater numbers of fragments that will start an unstoppable chain reaction of collisions. In this process, the debris will increase more than the amount of debris burned up by orbital decay, and will make the use of low Earth orbits impossible.

Most objects that go beneath LEO, through orbital decay or due to a collision, fall back to Earth and harmlessly burn-up in the atmosphere. Larger space junk is more of a problem. This was emphasised by the accidental crash of Cosmos 954 in January 1978. The Soviet reconnaissance satellite carried an on-board nuclear reactor, which instead of reaching a safe orbit fell over northwest Canada. A huge recovery operation found 12 large pieces, ten of

which were radioactive and one that carried a lethal radiation level of 500r/hr.

In 2001, the Russian Mir space station was deliberately crashed into the southern Pacific Ocean. The re-entry of the 130,000 kg station created a spectacular display, and metal fragments from it were recovered and sold on eBay.

So far, such crashes have been in oceans or remote parts of the world, but certainly there is a risk of a rogue piece of space junk causing serious damage to a highly populated area.

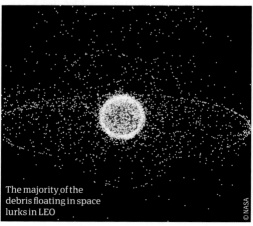

The majority of the debris floating in space lurks in LEO

© NASA

First and oldest
1 Vanguard 1, launched by the USA back in 1958, is the oldest piece of space junk. It stopped operating in 1964, but will continue orbiting Earth for another 240 years.

Long-term problem
2 The length of time junk stays in orbit before re-entering the atmosphere is only a few days when it's below 200 km, but increases to a few years between 200 and 600 km.

Working
3 The 902 operational satellites that were orbiting Earth in 2009 are dwarfed by the vast amount of junk debris and dead spacecraft that surrounds them.

Lethal
4 A 2-mm piece of debris can rip a lethal hole in an astronaut's spacesuit. The chance of such an object hitting an astronaut during a six-hour spacewalk is 31,000 to one.

Hit
5 The chance of being hit by space junk on Earth is 20 billion to one. Unlucky Lottie Williams was hit but unharmed by a 13 cm piece of a Delta II rocket in 1997.

DID YOU KNOW? More than 178,000 kg of hardware has been junked on the Moon, including Apollo's Lunar modules

Damages

The relative velocity of a space vehicle and a piece of junk can be 10 kmps, making a collision very damaging. In the case of manned flight, it is even more threatening. The US space shuttles often encountered debris, causing NASA to regularly replace cabin crew windows and thermal tiles damaged by flecks of paint or micrometeorites.

A more threatening incident happened to the Columbia shuttle in 1995, when an object penetrated the protective layers of its payload bay door. Another collision, between a circuit board and an Atlantis shuttle payload door in September 2006, created a 12 mm deep hole. To reduce such impacts Shuttles flew tail-first in orbit, or when docked to the ISS they were positioned so that the station took the worst impacts.

Whipple shields that absorb debris impacts before they can do any significant damage can protect manned and unmanned spacecraft. Unfortunately, such shields cannot protect vital solar panels or stop the impact of larger debris. To tackle large debris, spacecraft have to manoeuvre out of the way to avoid a collision.

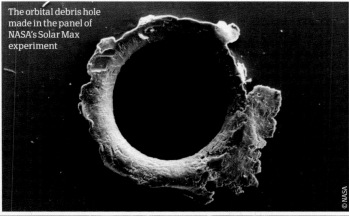

The orbital debris hole made in the panel of NASA's Solar Max experiment

© NASA

Shielding
Vulnerable areas of the space station are protected by shields.

Zvezda module
Zvezda is fitted with six Service Module Debris Protection shields.

One idea for ridding space of detritus is using satellites to destroy the litter with lasers

© Science Photo Library

Dealing with the space junk

The European Space Agency is currently building a radar system to catalogue and track hazardous objects in Earth orbit. At the moment, the US military Space Surveillance Network (SSN) tracks 19,000 objects and its Space Fence radar system scheduled for 2015 expects to track as many as 100,000 objects.

To mitigate the problem of space junk the Inter-Agency Space Debris Co-ordination Committee (IADC) was formed in 1993 to produce a set of guidelines. It advocates several preventative measures, including reducing the amount of hardware ejected or rendered inoperative by a space mission. Since accidental orbital explosions have accounted for at least 200 incidents, it is recommended that explosive gases or fuels be vented to stop this happening. The deliberate explosion of satellites should be stopped, and where possible satellites should be steered clear of debris. As LEO satellites are the biggest culprit, they should be designed to only have an orbital life of 25 years, and carry drag devices or a propulsion system to send them into re-entry if its orbit is not low enough for it to naturally re-enter. Higher satellites should be designed to enter a 'graveyard' orbit at the end of their operating life.

Several ideas have been proposed to dispose of existing junk. They range from shooting it down using lasers, scooping it up with Aerogel material or netting it with 'trawler' satellites. For the smallest debris, large panels of porous foam could slow down junk that passes through it, making it re-enter the atmosphere. For larger debris, it could be collected by the robotic arm of an unmanned spacecraft.

The Hypervelocity Ballistic Range at NASA's Ames Research Center simulates orbital debris hitting a spacecraft by launching a projectile at speeds of up to 27,360 kmph at a solid surface. This image shows the resulting energy flash.

Hypervelocity picture and starry background © NASA

Titan:
Saturn's largest moon

Discover one of the most Earth-like bodies in our solar system

Of Saturn's more than 60 natural satellites, Titan is not only the largest, but also one of the most fascinating and mysterious. It is about 50 per cent larger than Earth's moon and a few hundred kilometres larger than the planet Mercury, but Titan is often compared to Earth. It has clouds in its atmosphere that produce rain, which has resulted in large lakes at the poles. Stable bodies of water like these do not exist anywhere else but Earth. Titan also has predictable wind patterns, as well as volcanoes and evidence of plate tectonics. These processes have given it a landscape dotted with mountain ranges, dunes, valleys and shorelines.

Scientists often call Titan 'early Earth' because they believe that its atmosphere and surface – which is mostly free of impact craters – are similar to our planet around the time that life began. However, Titan only gets about one per cent of the sunlight that Earth gets, thanks to its thick, hazy atmosphere mostly made of nitrogen. Because of its distance from the Sun and its thick atmosphere, just about everything related to the moon is very frigid. Titan's average surface temperature is –179°C. Titan's rain is called a 'methane drizzle', and its lakes are composed not of water, but of liquid methane and ethane. Even Titan's volcanoes are cold; instead of scorching lava made of liquid rock, it is believed that these 'cryovolcanoes' spew ammonia and water-ice. ✿

Atmosphere
Titan's atmosphere is mostly nitrogen, but also contains methane, hydrogen and trace amounts of other hydrocarbons and gases.

Ice Ih crust
This layer comprises ice Ih, a hexagonal form of ice with a very low density. It is thought to be floating on the surface of the water and ammonia layer.

Water and ammonia layer
The Hugyens probe detected extremely low-frequency radio waves (ELF), which likely reflected off this sub-surface ocean. The ammonia would keep the water as a liquid even at low temperatures.

High-pressure ice layer
Pressures within the moon's structure during its formation probably created high-pressure forms of ice with tight crystalline structures.

Silicate core
Titan's core is thought to comprise silicate rock approximately 5,000 kilometres in diameter.

Inside Titan
Titan's internal structure is thought to be mostly ice; scientists believe that it has a rocky core (which could be hot) surrounded by a high-pressure form of ice, a liquid ammonia and water layer and a crystalline icy crust.

© NASA

Orbit and rotation

1 Titan both rotates and orbits Saturn once every 15 days and 22 hours. It is also synchronous with Saturn, meaning that the same side of the moon always faces the planet.

Life on the moon?

2 There is speculation that Titan could support life, based on a lack of the organic compound acetylene and lower levels of hydrogen than some have previously predicted.

Observing Titan

3 Titan can be very difficult to see from telescopes on Earth because it is so close to Saturn and its countless number of rings, which are extremely bright.

Titan as a colony

4 Titan has been considered as a candidate for colonisation. This is due to its high levels of hydrocarbons, which are far beyond all of the oil and natural gas reserves on Earth.

Flying on the moon

5 Scientists believe that people could theoretically fly on Titan with wings attached to their arms due to the low gravity and the thick atmospheric haze.

DID YOU KNOW? Titan was discovered in 1655 by Dutch astronomer Christiaan Huygens, who called it Luna Saturni

The Statistics

Titan

Diameter: 5,151 kilometres
Mass: 0.0225 Earths
Density: 1.88 grams per cubic centimetre
Average surface temperature: -178°C
Average distance from the Sun: 1,427,000,000 kilometres (9.54 AU)
Surface gravity: 0.14 g-force

Titan has a multi-layered atmosphere with very low temperatures and high pressure at its surface. Methane condenses, while surface activity such as volcanic eruptions and rain keep atmospheric gases circulating

© NASA

© NASA

Orange haze

Other moons in our solar system have little-to-no atmosphere, but Titan is unique. Its atmosphere is quite dense – the atmospheric pressure is almost one and a half times that of Earth's. It is also very thick due to the moon's low gravity (lower even than our own moon's gravity), extending ten times further into space than Earth's atmosphere. Titan's atmosphere has multiple layers and is extremely complex, comprising about 98.5 per cent nitrogen, 1.3 per cent methane and 0.2 per cent hydrogen as well as traces of numerous other hydrocarbons and gases.

Both the atmosphere's orange-brown colour and thick haze are likely due to organic molecules such as tholins, which form when ultraviolet radiation from the Sun breaks apart the nitrogen and methane in the moon's upper atmosphere. The molecules that do not hang in the atmosphere fall down to the surface, contributing to the sand dunes that cover the planet.

Methane rain

Titan has rain like Earth, but it is made of methane instead of water. Scientists believe that the Sun should have converted all of Titan's atmospheric methane into tholins and other organic molecules millions of years ago. This means that there is a source of methane on the moon itself, and it is likely circulated back into the atmosphere through volcanic eruptions.

The thick, dense atmosphere and low gravity means that the methane rain falls very slowly and in drops twice as large as raindrops on Earth, mostly near the moon's poles. It doesn't rain very often on Titan – perhaps as little as once every few decades. When it does rain, however, there's a lot of it and it carves out ridges, dunes and valleys.

© NASA / Mark A. Garlick / markgarlick.com

Chart (Altitude, km vs Temperature, K / Pressure, bar):
- Tholin haze
- Temperature
- Condensate haze
- $CH_4 - N_2$ clouds
- Pume
- $C_{20}H$ Fog
- Lake
- River
- HO/NH_3
- Volcanism?
- Organic sediments
- Impacts HO/NH_3
- Melt

Pressure bar values: 0.003, 0.01, 0.03, 0.1, 0.3, 1.0, 1.5
Altitude values: 140, 120, 100, 80, 60, 40, 20, 0
Temperature values: 80, 100, 120, 140, 160, 180

Missions to Titan

The Cassini-Huygens Mission was a joint project of NASA, the ESA and the Italian Space Agency. After several fly-bys of Titan, the Huygens probe landed on Titan's surface in 2005 and transmitted images and data back to the Cassini spacecraft. The probe provided the most in-depth look at Titan ever seen, including information about the moon's atmospheric make-up, weather and landscape. Its landing site showed a vast plain covered in water-ice rocks.

A joint NASA/ESA mission called the Titan Saturn System Mission (TSSM) has been proposed to launch as early as 2018. This mission would explore Saturn as well as Titan and another of Saturn's moons, Enceladus. It includes deploying two different types of probes on Titan: a montgolfière (or hot-air balloon) and a lander. The montgolfière would circulate in Titan's clouds and circumnavigate the moon, while the lander would splashdown in one of Titan's lakes.

© NASA

"Brown dwarfs are often considered to be the missing link between gas giant planets and red dwarf stars"

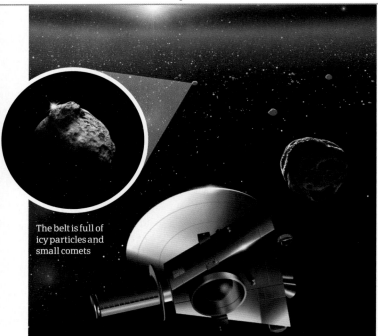

The belt is full of icy particles and small comets

Where is the Kuiper belt?

If you were looking for a gigantic asteroid field and a cloud of icy particles, where would you look?

If you were to scale down the Sun and planets so the Earth sat just one centimetre away from the Sun, the furthest dwarf planet would sit some 30 centimetres away. Just beyond the orbit of Nepture, however, lies a wide belt of the remnants from the construction of our solar system. The Kuiper belt contains hundreds of thousands of icy particles thought to be up to 100 kilometres in diameter, along with up to a trillion smaller comets.

But the solar system doesn't end there – our entire solar system is entombed in an almost perfect sphere of ice, the Oort Cloud, that lies some half a kilometre further away on our previous scale (where the distance from the Earth to the Sun is just one centimetre). Lying on the boundaries of interstellar space, this shell is thought to contain up to 2 trillion icy bodies teetering on the very cusp of our Sun's gravitational grasp. ✿

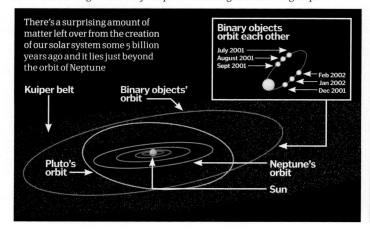

There's a surprising amount of matter left over from the creation of our solar system some 5 billion years ago and it lies just beyond the orbit of Neptune

Binary objects orbit each other

July 2001
August 2001
Sept 2001
Feb 2002
Jan 2002
Dec 2001

Kuiper belt

Binary objects' orbit

Pluto's orbit

Neptune's orbit

Sun

What is a brown dwarf?

These so-called 'sub-stellar' objects are barely bigger than planets, so what makes these failed stars stellar at all?

It's a conundrum that's puzzled the field of astronomy for the last 30 years – is a brown dwarf star really a star at all? Since they don't have the mass to initiate nuclear fusion like a normal star during its formation, they're often referred to as 'failed stars'. With masses that range from just a few times larger than our solar system's gas giant Jupiter, to around 75 times its size, brown dwarfs are often considered to be the missing link between gas giant planets and red dwarf stars – the smallest known 'true stars'.

Measuring or even discovering the presence of a brown dwarf star is notoriously difficult because they're so cool and small, so scientists use the presence of lithium as a determining factor. The presence of lithium is actually common in all young stars, but is usually burned up in the first 100 million years of its life. Since the core of a brown dwarf isn't hot enough to get rid of the lithium it's a very useful indicator in labelling low-mass stellar objects 'brown dwarf stars'. ✿

Size difference
Though an entirely hypothetical scenario, this artist's conception demonstrates the relative size difference between our own solar system and that of a particularly small brown dwarf system.

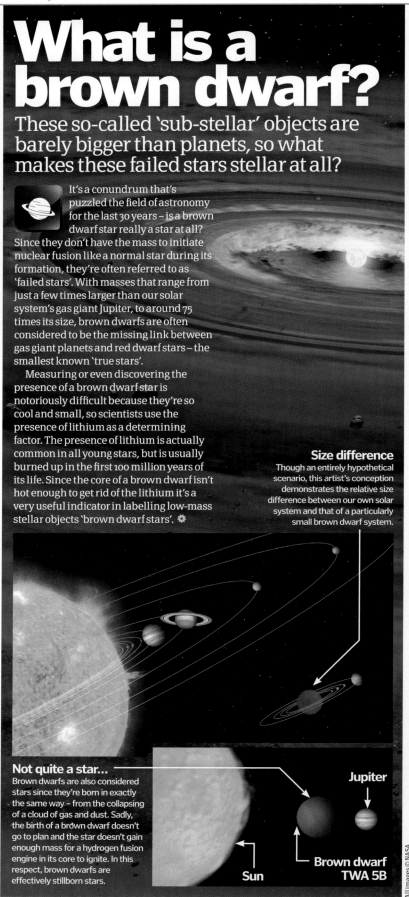

Not quite a star...
Brown dwarfs are also considered stars since they're born in exactly the same way – from the collapsing of a cloud of gas and dust. Sadly, the birth of a brown dwarf doesn't go to plan and the star doesn't gain enough mass for a hydrogen fusion engine in its core to ignite. In this respect, brown dwarfs are effectively stillborn stars.

Sun

Jupiter

Brown dwarf TWA 5B

Head to Head
PICTURING THE SUN

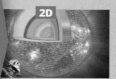

1. SOHO
Launched in 1995, SOHO is a Europe-led mission designed to study the Sun. Compared to both following missions, the visual fidelity of its findings were limited.

2. STEREO
NASA's next step was to take the study of the Sun into the third dimension. Utilising two spacecraft its mission was to study the nature of CMEs.

3. SDO
The SDO's visual capabilities dwarf both previous missions. Just three seconds of HD video revealed more detail about solar flares than many scientists ever knew.

DID YOU KNOW? The total mass of the SDO spacecraft at launch was 3,100 kg, yet the SDO itself weighs just 290 kg

NASA's Solar Dynamics Observatory

If you think 1080p HD video is impressive, your tech-buds are in for a treat with the SDO...

The Solar Dynamics Observatory (SDO) is the crowning mission of a new scientific endeavour designed to study our Sun. As the cornerstone of NASA's Living With a Star programme, the SDO is quite simply the most advanced spacecraft ever devised to help unlock the secrets of our Sun. Using the very latest technology, the SDO can gather high-quality data, process it with more advanced instruments and beam it back to Earth faster than any other scientific experiment undertaken by man.

And an important mission it is too as being able to understand and predict the processes of our Sun is becoming evermore important in this digital age. Launched in February 2010, the SDO will hopefully furnish us with the capability to better protect ourselves from 'space weather' side effects like power grid failures, long-haul flight radiation, not to mention satellite, telecommunications and GPS disruptions. ✦

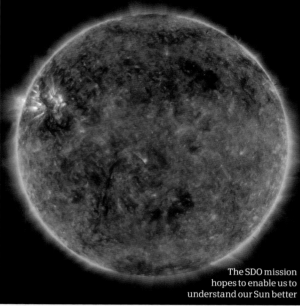

The SDO mission hopes to enable us to understand our Sun better

Road to discovery

The SDO is designed around a five-year mission, though has enough resources to ensure a ten-year life span. In that time scientists hope to gain in-depth information about how and why changes in the Sun produce its 11-year solar cycle brought on by changes in its magnetic field. As a major component of the Heliophysics System Observatory (essentially a whole fleet of solar, heliospheric and geospace spacecraft working together) it'll also help unlock the secrets of the complex processes at work in space in general.

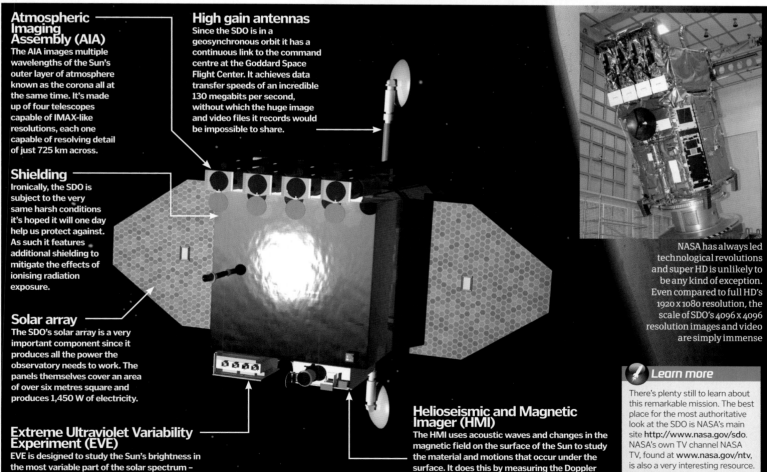

Atmospheric Imaging Assembly (AIA)
The AIA images multiple wavelengths of the Sun's outer layer of atmosphere known as the corona all at the same time. It's made up of four telescopes capable of IMAX-like resolutions, each one capable of resolving detail of just 725 km across.

High gain antennas
Since the SDO is in a geosynchronous orbit it has a continuous link to the command centre at the Goddard Space Flight Center. It achieves data transfer speeds of an incredible 130 megabits per second, without which the huge image and video files it records would be impossible to share.

Shielding
Ironically, the SDO is subject to the very same harsh conditions it's hoped it will one day help us protect against. As such it features additional shielding to mitigate the effects of ionising radiation exposure.

Solar array
The SDO's solar array is a very important component since it produces all the power the observatory needs to work. The panels themselves cover an area of over six metres square and produces 1,450 W of electricity.

Extreme Ultraviolet Variability Experiment (EVE)
EVE is designed to study the Sun's brightness in the most variable part of the solar spectrum – the extreme ultraviolet. It achieves this by utilising the highest spectral resolution ever achieved by a space observatory.

Helioseismic and Magnetic Imager (HMI)
The HMI uses acoustic waves and changes in the magnetic field on the surface of the Sun to study the material and motions that occur under the surface. It does this by measuring the Doppler shift (a change of wavelength depending on whether something is moving towards or away from you) to calculate velocities of movement.

NASA has always led technological revolutions and super HD is unlikely to be any kind of exception. Even compared to full HD's 1920 x 1080 resolution, the scale of SDO's 4096 x 4096 resolution images and video are simply immense

🔦 Learn more
There's plenty still to learn about this remarkable mission. The best place for the most authoritative look at the SDO is NASA's main site http://www.nasa.gov/sdo. NASA's own TV channel NASA TV, found at www.nasa.gov/ntv, is also a very interesting resource. There's plenty to see, including live feeds from this and other missions currently in progress.

"The Moon's gravity is about one-sixth that of our home planet"

The Moon

Understanding man's fascination with Earth's natural satellite

Not only is the Moon our only satellite, it's one of the biggest in the solar system and the only other celestial body upon which man has stood. It's much smaller than the Earth, with a diameter about 25 per cent that of Earth's diameter. The Earth's mass is also about 80 times that of the Moon. The Moon has a much lower gravitational force than the Earth – its gravity is about one-sixth that of our home planet.

The Moon is often referred to as dead, mainly because there is no life and its surface hasn't changed much over the billions of years. Temperatures at its poles can be as high as 127 degrees Celsius during the day and as low as -173 degrees Celsius at night. The Moon is also covered in deep craters that can stay as cold as -240 degrees Celsius.

Its apparent glow is just light reflected from the Sun. There's no atmosphere and no air, although there is a collection of gases above the surface known as an exosphere. The Moon does have days that last about 29.5 hours, although the sky is always dark with visible stars. It rotates on its axis in about the same time it takes for it to orbit the Earth, a phenomenon known as synchronous rotation. This means that the same side – called the near side – is typically facing the Earth. The far side is often called the dark side, but it's illuminated by the Sun once per lunar day just like the near side.

As the Moon orbits the Earth, it goes through four phases – the new moon, first quarter moon, full moon, and last quarter moon. During the new moon, the Moon is between the Sun and the Earth, so the sunlit side is turned away. Every seven days, more of the Moon becomes visible. This process is known as waxing. Halfway through the lunar month there is a full moon. Then as the Moon's orbit takes it further away from Earth, it wanes and less of it is visible. ✿

The average distance from Earth to the Moon is 384,403 km

The surface of the moon

Astronauts who have visited the moon describe the surface as being covered with a fine, powdery dust that was very slippery. Movements had to be planned several steps ahead. Although the gravity is one-sixth that of Earth's, simulations helped them to cope with the differences.

This photo of Buzz Aldrin was taken by Neil Armstrong during the Apollo 11 mission

All images © NASA

1. Maria
The darker areas of the Moon are cratered plains called maria (Latin for 'seas'). Originally they were thought to be water-filled, but they are actually filled with solid lava.

4. Ocean of Storms
Also known as Oceanus Procellarum, this is a massive mare covering more than 4 million square kilometres. The Apollo 12 mission and several lunar probes have landed in the Ocean of Storms.

5. Copernicus
The Moon is covered with numerous impact craters, and Copernicus is one of the most prominent. It's about 800 million years old and light in colour because it doesn't contain lava.

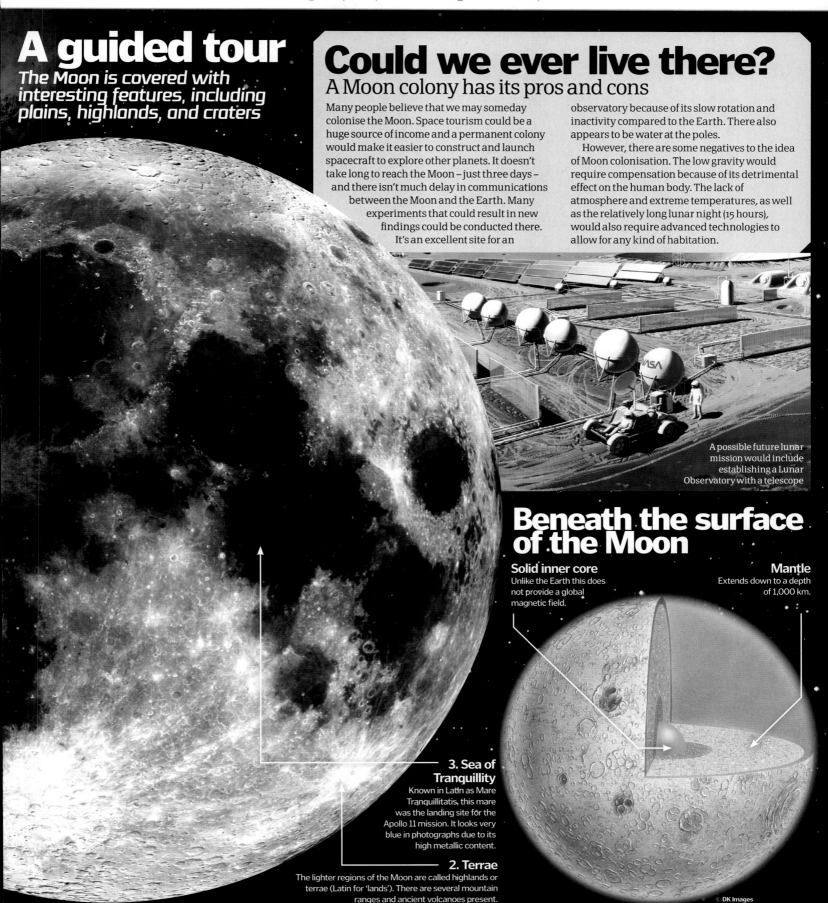

5 TOP FACTS
THE MOON

Nobody owns it
1 There are US flags and Soviet pennants on the Moon but they are purely symbolic. The Outer Space Treaty gives the moon the same status as international waters.

Man in the moon
2 The stark contrasts between the maria and terrae have been interpreted as various patterns including a human face, head or body and even a small dog.

No weapons allowed
3 Under the Outer Space Treaty, the Moon can only be used for peaceful purposes. In fact no nuclear weapons or WMDs are allowed to be in orbit or installed on any celestial body.

Were we really there?
4 Some believe that the Moon landings were faked by the US government, possibly to gain prestige, although these theories have been repeatedly disproved.

A second moon
5 3753 Cruithne is an asteroid in orbit around the Sun. It has been called "Earth's second Moon", although it is only a quasi-satellite with 364 day orbit of the Sun.

DID YOU KNOW? Our ocean tides are caused by the pull of the moon's gravitational force

A guided tour
The Moon is covered with interesting features, including plains, highlands, and craters

Could we ever live there?
A Moon colony has its pros and cons

Many people believe that we may someday colonise the Moon. Space tourism could be a huge source of income and a permanent colony would make it easier to construct and launch spacecraft to explore other planets. It doesn't take long to reach the Moon – just three days – and there isn't much delay in communications between the Moon and the Earth. Many experiments that could result in new findings could be conducted there. It's an excellent site for an observatory because of its slow rotation and inactivity compared to the Earth. There also appears to be water at the poles.

However, there are some negatives to the idea of Moon colonisation. The low gravity would require compensation because of its detrimental effect on the human body. The lack of atmosphere and extreme temperatures, as well as the relatively long lunar night (15 hours), would also require advanced technologies to allow for any kind of habitation.

A possible future lunar mission would include establishing a Lunar Observatory with a telescope

Beneath the surface of the Moon

Solid inner core
Unlike the Earth this does not provide a global magnetic field.

Mantle
Extends down to a depth of 1,000 km.

3. Sea of Tranquillity
Known in Latin as Mare Tranquillitatis, this mare was the landing site for the Apollo 11 mission. It looks very blue in photographs due to its high metallic content.

2. Terrae
The lighter regions of the Moon are called highlands or terrae (Latin for 'lands'). There are several mountain ranges and ancient volcanoes present.

© DK Images

"An object must be travelling nearly 7 miles per second to clear Earth's surface gravity"

Unlike later liquid-fuel rocket stages, solid-fuel rocket stages can't be stopped once lit. There's a one per cent chance it will explode due to over-pressurisation of the propellant.

Solid boosters are cheap to design and implement and supply in excess of 70 per cent of the required thrust to reach its destination.

Despite already being heavily pressurised, propellant is forced through a small nozzle at speeds up to 16,000 kmph.

Second stage rockets are liquid-fuelled and can be manually throttled and controlled after ignition.

Up to five rocket stages have been successfully deployed in the past, though this particular design utilises three to deliver its payload into space.

How do rockets work?

Despite their apparent ungainliness, rockets are still used to reach space. Here's how they work…

Every action has an equal and opposite reaction. Though it's highly unlikely Newton actually had space rockets in mind when he wrote his famous Third Law, it rather accurately and elegantly explains exactly how they work.

Of course to shift a giant rocket, replete with weighty payload, beyond the

Earth's gravitational pull requires quite a reaction – remarkably, an object must be moving at nearly seven miles per second to clear Earth's surface gravity.

To facilitate the sheer mass of fuel required to move a small payload into space, multi-staged rockets are used. By discarding these so-called 'stages' once spent, the mass of the remaining rocket

is less, therefore further thrust (and fuel) requirements are eased.

Some first stage rockets are solid-fuel boosters, which force highly pressurised propellant through a nozzle at up to 10,000 mph to generate their thrust. Second stage rockets are liquid-fuelled boosters which can be controlled to their destination, but generate less thrust. ✿

The Delta rocket family is based on a design originating from the mid-Fifties. These Delta II rockets have been in service since 1989.

The Kepler spacecraft used a plethora of small solid-fuel rockets, such as these, around its base to generate its initial thrust.

The Goldilocks Zone explained

Life-sustaining planets require such exacting standards that scientists call the area they occupy 'the Goldilocks Zone'

The Goldilocks Zone is an area 'just right' for a life-sustaining planet – the perfect distance from a star with a surface neither too hot nor too cold. It is an intersection of life-sustaining regions within both a solar system and a galaxy. Astronomers believe that the Goldilocks Zone ranges from 0.725 to three astronomical units (each about 150 million kilometres, or the mean distance between the Earth and the Sun).

Recently some planetary bodies have come close to fitting the bill. The April 2007 discovery of Gliese 581c in the Libra constellation, for example, seemed promising until further research proved it was too hot. However, a nearby planet, Gliese 581d, may turn out to be just right. At the same time, the definition of the Goldilocks Zone is expanding as scientists discover life on Earth in places previously thought too extreme to sustain it. ✿

HOTTER STARS

SUN-LIKE STARS

COOLER STARS

Solar systems must be in the right place in the galaxy to sustain the formation of terrestrial planets, but not receive high doses of radiation.

If the Earth had formed just a few percentage points closer or further from the Sun, it would be either covered in ice or have no oceans.

The Goldilocks Zone is also known as the Solar Habitable or Circumstellar Habitable Zone.

Life-sustaining planets require specific conditions

DID YOU KNOW? A spacesuit weighs approximately 127 pounds on the ground

Space suits inside and out
How a modern spacesuit works

Hard upper torso
The HUT is a hard fibreglass vest shape shell. Its primary function is to support arms, lower torso, helmet, life-support backpack and control module. It also acts as a mini-tool carrier.

Liquid cooling and ventilation garment
The LCVG is produced from nylon tricot and spandex long underwear, laced with thin plastic tubes. Cool water flows through these to elevate the heat.

Lower torso assembly
This one-piece unit contains pants, knee and ankle joints, boots and lower waist. The LTA is fitted to the upper half of the EMU by a metal connect ring, looping to tether tools so these don't float away.

Maximum absorption garment
Astronauts can spend up to several hours moon-walking and the absorbent MAG permits them bathroom trips on the go, without having to pressurise and depressurise both the space suits and the spacecraft.

Helmet
This has a purge valve to remove carbon dioxide if the backup oxygen supply must be used. Here oxygen flows from behind the astronaut's head, over the head and down his or her face.

Helmet lights and camera
Important for seeing in dark spots, these devices are mounted on the EVA and fitted over the helmet.

Communications carrier assembly
The CCA is a vital comms tool for mission control. This fabric cap contains microphones and speakers for use with the radio. This permits hands-free radio communications inside the suit.

In-suit drink bag
Hydration is essential with astronauts exerting so much energy. The IDB plastic pouch is mounted inside the HUT, containing 1.9 litres of water. Astronauts drink this through a small tube positioned next to their mouth.

Primary life-support subsystem
The PLSS is an essential backpack worn by Astronauts. It contains all manner of essential life-support apparatus, such as oxygen tanks, carbon dioxide scrubbers/filters, cooling water, radio, and electrical power, ventilating fans and warning systems.

Keeping an astronaut safe
It may not look comfy, but every part is necessary

Astronaut Edwin E "Buzz" Aldrin walks on the surface of the moon during the Apollo 11 extravehicular activity

The modern space suit, or Extravehicular Mobility Unit – that's EMU for short – is an environmental simulator, built intricately to ensure maximum life support and mobility for an astronaut in strenuous space conditions.

The EMU is far removed from old-fashioned styles. Instead of being specifically tailored for individual astronauts, the EMU is assembled by component pieces of varying sizes that can be put together to fit any given astronaut. One size fits all. The EMU is made from a mix of hard and soft components, including nylon tricot, spandex, urethane-coated, nylon, Dacron, neoprene-coated nylon, Mylar, Gore-Tex, Kevlar and Nomex.

Dacron, neoprene-coated nylon and Gortex are integral. These are used as primary insulators in the tailored EMU. Both are vital in regulating body heat from interstellar environments. Mylar, a white fabric, produces a reflective layer, minimising UV radiation effects on the astronaut. The EMU also includes either heat exchangers to blow cool air or water-cooled garments to stop condensation within the helmet and on the visor.

The EMU helmet is as elaborate as the main torso. These are made from clear plastic or durable polycarbonate. Coverings are included to reflect sunlight, with visors tinted to reduce sun glare, much like a pair of sunglasses.

Dacron and Kevlar are used to protect astronauts from micrometeoroids. The EMU has multiple layers of these durable fibres to ensure no tearing occurs from exposed surfaces of the spacecraft. ❉

Inside a black hole

Almost incomprehensible in size, black holes are hauntingly beautiful phenomena where the laws of space and time are rewritten. We take a look at the Sagittarius A* black hole at the centre of our galaxy

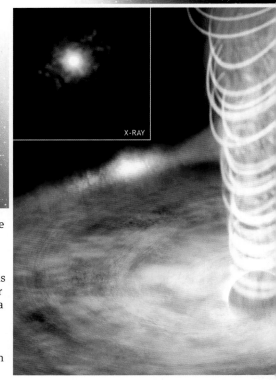

X-RAY

A black hole is a region of space containing, at its centre, matter compressed into a point of infinite density called a singularity (an area where spacetime curvature becomes infinite), which itself is surrounded by a sphere of space where the gravitational pull is so total that not even light can escape its pull – hence its name. The black hole is the result of the deformation and warping of spacetime (a mathematical model where space and time are combined into a single continuum) caused by the total collapse of individual stars or by the coalescence of binary neutron stars.

This collapse occurs at the culmination of a star's life span when, under the pressure of gravity, it is compressed perpetually – unable to resist due to the non-existence of nuclear fusion in its core – until it reaches critical mass. At this point, providing the star is over 1.4 to three solar masses (our Sun equals one solar mass) – a necessity for black hole formation instead of a white dwarf – the star will go into core-collapse supernova, expelling much of its remaining outer layers at one tenth the speed of light and leaving behind either a neutron star or, if the solar mass is high enough, a black hole. ✿

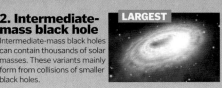

LARGE

1. Stellar-mass black hole
Stellar-mass black holes have masses up to 15-20 solar masses. These mainly form from stars going into core-collapse supernova.

LARGER

2. Intermediate-mass black hole
Intermediate-mass black holes can contain thousands of solar masses. These variants mainly form from collisions of smaller black holes.

LARGEST

3. Supermassive black hole
The biggest black holes by far, supermassive variants can contain hundreds of thousands even to billions of solar masses.

DID YOU KNOW? Sagittarius A* is a massive 26,000 light years from Earth

The Milky Way
The position of Sagittarius A* in our galaxy

Sagittarius A* lies at the heart of out galaxy the Milky Way. Unfortunately, from Earth Sagittarius A* is blocked from optical sight and presently scientists can only observe it through the actions of its surrounding stars.

Sagittarius A*

Introducing the Milky Way's very own supermassive black hole

An x-ray image of a black hole with accompanying illustration

At the heart of almost every galaxy lies a black hole, even our own the Milky Way, which centres on a region of space called Sagittarius A* – at the middle of which lies a supermassive black hole. Black holes like these, however, do not form directly but from the coalescence of multiple smaller-stellar-mass and intermediate-mass black holes, which then form a supermassive black hole such as Sagittarius A*. Supermassive black holes also often form from the slow accretion of matter from neighbouring stars, the mass collapse of large stellar gas clouds into a relativistic star (a rotating neutron star), or directly from external pressure caused by the Big Bang.

While unimaginable due to its very nature (it absorbs all light), its distance from Earth and the fact that the Sagittarius A* region is removed by 25 magnitudes of extinction from Earth (blocked from optical sight), our own supermassive black hole can only be observed by scientists through the actions of neighbouring cosmic phenomena. Indicating the presence of its existence most notably is the movement of star S2, which has been monitored by scientists following a slow elliptical orbit with a period of 15.2 years and a closest distance of less than 17 light hours from its orbit centre. From the slow motion of S2, scientists have extrapolated that the object which it is orbiting around has a solar mass of 4.1 million, which when taken with its relatively small diameter, strongly affirms that it is a black hole as no other known object can have such a large mass at such a small volume.

Sagittarius A* is a relatively small supermassive black hole when compared with others of its ilk, such as the black hole at the centre of the OJ 287 galaxy, which has a mass of 18 billion solar masses.

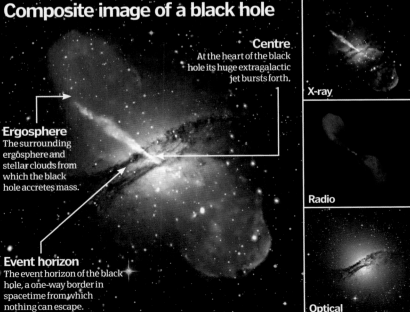

Composite image of a black hole

Centre
At the heart of the black hole its huge extragalactic jet bursts forth.

Ergosphere
The surrounding ergosphere and stellar clouds from which the black hole accretes mass.

Event horizon
The event horizon of the black hole, a one-way border in spacetime from which nothing can escape.

X-ray

Radio

Optical

All Images © NASA

"The simplest black holes have mass but neither charge nor angular momentum"

Inside our black hole

What are its properties and structure?

To understand our Sagittarius A* black hole it is important to understand how black holes in general work. After any black hole stabilises post formation, it has only three possible independent physical properties: charge, mass and angular momentum. Now, when an object is accreted (swallowed) by a black hole its own mass, charge and momentum is equalised with the black hole's own, distributing the matter evenly along its event horizon (a one-way spacetime boundary), which then oscillates like a stretchy membrane. The course that this pattern follows, however, depends on the individual black hole's properties and type.

The simplest black holes have mass but neither charge nor angular momentum, accreting mass to a point-singularity centre. However, most types of black hole formed from the core-collapse supernova of a star are thought to retain the nearly neutral charge it once possessed. Other, and theorised by scientists to be far more common, types of black holes – due to the spinning nature of stars – are rotating variants. These form from the collapse of stars or stellar gas with a total non-zero angular momentum and can be both charged and uncharged. These black holes, unlike the totally round, static variants, bulge near their equator under the phenomenal velocity of their spin (the quicker the rotation the more deformed the black hole will be) and instead of accreting matter to a point-singularity do so to a smeared disc singularity. Eventually all black holes – however dependent on their charge or rotation – revert to a non-rotating, uncharged variant.

Unfortunately, from the measurements taken from the stars surrounding our Sagittarius A* black hole, scientists have been left unsure about its physical properties. However, recent research from the University of California, Berkeley, suggests that A* rotates once every 11 minutes or at 30 per cent the speed of light. This information, when combined with the known close proximity of the surrounding stars (a spinning black hole drags space with it, allowing atoms to orbit closer to one that is static), would seem to suggest that not only is the gravitational pull of Sagittarius A* mitigated to a degree by its rotation but also that these measurements are accurate.

Microlensing magnification region
An illustration depicting swirling clouds of stellar gas pouring into a black hole.

Formation of extragalactic jets from black hole accretion disk

Extragalactic jet
Relativistic jets, extremely powerful streams of plasma, carry energy away from the heart of the accretion disk.

EXTRAGALACTIC JET

Black hole
The singularity at the centre of the black hole. All mass that reaches this point is crushed to infinite density.

Accretion disk
The black hole's accretion disk is formed from diffuse material orbiting around its centre.

As mass is accreted by a black hole it is heated up under the pressure of gravity

How spacetime is distorted

Away from a black hole, particles can move freely in any direction, only restricted by the speed of light.

EVENT HORIZON

As particles approach the event horizon of the black hole, spacetime starts to deform, restricting the freedom of the paths in which particles can follow.

TIME

SPACE

BLACK HOLE

TIME

SPACE

5 TOP FACTS
BLACK HOLES

Do the worm
1 Certain theories postulate that rotating black holes could be avoided by entities and actually used as a wormhole short-cut through space and time.

Weakling
2 Despite their colossal size and perpetual accretion of matter, black holes can only suck in matter from a very small surrounding region as gravity is incredibly weak.

Primordial
3 In the current epoch of the universe only the collapse of stars carry the requisite density to form a black hole. However, shortly after the big bang densities were greater.

Micro-management
4 Theoretically it is possible for micro-black holes to form through the high-speed collision of sub-atomic particles, although this is unlikely to ever happen.

Spaghetti
5 Any object that passes an event horizon will be stretched into long thin strands under the strong gravitational field of the black hole.

DID YOU KNOW? *The coinage of the phrase 'black hole' didn't occur until 1967*

Let's do the time warp
The theoretical consequences of time and space distortion

The event horizon (a boundary in spacetime through which matter and light can only pass inwardly) of a black hole is one of its central characteristics – and one that brings a host of issues for any object that passes through it. As predicted by general relativity (our geometric theory on gravitation) due to the colossal mass of the black hole – which, by these rules, is infinite at the heart of the black hole – spacetime is deformed, as mass has a direct bearing on it. Indeed, when the event horizon is passed, the mass's

distortion becomes so great that particle paths are bent inwardly towards the singularity (centre) of the black hole, unable to alter their course. At this point both time and space begin to be warped.

The consequences of this, while theoretical, are mind blowing. For example, theory states that if a hypothetical astronaut were about to cross the event horizon of a black hole, then apart from being stretched physically (spaghettification), they'd also be stretched in time. So, while the astronaut would pass

the event horizon at a finite point in his own time, to a hypothetical distant observer, he'd appear to slow down, taking an infinite time to reach it. Further, if the astronaut were wearing a watch, it would tick more slowly as he approached the event horizon than a watch worn by the observer, an effect known as gravitational time dilation. Finally, when the astronaut reached the singularity, he'd be crushed to infinite density and over an infinite time (to the observer) before having his mass added to that of the black hole.

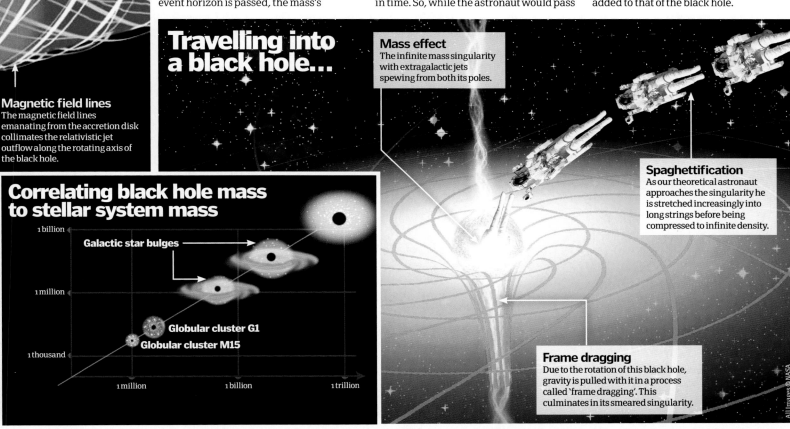

Travelling into a black hole...

Magnetic field lines
The magnetic field lines emanating from the accretion disk collimates the relativistic jet outflow along the rotating axis of the black hole.

Mass effect
The infinite mass singularity with extragalactic jets spewing from both its poles.

Spaghettification
As our theoretical astronaut approaches the singularity he is stretched increasingly into long strings before being compressed to infinite density.

Frame dragging
Due to the rotation of this black hole, gravity is pulled with it in a process called 'frame dragging'. This culminates in its smeared singularity.

Correlating black hole mass to stellar system mass

- 1 billion
- Galactic star bulges
- 1 million
- Globular cluster G1
- Globular cluster M15
- 1 thousand

  - 1 million
  - 1 billion
  - 1 trillion

All images © NASA

EVENT HORIZON

BLACK HOLE

Once the event horizon is passed all paths bring particles closer to the black hole's singularity. Gravitational time dilation, gravitational redshift and spaghettification are now in effect and consistent.

TIME
SPACE

EVENT HORIZON

BLACK HOLE

HOW IT WORKS

TRANSPORT
Explaining road, rail, sea and air

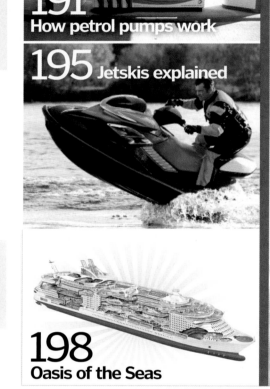

categories explained

Extreme vehicles

Road

Future vehicles

General

HOW IT WORKS
TRANSPORT

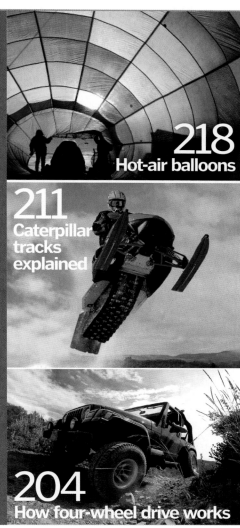

222
Jet engines

218
Hot-air balloons

211
Caterpillar tracks explained

204
How four-wheel drive works

"The Eurofighter Typhoon is changing the way the world's air forces think about fighter planes"

Eurofighter Typhoon

The fighter plane that's so advanced it can't be flown by a human without the help of a computer

Under construction
The building of a Typhoon is certainly no easy task...

"It is impossible for a human to fly the plane without the aid of a complex computer system that makes constant adjustments to the wings' flaps"

The Eurofighter Typhoon may be the world's most advanced killing machine, but it is also an extraordinary symbol of peace and co-operation. After centuries of fighting, a handful of European countries came together to produce this incredible aircraft.

From a plan started as way back as 1979, the Eurofighter was developed by Germany, Italy, Spain and the UK (France was involved for a while but then snuck off to do its own thing), and production is split between the four countries. At present there are plans to produce no less than 707 examples of the fighter jet. As well as the four core countries, the plane is also being used by other air forces around the world, including those of Austria, Saudi Arabia and Greece.

Why? Because it's quite simply the most technologically advanced fighter jet on the planet, and also the most capable.

It's what's known as a swing-role weapon system, which means that it is capable of different operational tasks and can even switch from one duty to another on a single mission. For instance, it can be used as an air-to-air (short and medium range) fighter to gain all-important air superiority, while at the same time carrying large, long-range ground-attack weapons for taking out an enemy's air defence systems.

This flexibility is further enhanced by the plane's incredible flying prowess. It boasts STOL (short take-off and landing) which means that it needs just 700 metres to take-off or land (the 747 you go on holiday in requires over 3,000 metres).

More impressively, the Eurofighter is incredibly manoeuvrable. This is thanks in part to its 'relaxed stability' design, which is a reassuring way of saying that the aircraft is inherently unstable, especially at subsonic speeds. Put simply, the plane's delta wings and small fore fins create a pressure (lift) point which is forward of the centre of gravity during subsonic flight. And that means it is impossible for a human to fly the plane without the aid of a complex computer system that makes constant adjustments to the wings' flaps quicker than the pilot could. Once the speed of sound is broken, though, the pressure point moves back and the aircraft becomes much more stable (although the computer aids remain).

The same flight control systems also make the Eurofighter easy to fly, freeing up the pilot to concentrate on tactical tasks.

No wonder the Eurofighter Typhoon is changing the way the world's air forces think about fighter planes.

Eurofighter in action

Just what makes the Eurofighter so formidable?

Armed and ready for action

The Eurofighter has a formidable arsenal. The large items are in fact fuel tanks, although long-distance missiles can be fitted. The yellow devices are laser-powered bombs, while the smaller grey items are short-range air-to-air missiles. The thin armaments visible at the back of the fuselage are beyond-visual-range air-to-air missiles. There is also a Mauser BK-27 automatic cannon.

Small but perfectly formed

The Eurofighter is remarkably compact – look at the size of the pilot in the cockpit to get an idea. The wingspan is 10.95 metres (less than that of a WWII Spitfire) and the length is 15.96 metres. This helps the aircraft to be incredibly agile, allowing it to change direction fast, as well as accelerate at an astonishing rate.

Giving it full throttle

The Eurofighter's twin Eurojet turbofan engines combine a jet nozzle with a ducted fan. This allows efficiency at low speeds combined with relatively quiet operation. They are equipped with afterburners (shown in operation here) that inject neat fuel into the jet stream to give a short increase in power. However, the Eurofighter can cruise at supersonic speeds without afterburner help.

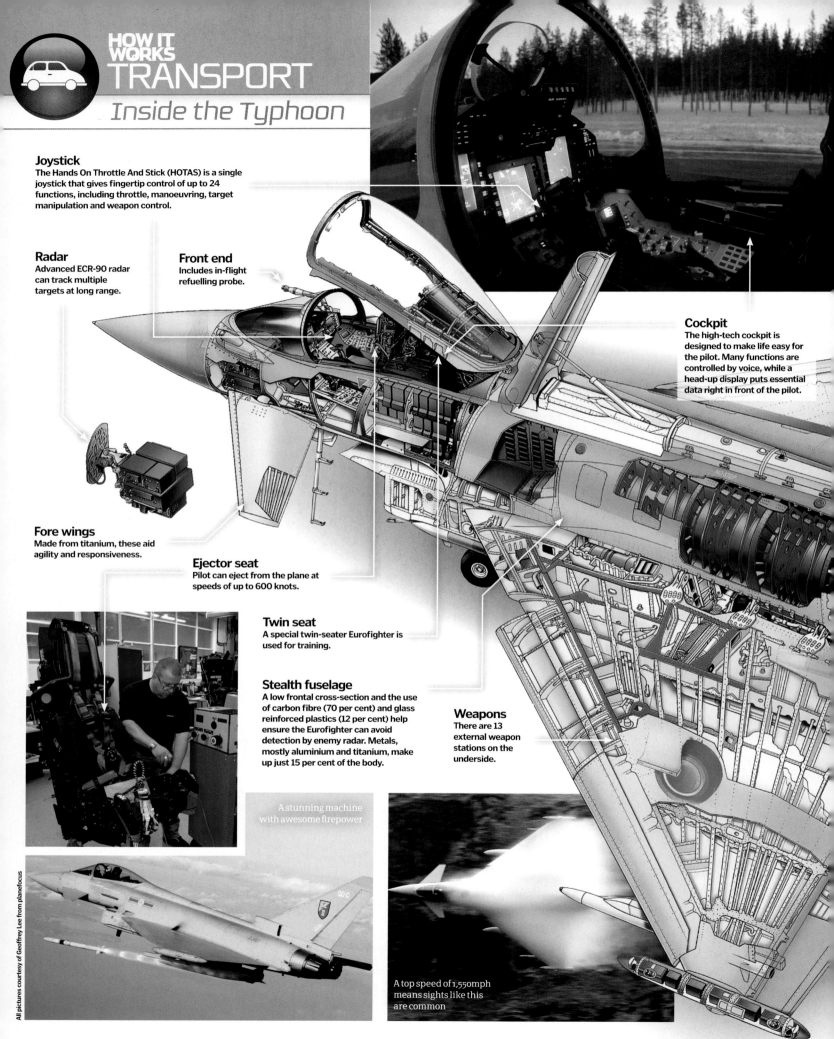

Joystick
The Hands On Throttle And Stick (HOTAS) is a single joystick that gives fingertip control of up to 24 functions, including throttle, manoeuvring, target manipulation and weapon control.

Radar
Advanced ECR-90 radar can track multiple targets at long range.

Front end
Includes in-flight refuelling probe.

Cockpit
The high-tech cockpit is designed to make life easy for the pilot. Many functions are controlled by voice, while a head-up display puts essential data right in front of the pilot.

Fore wings
Made from titanium, these aid agility and responsiveness.

Ejector seat
Pilot can eject from the plane at speeds of up to 600 knots.

Twin seat
A special twin-seater Eurofighter is used for training.

Stealth fuselage
A low frontal cross-section and the use of carbon fibre (70 per cent) and glass reinforced plastics (12 per cent) help ensure the Eurofighter can avoid detection by enemy radar. Metals, mostly aluminium and titanium, make up just 15 per cent of the body.

Weapons
There are 13 external weapon stations on the underside.

A stunning machine with awesome firepower

A top speed of 1,550mph means sights like this are common

All pictures courtesy of Geoffrey Lee from planefocus

Take a look inside the Eurofighter

Find out what makes the Eurofighter Typhoon the most advanced fighter on the planet

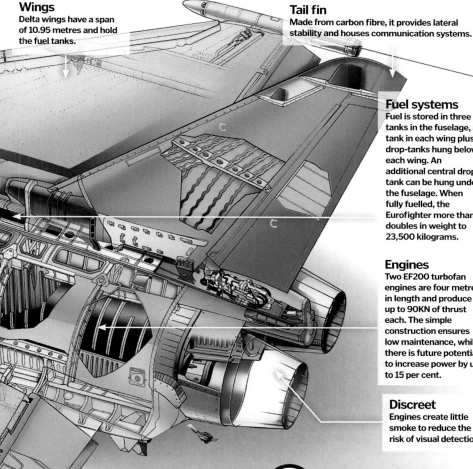

Wings
Delta wings have a span of 10.95 metres and hold the fuel tanks.

Tail fin
Made from carbon fibre, it provides lateral stability and houses communication systems.

Fuel systems
Fuel is stored in three tanks in the fuselage, a tank in each wing plus drop-tanks hung below each wing. An additional central drop-tank can be hung under the fuselage. When fully fuelled, the Eurofighter more than doubles in weight to 23,500 kilograms.

Engines
Two EF200 turbofan engines are four metres in length and produce up to 90KN of thrust each. The simple construction ensures low maintenance, while there is future potential to increase power by up to 15 per cent.

Discreet
Engines create little smoke to reduce the risk of visual detection.

Typhoon vs F-22 Raptor

So after taking an in-depth look at Europe's most advanced fighter jet, the question of its performance against the American F-22 remains. It's an argument that rages on many an aviation-based internet forum and it's also one that is unlikely to ever have a truly real-world answer.

There's a very strong argument for USAF's F-22 Raptor having air dominance over the Typhoon because of its versatility: the Raptor has stealth capabilities and supercruises at a much higher speed than its European rival, which many agree would give it the edge in all but a WVR (Within Visual Range) encounter. Due to its tiny radar signature the F-22 could obliterate the Typhoon before the latter was even aware of its presence. However, development of the third phase of the Typhoon will endow the fighter with full strike capabilities and improved radar to match the Raptor. The cost of the Raptor is also worth weighing in the Typhoon's defence: initially £140 million for each Typhoon versus around $339 million (£212 million) for the Raptor, including research and development costs.

The most reliable source of comparison comes from General John P Jumper, Chief of Staff of the United States Air Force from 6 September 2001 to 2 September 2005 and one of the few pilots to have flown both aircraft. Speaking to the Air Force Print News shortly before he retired, General Jumper said: "It's like asking us to compare a NASCAR car with a Formula 1 car. They are both exciting in different ways, but they are designed for different levels of performance." He continued, "The Eurofighter is certainly, as far as smoothness of controls and the ability to pull (and sustain high g-forces), very impressive," he said. "The manoeuvrability in close-in combat was also very impressive." All very complimentary, but on the question of dominance, Jumper stated :"The F-22 Raptor has stealth and supercruise," he said. "It has the ability to penetrate virtually undetected because of [those] capabilities. It is designed to be a penetrating aeroplane. It can manoeuvre with the best of them if it has to, but what you want to be able to do is get into contested airspace no matter where it is." However it would seem that the real measure of success between the two planes is a financial one. The US Senate discontinued production of the F-22 in July 2009, with President Obama himself stating "at a time when we're fighting two wars and facing a serious deficit, [expanding the F-22] would have been an inexcusable waste of money." Conversely, in May 2009, then Prime Minister Gordon Brown committed to buying a third tranche of Eurofighters, perhaps making it a winner without even leaving the hanger. ⚙

Eurofighter VS F-22 Raptor

	Eurofighter		F-22 Raptor
Engine Thrust:	20,000lbs	Engine Thrust:	35,000lbs
Max Speed:	1,550mph	Max Speed:	1,500mph
Supercruise:	840mph	Supercruise:	1,220mph
Altitude:	65,000 feet	Altitude:	60,000 feet
Max Range:	2,045 miles	Max Range:	1,840 miles
Cannon:	Mauser BK-27 (150 rounds)	Cannon:	M61A2 Vulcan (480 rounds)

Maglev technology eliminates the rolling friction that restricts conventional trains, making Maglevs faster, quieter and more efficient

Explained:
Maglev trains

Maglev train lines cost more than £1 billion, but they employ the same forces as a £5 magnet set. Every kid knows that the 'north' ends of bar magnets repel each other, while the 'north' and 'south' ends attract each other. This lets you push or pull one magnet around with another. Maglev technology uses magnetic fields to levitate a train and propel it forward. Three alternative designs use various arrangements of different magnet types.

The only commercial maglev, the German-engineered Transrapid in Shanghai, is powered by electromagnets. An electromagnet is a coil of wire with electric current running through it. Magnetism and electricity are sides of the same coin – any electric current generates a magnetic field, and any fluctuating magnetic field induces an electric current. Running current through a coil of wire generates a strong magnetic field. And switching the direction of the current reverses the polarity of the magnet (from north to south).

The Transrapid train undercarriage envelopes a T-shaped steel guideway. Inside the guideway, there's an electromagnetic linear motor – essentially a string of coiled wires. Current running through these wires generates a fluctuating magnetic field that travels along the guideway. This magnetic field interacts with the magnetic fields generated by lift electromagnets on the undercarriage of the train, under the guideway. The moving magnetic field pushes and pulls the train along, in the same way two toy magnets move each other.

The lift electromagnets also levitate the train – the magnetic attraction between the electromagnet and the guideway lifts the train up. A feedback control system constantly adjusts the electromagnetic field to keep the train hovering a centimetre above the guideway. Guide electromagnets along the side of the train adjust as well, to keep the train from wobbling.

The Shanghai maglev opened for business in 2004. It runs between the Shanghai financial district and the Shanghai airport, at a top speed of 268 mph. An experimental electrodynamic maglev in Japan has reached 361 mph. In 2006, a demonstration Transrapid train in Germany collided with maintenance equipment, killing 23 people. ✿

Levitation methods
There are three major maglev technologies...

ELECTROMAGNETIC
Electromagnets in the train undercarriage and an electromagnetic linear motor in the guideway generate magnetic forces that interact to levitate and propel the train.

ELECTRODYNAMIC
Superconductor metals kept at super-cool temperatures on the train generate a magnetic field. This induces a separate field in guideway coils, levitating the train. A linear motor in the guideway then propels it.

INDUCTRACK
In this variation on the electrodynamic design, magnets on the train generate a magnetic field. This induces a separate field in passive coils in the guideway, levitating the train.

Lift electromagnet
The lift electromagnet lifts the train undercarriage so it levitates a centimetre below the guideway.

How magnetic levitation works
Electromagnets create a force field that pushes the train along the tracks

Guideway motor
The electromagnetic linear motor in the guideway generates a moving magnetic field that propels the train forward.

Train undercarriage
A control system continually adjusts the electromagnets in the undercarriage to keep the train stable.

Guide electromagnet
The guide electromagnet prevents the train wobbling side to side.

🚗 Learn more
For more information about the Shanghai Maglev Train visit **www.smtdc.com/en/**, where you can view images, watch video of the train in action and learn all about the background of the project, along with interesting facts and figures.

1. Unleaded petrol
The higher the octane rating, the more compression it can take before igniting. High-octane petrol is a must for high-performance engines.

UGLY BUT EFFICIENT

2. Diesel
Diesel packs more energy into the same amount of fuel. A litre of diesel contains 130,500 Btu/gallon compared to petrol's 115,000 Btu/gallon.

ECO-FRIENDLY

3. Biodiesel
Derived from the fatty oils of plants instead of fossil fuels, biodiesel is more fuel-efficient than petrol and burns far cleaner than diesel or regular unleaded.

DID YOU KNOW? *New 'clean diesel' engines have fuel efficiency and emission levels rivalling hybrids*

How petrol pumps work

Peek inside the fuel-pumping petrol dispenser

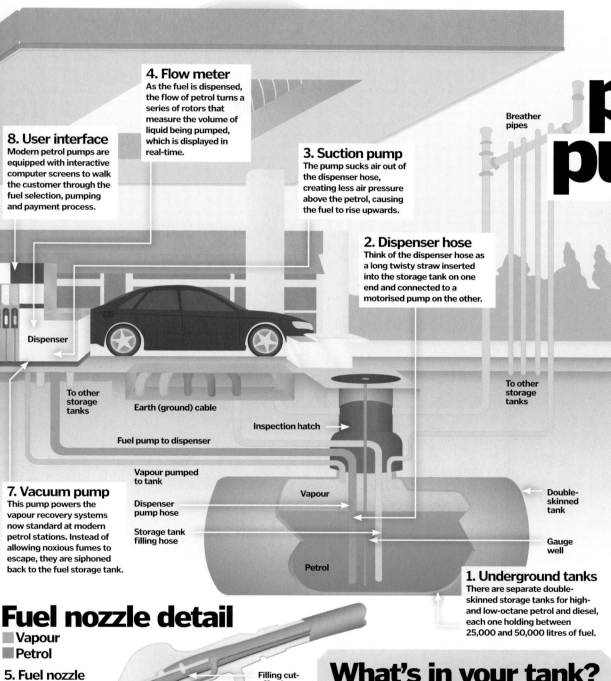

4. Flow meter
As the fuel is dispensed, the flow of petrol turns a series of rotors that measure the volume of liquid being pumped, which is displayed in real-time.

8. User interface
Modern petrol pumps are equipped with interactive computer screens to walk the customer through the fuel selection, pumping and payment process.

3. Suction pump
The pump sucks air out of the dispenser hose, creating less air pressure above the petrol, causing the fuel to rise upwards.

2. Dispenser hose
Think of the dispenser hose as a long twisty straw inserted into the storage tank on one end and connected to a motorised pump on the other.

Breather pipes

Dispenser

To other storage tanks

Earth (ground) cable

Inspection hatch

Fuel pump to dispenser

To other storage tanks

7. Vacuum pump
This pump powers the vapour recovery systems now standard at modern petrol stations. Instead of allowing noxious fumes to escape, they are siphoned back to the fuel storage tank.

Vapour pumped to tank

Dispenser pump hose

Storage tank filling hose

Vapour

Petrol

Double-skinned tank

Gauge well

1. Underground tanks
There are separate double-skinned storage tanks for high- and low-octane petrol and diesel, each one holding between 25,000 and 50,000 litres of fuel.

Fuel nozzle detail

■ Vapour
■ Petrol

5. Fuel nozzle
When you pull the nozzle trigger, it dispenses petrol and sucks out vapours from your fuel tank.

Filling cut-off valve

Nozzle trigger

Vapour recovery

Vapour

Petrol

6. Overfill detector
A vacuum pump sucks air from a narrow tube next to the fuel nozzle. If the petrol level rises up to the tube, the pump senses the change in pressure and triggers a cut-off valve.

What's in your tank?

In its purest form, petrol is nothing but a string of carbon and hydrogen atoms. It is distilled and separated from crude oil (petroleum) through the refining process. Unlike other oil-based fuels like butane or propane, petrol has a relatively high boiling point, making it more stable.

But the gas at the pump isn't pure petrol. It contains a blend of additives and stabilisers that help the fuel burn cleaner, store longer and make your engine run efficiently. Additives called oxygenates increase the oxygen content of petrol, enhancing its octane level and helping it burn cleaner. Antioxidants are added to decrease the formation of sediments in tanks. Finally, detergents and anti-corrosive agents are added to keep engines running clean.

Next time you're lost in boredom at the petrol pump, pretend you have a pair of x-ray specs on. If you stare straight down, several metres below you are three massive storage tanks. Two of them contain regular unleaded petrol – one with the highest-octane grade of fuel, the other with the lowest – and the third holds diesel.

When you select your fuel grade and pull the trigger, suction pumps inside the petrol dispenser draw up fuel from both the high- and low-octane tanks and blend them to the precise octane level. A spinning 'fuel-o-meter' inside the pump records how much petrol flows past, keeping track of your purchase. Since petrol expands and contracts with hot and cold weather, a temperature probe compensates for fluctuating volume, ensuring that you get what you pay for.

In the old days, caustic petrol vapours seeped out of the tank during a fill-up. Modern petrol stations are equipped with vacuum pumps that siphon out the offending fumes and store them below ground in the fuel tanks. Aim those x-ray glasses at the fuel nozzle itself and you'll see that the dispenser line is held open by air pressure from within the tank. When the fuel level reaches the tip of the nozzle, the air pressure is choked off and the dispenser switches off automatically. ✿

Imagine driving one of these on your morning commute. The M1 Abrams tank, used throughout the Eighties and Nineties for both Gulf wars and yet still more advanced than any other tank since, is a 74-ton monster that can crash through walls and over terrain.

"The design of this tank is what makes it unique from its first inception," says Mike Peck, the director of business development at General Dynamics, who designs and manufactures the M1. According to Peck, the M1 uses a "combat platform" suspension with a low-to-the-ground chassis with a contoured body that allows the turret to be nestled down lower than other tanks, making the tank about three feet lower to the ground than similar vehicles. In the mid-Nineties, the M1 was updated with all digital components. Peck says it actually has more electronics than an F16 fighter.

Kevin Benson, a retired Lt Colonel who commanded entire battalions of M1 tanks, says the main advantage of the M1 is that it can fire 120 mm rounds between 3,000 and 4,000 metres whereas other tanks – especially those used by Iraqi forces in Operation Desert Storm – could only fire about 1,500 metres. In that campaign, US forces would surround the Iraqi

The approaching camel didn't know what hit it...

Abrams M1 in action
Just what makes the Abrams M1 so formidable?

Long-range, 120mm rounds
A key feature on the M1 is that it fires 120 mm rounds up to 4,000m, a decided advantage on the battlefield. The rounds are made of high-density steel, travel one mile per second, and weigh around 30 pounds. "It's like firing a big nail," says Benson.

Heavy armour protection
Another major advantage to this tank is that the M1 is heavily armoured. Tank returning for repairs barely ever come back with any noticeable dents. In fact, many M1's have fought in multiple campaigns and remain in pristine condition.

High-torque engine
The high-torque engine on the M1 is also extremely advanced: it uses a form of jet fuel and produces so much energy that – even at 74 tons – the tank can reach speeds approaching 45 miles per hour.

Abrams M1 Battletank
74-ton, 1,500-horsepower behemoth fires long-range cannons

tanks, safely out of range but well within the range of the M1. Peck says the M1 has a forward-range infrared sensor that works in day or night for long-range shots.

The engine on the M1 is also unique. It uses a turbine engine running at 1,500 horsepower, providing a distinct advantage: because the tank has such a high torque in the engine, it is almost unstoppable on the battlefield. "The engine has the most dense horsepower-per-weight ratio we could find," says Peck.

The M1 also has a pulse jet air cleaner to remove sand and other hazards, which Peck says has doubled the life of the engine. The tank is also outfitted with a 50 calibre machine gun that can turn 360-degrees, an aid for urban warfare. The M1 Abrams cruises at a top speed of 45 miles per hour on paved roads or 35 miles per hour over sand. ❖

A US tank provides suppressive counter fire in Fallujah, Iraq

THE STATS
M1 TANK

GUN RANGE **4,000m**	ROUND LENGTH **120mm**	TRACK WEIGHT **2 tons**
WEIGHT **74 tons**	ROUND WEIGHT **30lbs**	FIRST ENTERED SERVICE **1980**

DID YOU KNOW? TUSK (Tank Urban Survival Kit) allows commanders to fire using an LCD viewfinder

Under the hood of the Abrams M1

Find out what makes the Abrams M1 the most advanced battle tank on the planet

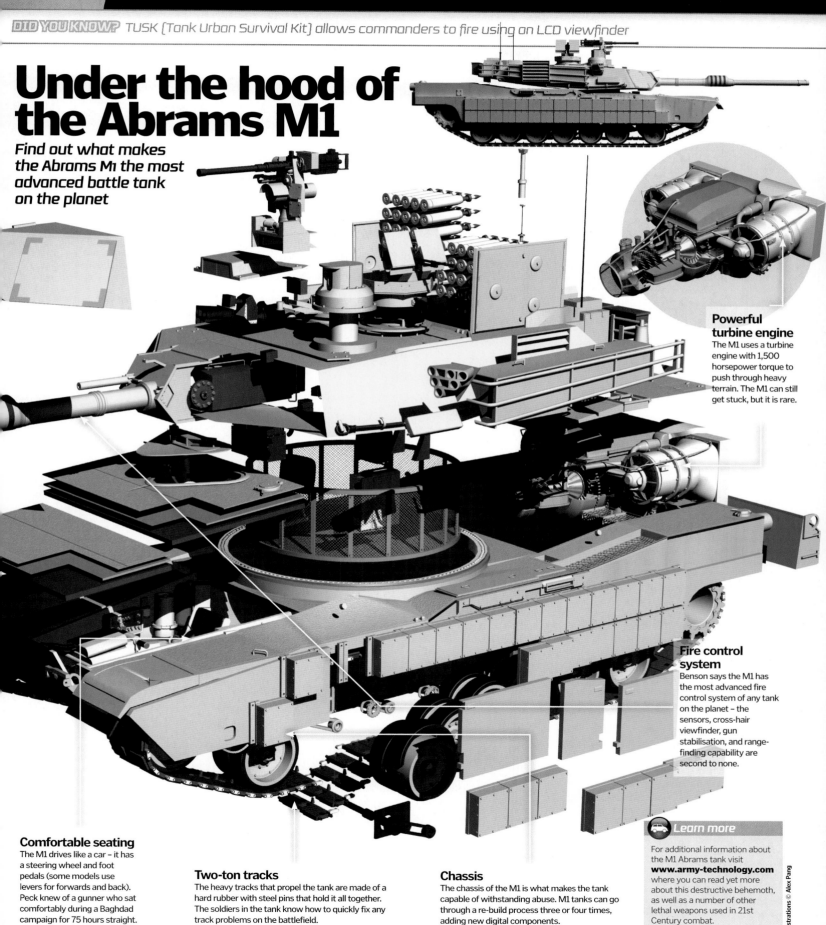

Powerful turbine engine
The M1 uses a turbine engine with 1,500 horsepower torque to push through heavy terrain. The M1 can still get stuck, but it is rare.

Fire control system
Benson says the M1 has the most advanced fire control system of any tank on the planet – the sensors, cross-hair viewfinder, gun stabilisation, and range-finding capability are second to none.

Comfortable seating
The M1 drives like a car – it has a steering wheel and foot pedals (some models use levers for forwards and back). Peck knew of a gunner who sat comfortably during a Baghdad campaign for 75 hours straight.

Two-ton tracks
The heavy tracks that propel the tank are made of a hard rubber with steel pins that hold it all together. The soldiers in the tank know how to quickly fix any track problems on the battlefield.

Chassis
The chassis of the M1 is what makes the tank capable of withstanding abuse. M1 tanks can go through a re-build process three or four times, adding new digital components.

🚗 Learn more
For additional information about the M1 Abrams tank visit **www.army-technology.com** where you can read yet more about this destructive behemoth, as well as a number of other lethal weapons used in 21st Century combat.

Illustrations © Alex Pang

> "The Cockpit Voice Recorder picks up sound from inside the cockpit, including the pilot and copilot's headset"

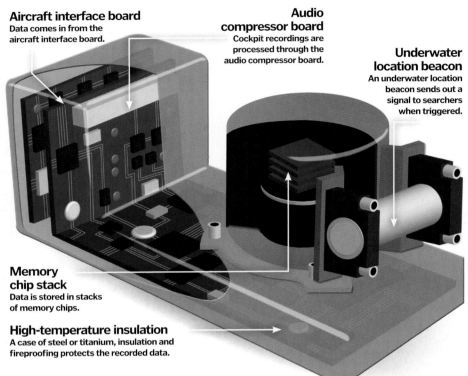

Aircraft interface board
Data comes in from the aircraft interface board.

Audio compressor board
Cockpit recordings are processed through the audio compressor board.

Underwater location beacon
An underwater location beacon sends out a signal to searchers when triggered.

Memory chip stack
Data is stored in stacks of memory chips.

High-temperature insulation
A case of steel or titanium, insulation and fireproofing protects the recorded data.

Black box
How important aircraft data is designed to survive the worst disasters

Black box recorders are used to retrieve data about an aeroplane and its operating environment in the event of a crash. There are two types of black box: the CVR or Cockpit Voice Recorder, and the FDR or Flight Data Recorder. Both record different types of information, and when combined this information can be used to build up a picture of what happened during a crash.

The Cockpit Voice Recorder picks up sound from inside the cockpit, including the pilot and copilot's headset microphones and those of any other cockpit staff. There's also a microphone placed centrally in the cockpit to record any other ambient sound, such as conversations with other crew members, radio, and even the noise of switches and dials. They used to be magnetic tape recorders but are now more reliable solid-state devices akin to flash drives. These record around two hours of information at a time, recording over and replacing older audio. The CVR allows listeners to find out what the cockpit staff were doing in the event of the crash; what they observed and reacted to

among the circumstances that caused it, if they sent out a Mayday message or signal or recorded any grid co-ordinates.

The Flight Data Recorder, on the other hand, records important information about what the plane was doing at the time. The data is taken from several areas, including the wings, engines,

landing gear and rudders. This information is aggregated in the Flight Data Acquisition Unit at the front of the plane and fed into the FDR at the back. Typically it includes factors like speed, altitude, engine performance and the positions of the wings, rudder and landing gear. ✿

Where is it kept?
Where is the recorder most likely to survive?

Sensors that feed data to black box recorders are located in key areas of the plane, such as the engines, wings, rudder and landing gear. Microphones and data recording and processing units are stored around the cockpit to record voices, ambient noise and data from the cockpit instruments. The actual black boxes themselves though – the units in which the recorded data is stored – are located at the back of the plane beneath the tail. This location lessens the chance of the black box being destroyed, as it's not in an area that would take the impact of a head-on or belly-down crash, and it's as far away as possible from the most combustible areas of the engine.

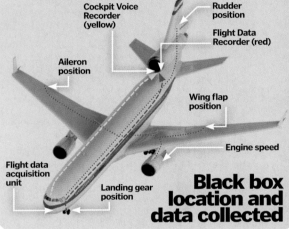

Cockpit Voice Recorder (yellow)

Rudder position

Flight Data Recorder (red)

Aileron position

Wing flap position

Engine speed

Flight data acquisition unit

Landing gear position

Black box location and data collected

The black box can be more eyecatching than the name suggests...

Brazilian Air Force personnel recover the flight data recorder of PR-GTD, the Boeing 737-8EH used for Gol Transportes Aéreos Flight 1907, in the Amazon Rainforest. PR-GTD crashed after a mid-air collision.

5 TOP FACTS
BLACK BOXES

1 The Wright Brothers
Many years ago, the Wright Brothers pioneered a device that recorded propeller speed.

2 What's in a name?
The black box name may be linked to a device designed in 1939 by Francois Hussenot, which recorded photographic data using lines of light reflected inside a black case.

3 High temperatures
The housing around a black box is specified to withstand temperatures of 1,000° Celsius.

4 Satellite beacon
A black box recorder's locator beacon uses a satellite network connection to send radio signals.

5 On-board cameras?
The US is now looking into placing image recorders in commercial flight cockpits.

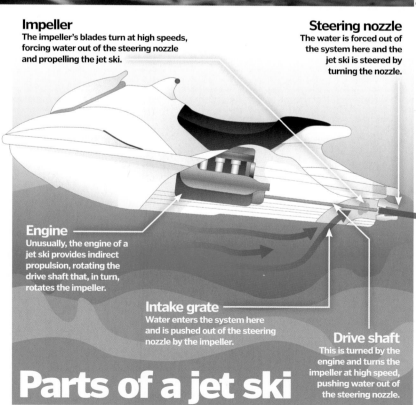

Spending time on jetskis is now a highly popular pastime. And let's face it, it makes you look cool

© Sea-doo

Jet skis

Isaac Newton has no idea how much fun he's responsible for

Jet skis work off Newton's third principle, that each action has an equal and opposite reaction. Here, the action is pushing a large volume of water out of the back of the jet ski and the reaction is pushing the jet ski forwards through the water at speed. It's a remarkably simple principle achieved with the use of an equally simple device: an impeller drive.

The impeller sits inside a shaft that runs the length of the craft and is driven by the ski's engine. It's designed like a propeller and when the engine spins it, the blades of the impeller rotate at speed, forcing water through the shaft and out through the nozzle at the rear of the ski, pushing it along.

Of course, everyone falls off every now and then, so modern jet skis all have a 'starter pin' or key that's placed in a slot near the ignition and is attached to the driver. If they fall overboard, the pin is yanked out and the ski coasts to a halt, preventing collisions and meaning the driver never has to swim too far to get back to it. ✿

Turning on a wave

Jet skis are steered by controlling the direction of the steering jet at the rear of the ski. This is done by attaching two steering lines to the handlebars which run through the craft to either side of the nozzle meaning that if you turn left, the nozzle is pulled to the left, the jet ski turns left and vice versa.

Impeller
The impeller's blades turn at high speeds, forcing water out of the steering nozzle and propelling the jet ski.

Steering nozzle
The water is forced out of the system here and the jet ski is steered by turning the nozzle.

Engine
Unusually, the engine of a jet ski provides indirect propulsion, rotating the drive shaft that, in turn, rotates the impeller.

Intake grate
Water enters the system here and is pushed out of the steering nozzle by the impeller.

Drive shaft
This is turned by the engine and turns the impeller at high speed, pushing water out of the steering nozzle.

Parts of a jet ski

Images © BMW Motorsport

MINI-GUIDE KEY
Parts of the steering wheel explained

1. FIA/Race control
2. Shift lights
3. Multifunction display
4. Neutral
5. Activate front wing
6. Multipurpose button
7. KERS boost button
8. Presettings down
9. Presettings up
10. Acknowledge
11. Pitlane limiter
12. Spare
13. Radio
14. Pit stop
15. Clutch
16. Safety car
17. Differential
18. Differential settings
19. Differential
20. Cruise control
21. Selector
22. Tyre adaption
23. Presettings front wing
24. Pedal map
25. Fuel mix
26. Upshift
27. Downshift
28. Clutch

Formula One cockpit

The cockpit of a Formula One car is a high-tech and surprisingly safe place to be

The cockpit of a modern Formula One car is much more than just a place for the driver to sit – it's also his survival cell and an integral part of the car's structure.

The carbon fibre 'tub' of the car is the principal component of the vehicle and the engine and front suspension are attached directly on to it. This makes for a much lighter structure than having to rely on a separate chassis. As well as being stiff to cope with the forces involved when the car is driving at high speed around a track, the tub is also incredibly

strong to protect the driver in the event of an accident. Today's FIA regulations insist on this, which is one reason fatalities are so rare in modern Formula One. The front and rear of the tub incorporate crash protection areas to absorb impact, and there is also a roll-hoop behind the driver's head. The sidewalls of the cockpit are as high as possible to protect the driver from flying debris.

The carbon fibre seat is made especially for the driver so that it is a perfect fit, and there is a five-point harness to hold him in place.

Regulations insist that in an emergency the driver be able to get out of the car in just five seconds, without having to remove anything but the harness and the steering wheel. And he must also be able to replace the wheel in the same time, in case the damaged car needs to be manoeuvred off the track.

The steering wheel holds all the controls (except for throttle and brake, which remain foot-operated) and instrumentation, so that they're immediately to hand. Formula One cars now have power-assisted steering, which allows the wheel to be very small.

Volkswagen's car vending machine

Glass and steel car towers are the centrepieces of Volkswagen's AutoStadt in Wolfsburg, Germany

Image courtesy of DooMeer

AutoStadt (car city) is part factory, part dealership, and part theme park. All the elements come together in two 20-storey car towers. When a car rolls off the factory assembly line, a robotic rail system carries it to one of two 145-foot towers, which can each hold 400 cars. A robotic lift hoists the car with a hydraulic arm and deposits it into an empty compartment. When the buyer comes to pick up the car, the lift system retrieves the car and places it on a conveyer belt leading to the KundenCenter (customer centre). The system uses only 20 per cent of the land of a conventional car park with equal capacity. Each tower has two lifts, and can 'process' one car every 45 seconds. On average, the towers deliver 600 cars a day. All in all, it's an amazing machine. Just don't kick it if your car doesn't drop.

Gliders

How do these engineless aircraft stay airborne?

A trainer and pupil in a dual-seated trainer glider

Gliders work by maximising the dynamic properties of air to remain airborne. They do this by optimising their lift-to-drag (L/D) ratio: that is the amount of lift generated by a wing or vehicle, divided by the drag it creates by moving through the air. This is achieved by extending the surface area of their lifting surfaces (wings) streamlining their physical construction, and utilising the lightest possible construction materials.

The glide ratio – the distance a glider falls for the distance it travels forward – of any glider is also reliant on its airspeed and the prevalence of rising air in the aircraft's vicinity. For example, if a glider is too light then its fall rate will be low but its travel distance forward will also be low, meaning high speed and long distance glides are impossible, as it will never reach the next area of lift. However, if a glider is weighted correctly, then the polar curve of distance travelled to distance fallen is optimised, carrying the glider between areas of uplift.

> "Weighted correctly, the polar curve of distance travelled to distance fallen is optimised"

Airspeed (knots) →

Sink rate (knots)

Best glide angle

5 TOP FACTS
GLIDERS

1 Recreational
Modern gliders were developed post-World War II, mainly by enthusiasts just to have fun during their time off work. Back then they were made primarily out of wood, not fibreglass.

2 Tow
Gliders were used in the Second World War to drop soldiers and equipment into war zones. The gliders were towed half the way and then left to glide to a set drop-off point. They were considered expendable.

3 Cheat
Not all gliders are engineless, with many fitted with one to allow them to take-off on their own, removing the need for them to piggyback on another aircraft in order to get airborne.

4 Boom
The principles of gliding have been extrapolated to the armament industry, where numerous companies make gliding bombs designed to travel great distances without the need for any propellant.

5 Training
Many gliders are used by instructors to educate amateur pilots in the basic principles of flight before they are given an engined aircraft. Trainer gliders contain a dual-seated cabin.

Experiments with gliding

Gliding isn't a new pursuit for humans, although it only reached substantial success in the 20th and 21st Centuries. In fact, the first record of someone attempting to glide through the air occurred in a 17th Century account of a 9th Century attempt by Abbas Ibn Firnas of Cordoba, Spain. Unfortunately for Firnas – who was a respected polymath and inventor – the attempt was reliant on covering himself with vulture feathers and resulted in bad back injuries. Where Firnas failed, however, the Wright brothers succeeded, and in 1911 they successfully glided in a modified, engineless variant of their famous aircraft. Since then the engineless glider has evolved into the sleek, streamlined aircraft we see today.

The Wright brothers' aircraft without motor in 1911 successfully gliding

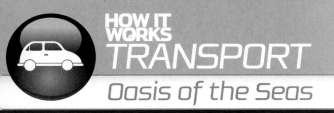

The world's larg cruise ship

Evolving out of the transatlantic crossing tradition, cruise liners have developed exponentially since their creation in 1900. The Oasis of the Seas is the latest and arguably greatest variant sailing today

The design of the cruise ship has changed wildly in the past hundred years, from the compact passenger ship designed to carry a small number of passengers across the Atlantic, to the Oasis of the Seas, a massive floating city resplendent with parks, theatres, restaurants, golf ranges, swimming pools and shops. Indeed, the Oasis of the Seas is truly a monumental feat of engineering and its lineage can be traced through several iterations of the cruise ship over the past 20 years, culminating in the creation of an entirely new category of liner (Oasis Class).

The Oasis of the Seas was built by Royal Caribbean International to replace its previous top-of-class liner, the Freedom Class. In order to build such a colossal ship, over 37 design firms, 20 architectural firms, the full 130 members of Royal Caribbean's Newbuilding & Fleet Design group, and the entire staff of STX Europe's Finnish shipyard were needed. The fine honing of 15 separate ship configurations, as well as the pioneering inclusion of a split-superstructure design, were also undertaken in a design and build process that would take almost six years.

Upon completion in October 2009, the Oasis of the Seas was over seven times bigger than the Titanic – the world's most famous cruise liner – and twice as heavy as its predecessor Freedom Class liner at a displacement weight of an estimated 100,000 tons. In addition, the Oasis is now the largest passenger ship and cruise liner in the world, with a total capacity of 6,296, incorporating a zonal design for its seven on-board neighbourhood areas.

The Oasis's primary role is as an all-in-one floating vacation – one in which the journey is part of the holiday just as much as the actual destination. Registered at the port of Nassau in the Bahamas, and sailing from Fort Lauderdale, Florida, to multiple destinations around the Caribbean, the ship specialises in touring passengers in ridiculous comfort and with an unequalled level of amenities. ✿

est

An under-construction shot of the ship's Central Park

"Upon completion in October 2009, the Oasis of the Seas was over seven times bigger than the Titanic"

The physical building of the Oasis of the Seas took over three years

All pictures © Royal Caribbean International

"It sounds more like a collection of city centre amenities than those traditionally found on a ship"

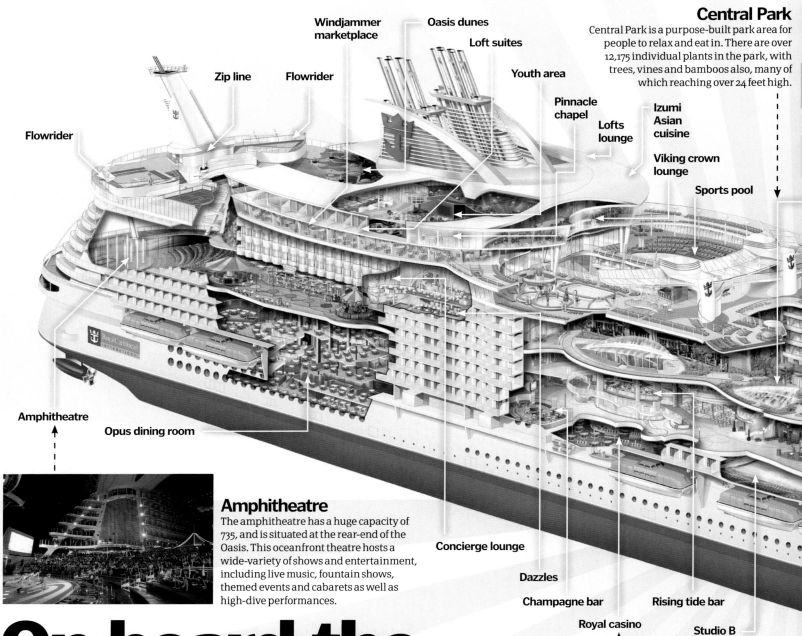

Zip line

Flowrider

Flowrider

Windjammer marketplace

Oasis dunes

Loft suites

Youth area

Pinnacle chapel

Lofts lounge

Izumi Asian cuisine

Viking crown lounge

Sports pool

Central Park
Central Park is a purpose-built park area for people to relax and eat in. There are over 12,175 individual plants in the park, with trees, vines and bamboos also, many of which reaching over 24 feet high.

Amphitheatre

Opus dining room

Concierge lounge

Dazzles

Champagne bar

Rising tide bar

Royal casino

Studio B

Amphitheatre
The amphitheatre has a huge capacity of 735, and is situated at the rear-end of the Oasis. This oceanfront theatre hosts a wide-variety of shows and entertainment, including live music, fountain shows, themed events and cabarets as well as high-dive performances.

On board the Oasis of the Seas

Take a look at the amenities that make this the world's most decadent cruise ship

The facilities available to those who travel on the Oasis of the Seas are quite staggering, sounding more like a collection of city centre amenities than those traditionally found on a ship. Split into seven distinct neighbourhoods, including Central Park, Pool and Sports Zone, Spa and Fitness Centre, Boardwalk, Royal Promenade, Youth Zone and Entertainment Place, no matter what your fancy, the Oasis in all probability can provide. From numerous restaurants, coffee houses, bars and high street shops, to a full theatre, casino, park and amphitheatre, the term 'floating city' has never been more apt.

DID YOU KNOW? *The Oasis of the Seas is the first ever ship to have a park built in, containing a whopping 12,175 plants*

Bars

Dotted around multiple neighbourhoods are over 35 drinking establishments, each differing in theme, style and service from the last, including a traditional English pub.

Central Park

Beach pool

Main pool

OASIS OF THE SEAS	VS	FREEDOM OF THE SEAS

	OASIS OF THE SEAS		FREEDOM OF THE SEAS
Cost:	$1.6 billion	**Cost:**	$800 million
Power:	3 x 18,590hp, 3 x 24,780hp	**Power:**	3 x 17,000hp
Capacity:	6,296	**Capacity:**	4,375
Decks:	16	**Decks:**	15
Speed:	22.6 knots	**Speed:**	22.6 knots
Length:	360 metres	**Length:**	339 metres
Weight:	225,282 gross tons	**Weight:**	154,407 gross tons

Solarium

Youth zone

Restaurants

There are a massive selection of restaurants on the Oasis. However, the biggest and most spectacular is arguably the 3,056 capacity Opus dining room.

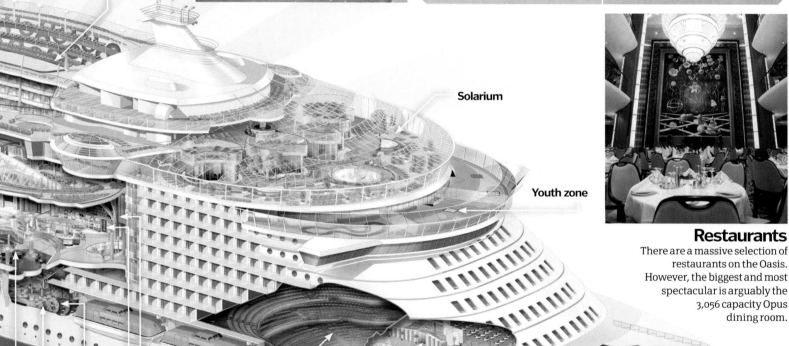

Boleros

Comedy live   **Jazz on 4**

On air club

Blaze   **Conference centre**

Helipad

Opel theatre

Fitness centre   **At sea spa**

Casino

Casino Royal is the largest and most sophisticated casino at sea, with over 450 slot machines, table games and separate bar and lounge. The casino is served by two main walkways that display the history of gaming.

Accommodation

The Oasis of the Seas has a grand total of 2,706 staterooms, including 1,956 with a balcony, 254 outside and 496 in the interior. In addition, the ship also has a selection of luxury two-storey loft suites, with floor-to-ceiling views of the sea and promenades.

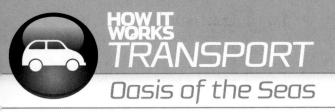

The technically advanced bridge control room of the Oasis

The king of all cruise ships

Exploring the statistics, performance and equipment of this oceanic behemoth

Despite a smorgasbord of amenities and its new class-creating size, the Oasis of the Seas is designed largely in the same way as any other ship, with performance and stability ultimately driving its design and construction.

For example, in order for any ship to float it must displace an equal amount of water to its weight, if it can't do this before it is submerged then it sinks as it is too dense. All ships accomplish this mainly through their hulls: the lightweight, watertight part of the ship that sits below the waterline. Considering the Oasis has a displacement weight of over 100,000 tons its hull is therefore super-wide (66 metres) to maintain stability and minimise drag, while its magnificent size and shape (nine metres deep with rounded edges) are tailored to disperse weight while maintaining smooth sailing.

The large, traditional hull of the Oasis however, has an increased burden when compared to its predecessors, as it has to accommodate the split-superstructure of the ship. The Oasis's superstructure is split right down its middle to minimise the amount of interior areas with no

access to the exterior – an issue that has grown in parallel with ship size over the last 20 years. By splitting the superstructure, however, the complexity and weight distribution of the ship is altered dramatically from previous liners and the hull's construction – notably its colossal width – is modified to account for this.

Due to the ship's gargantuan physical characteristics – over 360 metres long, 66 metres wide, 65 metres high from the water line and a draft of nine metres – it is

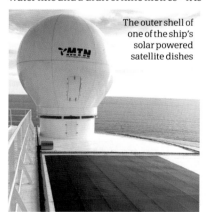

The outer shell of one of the ship's solar powered satellite dishes

Whale of a size

1 With an incredible displacement weight of 100,000 tons, the Oasis of the Seas weighs more than 500 blue whales, the largest known animal in the world.

A ship in bloom

2 The massive Central Park area on board the Oasis of the Seas contains approximately 12,175 plants, 62 vines and 56 trees and bamboos.

Plenty of power

3 The Oasis of the Seas' total power output is over 130,000hp... which is 130 times that of the incredibly nippy Bugatti Veyron, once the fastest car in the world.

Steering

4 No rudders are needed to steer the Oasis of the Seas, instead the action is performed by a series of 20-foot propellers suspended under the stern.

A mighty crew

5 The ship has a mammoth crew size of over 2,100, which is no huge surprise when you consider its sheer size and the number of activities and amenities on offer.

DID YOU KNOW? *The Oasis of the Seas is so wide at 66 metres that it cannot fit through the Panama Canal*

A shipyard worker gives one of the ship's bow thrusters a last-minute inspection

limited to certain ports. This is not surprising if you consider the Oasis is four times the length of a football pitch and over 20 storeys high.

The juice for such a leviathan comes courtesy of six engines, three Wärtsilä 12-cylinder diesels producing 18,590hp each, and three Wärtsilä 16-cylinder diesels producing 24,780hp each – a combined total power output of over 130,000hp. Amazingly, this massive power is justified as, once converted into electricity, it is used all over the ship, from the operation of individual lights and elevators, to the running of the on-board water treatment plant and ship's control room. Propulsion is also powered by these engines and is handled by three 20MW ABB Azipod electrically driven, rotatable propellers. In addition, to aid docking, the ship is also fitted with four 7,500hp bow thrusters.

Learn more

For additional information about the Oasis of the Seas – and her sister ship – head to **www.oasisoftheseas.com/** where you can watch videos and read about the history of the ship that could change the face of cruise liners forever.

Horse power
A look at the world's first carousel at sea

With a weight of 11,000 pounds, a height and diameter of seven metres as well as containing 21 handcrafted wood figurines, the Oasis of the Seas boasts the world's first carousel at sea. Constructed over eight months, the centrepiece of the ship's Boardwalk area needed 31 gallons of paint, 130 square feet of real gold leaf gilding,

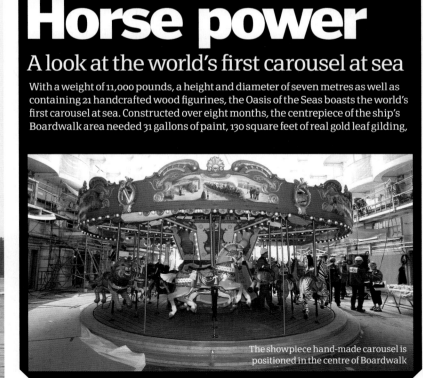

The showpiece hand-made carousel is positioned in the centre of Boardwalk

203

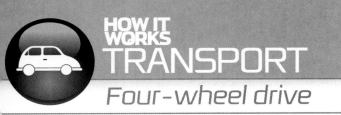
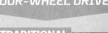

"Electronics are increasingly found in 4x4 systems, but the basic engineering remains the same"

Four-wheel drive

How does this technology allow you to keep moving over all terrain in all weather conditions?

Driving all four wheels in a car at the same time is a complicated process, but at the same time it is the purest way to propel a car. Instead of two wheels out of the four transmitting the full energy of the engine to the road, that effort is spread more equally between all of the wheels.

There are two classifications of four-wheel drive that relate to whether the system is 'permanent' or not. Older and more basic systems are only part-time, with the all-wheel drive selected when conditions demand – these are the traditional 'four-wheel drive' vehicles. Most modern systems, however, are full-time, and these are known as 'all-wheel drives'.

There are different technical solutions in passenger cars, which depend on whether the basic car is normally front-wheel drive or rear-wheel drive. The more commonplace systems are found in dedicated off-roaders, though. These are engineered from the outset to drive all four wheels, incorporating the necessary transfer box, drive shafts and differentials.

Electronics are increasingly found in 4x4 systems, but the basic engineering remains the same. All send drive simultaneously forwards and rearwards. It is the management of how much drive is sent to which wheels and when that electronics oversee. This has enhanced the abilities offered by these vehicles. ✿

Four square

2. Half shaft
Front half shafts are connected to the road wheels and transfer drive from the front differential.

3. Locking hub
On part-time 4WD systems, the front wheel hubs can be disconnected when running in 2WD mode.

6. Brains in the middle
Modern 4x4s frequently use 'torque-sensing' centre differentials. These constantly vary the drive split between front and rear axles according to grip available.

1. Transfer case
This divides torque produced by the engine between front and rear wheels.

4. Front differential
A differential allows wheels on the same axle to rotate at different speeds. This is important for cornering.

8. LSD
A limited-slip differential means that if one wheel rotates at a different speed to the other, the differential can partly 'lock' – ensuring drive still reaches the other wheel.

7. Front drive shaft
The front drive shaft transmits drive forwards from the transfer case to the front differential.

5. Spin the diff
If an 'open' differential is fitted at the rear, torque is evenly split between the wheels. So if one raises off the ground or spins, it can take on no torque, and neither can the other.

Now we're torquing

The product of an engine is a physical twisting force, this turns the drive shafts and moves the car. This is known as torque. Four-wheel drive systems work by optimising the spread of this force between all four wheels.

If you apply too much torque to a wheel, the tyre will slip. However, in four-wheel drive cars each wheel carries 25 per cent of torque, rather than 50 per cent. It means a more measured distribution of force across all four wheels.

Life-saver

A Virgin Pendolino derailed in Cumbria, UK, on 23 February 2007. The cause was determined to be faulty points, and Virgin chairman Sir Richard Branson credited the train's build for limiting the loss of life to one.

An aircraft's wingtip vortex is made visible with coloured smoke

Wingtip vortices

What are they and why do they occur?

Wingtip vortices are circulating tubes of air that emanate from the tips of aircrafts' wings as they generate lift. Each wing has its own vortex and their cores spin at a great speed and at low pressure. They are formed when an aircraft's wings generate lift by creating a region of low pressure above them, causing the high-pressure air beneath the wings to migrate towards the top via the wingtips. Consequently, air flows from below the wing and out around the tip to the top of the wing in a circular fashion, causing a rotating tunnel of air behind it.

Wing vortices can cause severe hazard to aircraft that pass through their vicinity, especially during take-off and landing phases. This is because the vortices persist often for many minutes, drifting about runways on the wind. Due to their size they can spin and destabilise the plane with much more intensity than can be actively managed by its ailerons (these are the hinged control surfaces attached to trailing edge of most fixed wing aircraft), leading to severe difficulties.

To counteract the negative effects that wingtip vortices have, it is standard procedure for air traffic controllers to leave a two- to five-minute gap between individual aircraft taking off or landing in the same airspace. This is especially necessary if a large plane is followed by a smaller aircraft. ⚙

What happens to the air?

An inevitable consequence of creating lift

Airflow above wing
The wings help generate a region of low pressure air above them.

Airflow below wing
The high pressure air under the wings pushes upwards but cannot escape due to airspeed.

The vortex
The trapped air flows down the wing before spiralling off at the tips in a circular fashion.

Air spillage
A spiralling vortex with a low-pressure core is created, proving hazardous to following aircraft.

Full tilt

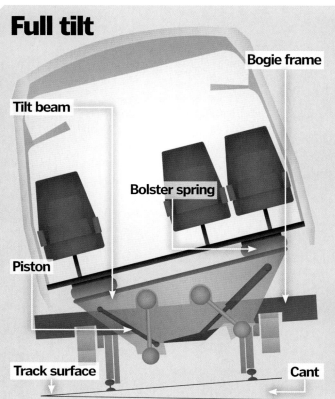

Bogie frame

Tilt beam

Bolster spring

Piston

Track surface

Cant

Tilting trains

How high-speed trains can corner without sending passengers hurtling

Tilting trains provide the solution to the awkward jerking motion caused by the centrifugal force that pulls on a passenger when a train takes a corner at high speed.

Virgin uses a train called the Pendolino, which uses powerful traction and tilting technology to lean into curves instead of slowing down, keeping journey times to a minimum. Tilting trains do not require special rails, instead the mechanism beneath the coach enables the train to corner quickly on regular mainline tracks. The wheels are attached to a hydraulic bogie, which is the chassis frame connected securely to the track. The bogie acts as a fulcrum in the centre, capable of tilting the coaches up to eight degrees in bends, using hydraulic or electromechanical jacks. Computerised pistons in the mechanism control the degree of tilt.

The Tiltronix technology inside the Pendolino provides either reactive tilting (using gyroscopes and accelerometers to determine the precise angle that is required) or anticipative tilting (using specific track information from a database together with on-board sensors). ⚙

© Virgin Trains

"The car's top speed is 'limited' to 253mph; no one knows what the car is truly capable of"

When Volkswagen decided in 1998 to resurrect the famous Bugatti name, it didn't hold back. The Veyron redefined the term supercar with power and torque figures unlike anything that had come before it. So let's cut straight to the chase. The Veyron's mid-mounted engine produces over 1,000bhp. Actually, the official figure is 'only' 987bhp, but in reality the output is believed to be closer to 1,035bhp. Indeed, an indicator on the dash lets you know when the power reaches the magic four-figure number (if you dare look because you are likely to be travelling at over 200mph when this happens). But perhaps even more impressive is the engine's torque figure of 1250Nm – that's almost double that of the McLaren F1, previously the world's fastest car.

Those impressive figures come courtesy of an impressive engine, with no less than 16 cylinders arranged in a 'W' configuration (essentially, two V8s joined at the crankshaft). The capacity is a hearty 8.3-litres and the cylinders are fed by no less than four turbochargers. And to keep it all cool, there are ten radiators and two independent cooling circuits.

The power is fed to all four wheels through a seven-speed gearbox with the

option of automatic or manual shifts, the latter courtesy of steering wheel-mounted paddles. And the power is then harnessed back by a set of massive ceramic disc brakes.

All this technology is clothed in an astonishingly beautiful body hand-made from carbon fibre and aluminium. The Bugatti Veyron is undoubtedly a very modern car and yet the designers managed to incorporate some of that old Bugatti charm into its lines – not least with the evocative radiator grille and badge. And, of course, the shape was defined by aerodynamic requirements to ensure that the car remains firmly on the road. Inside, the Veyron is pure luxury, with no plastic to be seen anywhere. Instead, you find leather and

aluminium, all hand-crafted. Even the hi-fi unit has bespoke aluminium controls.

The top speed of the Veyron is limited – if that's the right word – to 253mph because the tyres are not considered capable of faster speeds. No one knows what the car is truly capable of. Surely, in these politically correct days, no one will ever have the tenacity to produce a more outrageous machine. ☼

MID-MOUNTED ENGINE
8.3-litre W16 engine is mounted in the centre of the car to ensure good weight distribution which in turn helps ensure superb handling.

CERAMIC BRAKES
Massive brake discs are made from carbon fibre-reinforced silicon carbide, which is less likely to fade under heavy use, compared to steel discs.

There are supercars and then there is the Bugatti Veyron. Faster, more power and more advanced than most other vehicles, the Veyron is among the planet's ultimate cars

The speed and the beauty Bugatt

Head to Head
Which is the biggest, fastest, strongest?

FASTEST	**1. Bugatti Veyron EB 16.4** **Capacity:** 8.3-litre **Cylinders:** W16 **Max power:** 987bhp **Max torque:** 1250Nm **Gearbox:** Semi-auto, six-speed **0-60mph:** 2.9 seconds **Max speed:** 253mph	
 **FASTER**	**2. Pagani Zonda C12 F** **Capacity:** 7291cc **Cylinders:** V12 **Max power:** 620bhp **Max torque:** 400Nm **Gearbox:** Six-speed manual **0-60mph:** 3.6 seconds **Max speed:** 214mph	
 **FAST**	**3. McLaren MP4-12C** **Capacity:** 3800cc **Cylinders:** V8 **Max power:** 600bhp **Max torque:** 572Nm **Gearbox:** Semi-auto, seven-speed **0-60mph:** 3.4 seconds **Max speed:** 200+mph	

DID YOU KNOW? *The Veyron was named after the French racing driver, Pierre Veyron, who won the 1939 Le Mans race*

Inside the Bugatti
What makes the Veyron purr?

RADIATOR GRILLE
The central air intake is one of a number of apertures that feed air to the various radiators and intercoolers. This one also harks back to the design of classic Bugattis.

The W16 configuration enables a compact engine. Interestingly, the original Bugatti concept car of 1998 used a W18 engine

HIGH-SPEED TYRES
Michelin tyres were specially developed to cope with a 250mph top speed and also offer superb grip. They can run flat for around 125 miles – but only at 50mph.

FOUR-WHEEL DRIVE
To ensure good traction, the 1,000 bhp is transferred to the road via all four wheels.

Images © Bugatti

CATEGORY	BUGATTI VEYRON GRAND SPORT
On sale from	2009
Engine Type	7993cc litre quad-turbo W16
Torque	922lb-ft at 3500-5500 rpm
Acceleration	0-60 in 2.7 seconds
List price	1.4million euros
Horsepower	1001 bhp at 6000 rpm
Top Speed	253 mph
Transmission	7-speed dual clutch sequential manual with four-wheel drive
Weight	1,990 kg

Veyron Grand Sport

Unveiled in August 2008, the first Bugatti Veyron Grand Sport was sold at a charity auction for $2.9 million, though main production didn't start until early-2009. Essentially there's no difference between the original car and the Grand Sport, though the first Bugatti Veyron proved so popular (*Top Gear* endorsements withstanding) that it spawned several special edition models since. This latest in the Bugatti line is a targa top, with a removable roof for a top speed of 228 mph and a folding umbrella roof that can be activated in case of rain, for 80 mph max. Considering you could probably hit this speed simply resting your foot near the accelerator, you're going to want to take it somewhere reliably hot.

Under the hood
How does it make so much power?

The Veyron's engine is unusual in that it is has a W16 configuration – most supercars have a V12 engine. However, a V12 which produced 1,000bhp would have been restrictively large – both in capacity and in physical bulk, which is not ideal for a sports car. By using a W16 layout, Bugatti's engineers were about to create an engine that was relatively compact (it measures just 710 x 889 x 730 mm) and limited to 8.3 litres.

However, that alone would not be enough to create the desired power, which is why the Veyron's engine has four turbochargers – one for each bank of eight cylinders. These use the otherwise wasted exhaust gases to force air and fuel into the cylinders.

And how the Veyron drinks fuel. Using standard Combined Cycle tests, it manages to travel just 11.7 miles on one gallon of super unleaded. Floor the throttle, though, and that figure drops to an eye-watering 2.5 mpg. In other words, its rather modest 100-litre tank would be drained in just 12 exhilarating minutes.

Veyron

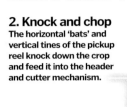
How combines work

More than overgrown lawn mowers, combines are mobile multitaskers

2. Knock and chop
The horizontal 'bats' and vertical tines of the pickup reel knock down the crop and feed it into the header and cutter mechanism.

3. Command in comfort
From the climate-controlled cabin, the farmer monitors and controls every aspect of the harvest through touch screens, video monitors and GPS trackers.

4. Thresh and churn
The chopped crop material moves over, under and through a series of specialised threshing drums that loosen the grain and shake it off through concave metal grates.

5. Dead straw walking
The rough, stepped surface of the straw walker is perfect for shaking off any leftover grain. The whole platform jostles back and forth as the straw is pushed toward the back for chopping and spreading.

1. GPS-guided
John Deere's AutoTrac system allows for 'hands free' navigation. Special sensors record GPS data when the crop is planted. The combine follows the GPS co-ordinates to harvest perfectly straight rows.

6. Temporary storage
The prized grain is stored in the belly of the combine until it reaches maximum capacity. Modern machines have cameras and sensors to detect when the storage tank is full.

7. Out you go
The unloader is a long, turbine-powered arm that empties the storage tank at a rate of 3.3 bushels of grain per second.

© John Deere

Semi-automatic transmission

The latest double-clutch automatic transmissions are a must-have

Double-clutch transmissions give you the choice of fully automatic changes or manual ones via steering-wheel mounted paddles. The key is a pair of compact wet clutches, one inside the other. In a typical system, one clutch is linked to even-numbered gears, the other to odd-numbered ones and reverse. The rest of the transmission is much the same as a manual gearbox. A hydraulic control unit and a series of pressure valves control the wet clutches and the shifters. The clutch on one transmission opens or disengages, while the clutch on the other closes or engages simultaneously. This means as one gear is selected, the next is pre-engaged ready to be used. ✿

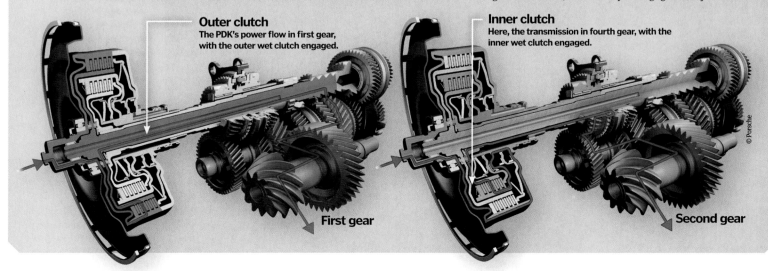

Outer clutch
The PDK's power flow in first gear, with the outer wet clutch engaged.

Inner clutch
Here, the transmission in fourth gear, with the inner wet clutch engaged.

First gear

Second gear

© Porsche

Air bags post deployment from steering wheel and dashboard

© Janipewter

Air bags

How do they inflate so quickly?

Air bags consist of three main parts: first the bag itself, which is constructed from a thin, nylon-type fabric and folded into the steering wheel or dashboard of a vehicle. Second, the air bag sensor, a device that tells the bag when to inflate. And thrd, the air bag's inflation system, a mechanism that produces and releases nitrogen gas quickly for inflation.

The inflation system is key to any air bag, as it must complete its process in a fraction of a second. The system operates akin to a solid rocket booster, igniting a solid propellant that burns extremely rapidly to create a large volume of gas. This gas inflates the bag at over 200 mph in order to mitigate the forward momentum the human is experiencing during the crash. Once inflated, the bag then releases the gas slowly through small holes in order for the passenger to then exit the vehicle. ✿

Air bag inflation
How does the air bag inflate?

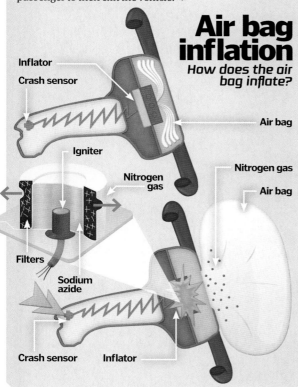

- Inflator
- Crash sensor
- Air bag
- Igniter
- Nitrogen gas
- Nitrogen gas
- Air bag
- Filters
- Sodium azide
- Crash sensor
- Inflator

© Segway

Microchip
User balance is maintained when operating a Segway by a series of inbuilt gyroscopes and electric motors that detect the subtle shifting of position and pressure of the user, as well as the tilt of the LeanSteer™ frame.

Frame
Segways are directionally controlled by their vertical LeanSteer™ frame. To turn left or right the user tilts the frame in that direction and leans forward. The column's position effects direction by the increase or decrease in the individual wheels' rotation.

Tilting column to steer

Lock
To avoid theft a heavy-duty lock mechanism allows the Segway to be secured to an immovable object. In addition, the wheels automatically lock when the included anti-theft alarm is activated.

Indicators
When fully balanced and ready to operate, a series of sensor lights gently pulsate.

Luggage
Luggage racks can be fitted to most variants of the Segway, allowing commuting users to attach briefcases, containers and bags to the device.

Tyres
All Segways are fitted with anti-marking tyres, meaning that the rubber leaves no trails on indoor or smooth surfaces. Off-road variants are also sold, with a beefier tread suited to uneven terrain.

Segway

Exploring the technology that drives this personal transporter

Segways use a combination of gyroscopes, electric motors and a user-controlled vertical steering column to propel individuals around outdoor and indoor environments. Direction is dictated by the tilting of the vertical frame – left to turn left, right to turn right. Forwards and backwards momentum, meanwhile, is dictated by the positioning of the user's weight and posture while on the Segway. Lean forwards and the internal microchips instruct power to be delivered from the electric motors to rotate the wheels forwards, lean backwards and the reverse is delivered. Power is derived from an internal series of cell batteries, which are recharged with electricity sourced from any standard power supply. ✿

The Statistics
Segway i2

Weight: 47.7kg (105lbs)
Tyre size: 19" (48cm)
Max speed: 12.5mph (20kph)
Max range: 24 miles (38km)

Parking sensors

It's so easy to do your car some serious damage when parking, but thankfully new technology can make us all parking masters

Parking sensors are now must-have technology. They enable us all to park ever-larger cars with expert finesse and avoid scrapes that can cost hundreds to repair. The most familiar type use ultrasonic technology – just like bats do.

When activated, these fire out high-frequency signals from a series of round sensors (usually four) attached to the bumper. When physical objects are detected within a set range, they will alert the driver via a visual or audible signal. Manufacturers programme the range of these signals within the logic board of the sensors – they can therefore be calibrated so the driver has an indication of how far away the object is.

Usually, widely spaced bleeps are issued. As the car gets closer to the object, the pause between these shortens, until a continuous tone is heard.

The alternative sensors are electromagnetic. These comprise a magnetic strip on the inside of the bumper – it is 'invisible' technology so is more aesthetically pleasing. When activated, a magnetic field is generated. From this, an elliptical magnetic field is sent out by a control unit. When something enters its range, the voltage in the control unit increases. The rate of this change is converted into a calibrated audible signal.

The car that (almost) parks itself

1. Smart sense
Active Park Assist uses a car's ultrasonic sensors in a smart way. Below a set speed, the two outside ultrasonic sensors on the bumpers scan sideways and measure sudden changes in distance that indicate the presence of a space.

3. The car steers itself
The Mercedes A-Class is fitted with electrically assisted power steering, so the motor can 'take over' the steering process. Engineers have defined the requisite steering movements to parallel-park, and stored these in the software.

4. Take out the guesswork
Once the system is engaged, it will steer in exactly the right way to perfectly park the car next to the kerb – there is no guesswork, as the steering profile of how to park that exact model has already been calculated.

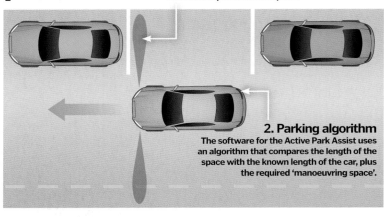

2. Parking algorithm
The software for the Active Park Assist uses an algorithm that compares the length of the space with the known length of the car, plus the required 'manoeuvring space'.

5. Driver remains in control
The driver still controls brakes, throttle and gears for safety. The system still uses parking sensors in a traditional sense for distance measurement, too. The tolerances are no different as the movement of the car is still under the driver's control.

Car immobilisers

Forget car keys; nowadays car makers use advanced electronics to guarantee your car remains yours

Thanks to electronic immobilisers, the days of thieves hotwiring cars are long gone. They have been mandatory on all new cars since the Nineties, and in their simplest form ensure the car cannot be started without a coded key fob or ignition – even if the ignition system is hacked.

In modern cars, the key fob transponder communicates directly with the car's electronic control unit (known as the ECU). By integrating the circuit into the car's central brain, it's virtually impossible for thieves to somehow hack into it. Because so many different aspects of modern cars are controlled by electronics, it is easy for makers to cut power supply to these components, therefore 'immobilising' the vehicle altogether.

The transponder itself is usually a coded chip. This is read by the car then the ignition is turned on. If it is missing – or if the coded chip doesn't match what the car is expecting – it will not start at all.

Many immobilisers use 'rolling code' technology. At the factory, a random table of codes is burned into the immobiliser unit, with a complimentary one installed in the immobiliser tag. Each time the car is started, a new code is utilised – and the car will only start if the key and the immobiliser unit match each and every time.

Immobilisers are a car thief's worst nightmare

How tyre treads work

Traction and handling are all about the tread

| Sipes aid traction | Circumferential grooves prevent aquaplaning | Blocks grab the road | Ribs can be solid or broken into blocks | Dimples cool the tire | Shoulders hug the road |

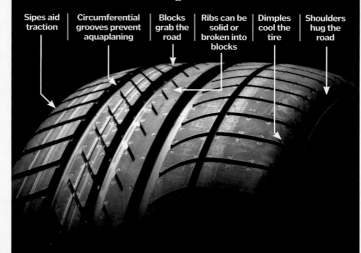

 Tyre-building machines spit out 'green tyres' with a completely smooth surface, which would spell disaster on the road. They would have terrible traction and would constantly be aquaplaning – skidding on a layer of water between the tyre and the road. A tyre isn't properly ready for action until it goes through a curing process that moulds a tread pattern into its rubber compound surface.

Tread patterns vary depending on the tyre's intended use, but the basic idea is to offer good traction in a range of conditions, while minimising aquaplaning, vibration and noise. There are several key tread elements that make that happen.

The basic unit of tyre tread is the rib – a raised area going all the way around the tyre, divided by circumferential grooves. Ribs are literally where the rubber meets the road, while grooves prevent aquaplaning. When you drive over a puddle, the grooves give the water somewhere to go, so it doesn't build up between the tread and the road. Ribs may be solid all the way around the tyre, or they may be divided into separate blocks (also called lugs) by transverse grooves (also called slots). One common design includes a solid rib running around the centre of the tyre, with two ribs divided into blocks on either side, and a shoulder at each edge.

Blocks are critical for traction – the edge of each block essentially grabs onto the road. Ribs generally include blocks of different sizes to create a particular sequence that minimises noise. Sipes are smaller horizontal slits within blocks. They give blocks more flexibility and provide additional edges that boost traction, especially in tricky conditions such as snow, ice, and mud. Dimples are smaller indentations that help cool the tyre. ✿

Tyre tread keeps this Porsche on the road, just about...

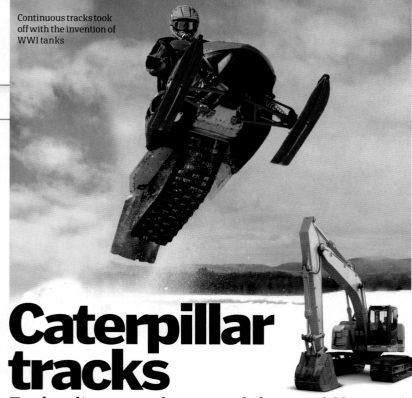

Continuous tracks took off with the invention of WWI tanks

Caterpillar tracks

Tanks, diggers and snowmobiles would be stuck without their innovative terrain-busting tracks

 Named after the Caterpillar company, continuous tracks took off with the invention of the military tank during World War I. Caterpillar tracks can cope much better with rough and muddy terrain than wheels with pneumatic tyres; they are much tougher and spread the weight more evenly.

The track belts are made from a number of identical steel or rubber segments joined by hinges, so that the assembly is flexible, and made into a continuous loop. This loop is wrapped around a row of closely spaced wheels, usually linked to some form of suspension. One or more grooves in the wheels locate with protrusions on the inside of the track to ensure it doesn't slip out of position.

One or more of the wheels – or a dedicated sprocket – is powered by the vehicle's engine and engages with holes in the belt to drive it around the wheels, and therefore move the vehicle forward.

The vehicle is steered by varying the speed – and sometimes direction – of the tracks on each side. To turn right, for instance, the left-hand track turns faster to pull that side of the vehicle forward. ✿

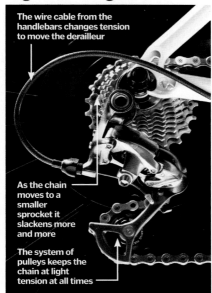

Bike derailleurs

How a modern bicycle gets into gear

We have unspoken trust in bike derailleurs. The front and rear derailleurs change our gears while we pedal hard, and we expect them to work, but what really happens?

The job of derailleurs is more than just changing from gear to gear. The tension of the wire from your handlebars moves the rear derailleur to 'derail' and change sprockets. The second job of the rear derailleur is to reduce slack on the chain. When you change gear to a smaller sprocket, the chain gains slack. The top of the chain is pulled tight as you pedal, and the bottom half is tightened by the rear derailleur. However, the chain is not completely tight so the derailleur can shift sprockets even if you're pedalling hard. The S-shape seen on the rear derailleur is a system of spring-loaded pulleys which automatically take up the slack as the chain shifts sprockets. ✿

The wire cable from the handlebars changes tension to move the derailleur

As the chain moves to a smaller sprocket it slackens more and more

The system of pulleys keeps the chain at light tension at all times

The world's nuclea

From the 16th to 21st Centuries, submarines have inspired shock and awe in equal measure. HMS Astute is the latest and perhaps greatest example

First theorised in the 16th Century by Leonardo da Vinci and first deployed during the American Revolution, submarines have afforded navies the advantage of moving unseen, striking without warning and then disappearing without trace. Their effectiveness was restricted by only two things: the time they could remain submerged and the range of the weapons they carried. All this changed in 1954 and again the following year, with the world's first nuclear powered submarine (the USS Nautilus) and the first submarine Launched Ballistic Missile (the Soviet R13). Today, at least six nations include nuclear subs in their arsenal, although since the end of the Cold War, most carry conventional rather than nuclear weapons. The most expensive and some would say deadliest of these is the HMS Astute.

The Astute was the first UK-built submarine in almost 20 years, developed and constructed by BAE and launched on 8 June 2007. Astute contains around 50 per cent more firepower than the sub classes it replaces, totalling around 30 weapons systems including six torpedo tubes armed with Spearfish torpedoes and 36 Tomahawk Cruise missiles. Approximately 30 per cent larger than previous British attack submarines thanks to the bigger PWR2 Pressurised Water Reactor that powers it, safety is a primary consideration, especially while operating in the harshest environment

on the planet: the deep ocean. It's a sobering thought that the 98-man crew will be living and working within a few metres of the core of a nuclear power plant more complex than a power station.

Astute's primary role is as an undersea hunter-killer, operating undetected hundreds of metres underwater while maintaining secure satellite communication. Its stealth credentials are enhanced by the 39,000 acoustic tiles that mask its sonar signature, as well as the 2076 Sonar System capable of tracking vessels across thousands of square miles of ocean. The Astute is capable of operating in isolation or as part of a taskforce with other naval vessels. It is expected to complete its 25-year life span without ever refuelling, patrolling submerged for 90 days at a time. In fact, the main limiting factor on its effectiveness is that it can only carry three months of food for the 98 strong all-male crew members onboard. Britain's contingent of new Trident submarines are being reduced to three and not deployed until 2025, so Astute class represents the immediate future of submarine warfare. ✿

"Construction required over 1 million components, 7,000 design drawings, 10,000 separate engineering requirements and 100km of pipework"

THE STATS
HMS ASTUTE

WEIGHT **7,800 tons**	LENGTH **97m**	SPEED **29 knots**	
CREW **98**	TIME TO BUILD **6 years 4 months**		

DID YOU KNOW? This 7,800 ton sub will make no more noise than a baby dolphin

deadliest submarine

Made in Britain
The vessel was built at BAE's submarine facility in Barrow

One of seven
HMS Astute is the first of seven Astute-class subs to replace the Swiftsure and Trafalgar-class

All images © BAE Systems

Team effort
Around six thousand people were involved in the Astute's construction

On board HMS
Beneath the hull of the most advanced submarine

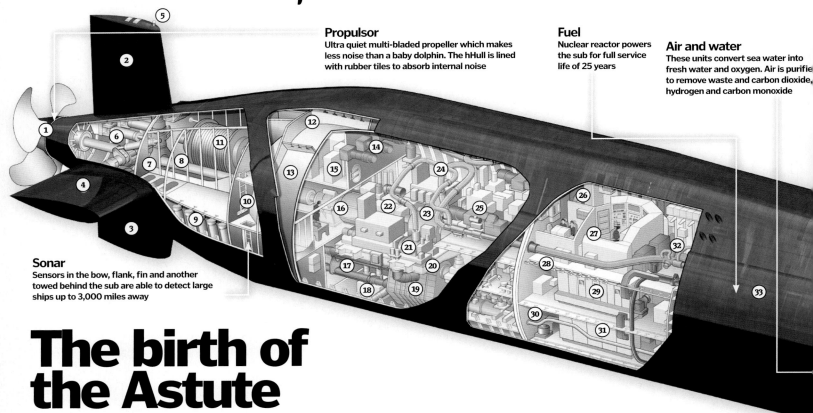

Propulsor
Ultra quiet multi-bladed propeller which makes less noise than a baby dolphin. The hHull is lined with rubber tiles to absorb internal noise

Fuel
Nuclear reactor powers the sub for full service life of 25 years

Air and water
These units convert sea water into fresh water and oxygen. Air is purifie to remove waste and carbon dioxide, hydrogen and carbon monoxide

Sonar
Sensors in the bow, flank, fin and another towed behind the sub are able to detect large ships up to 3,000 miles away

The birth of the Astute

Astute was the first nuclear submarine to be designed entirely in a 3D computer-aided design environment

HMS Astute is the first in a programme to design seven Astute-class subs to replace the Royal Navy's aging Swiftsure and Trafalgar-class. Three similar subs (Ambush, Artful and Audacious) have already been approved to follow.

Around six thousand people were involved in Astute's construction at BAE's Devonshire Dock Hall in Barrow-in-Furness, the largest shipbuilding construction complex of its kind in Europe, covering an area of 25,000 square metres. Astute's construction required over 1 million components including 7,000 design drawings., 10,000 separate engineering requirements and 100km of pipework.

A number of technical challenges had to be overcome during the 17-year cycle from concept design to nuclear powered vessel. Not least of these was the fact that with space at an absolute premium, Astute's machinery and equipment is three times more densely packed than that of a surface warship.

Astute was the first nuclear submarine to be designed entirely in a 3D computer-aided design environment. With neither much time nor budget for designing a prototype in the usual manner, this system of 'virtual' prototyping harnessed the power of computer test and visualisation, along with continuous design and careful systems analysis. Some areas of the Astute – such as the command deck and forward engine room – were manufactured in modules,

assembled in the workshop. They were then shipped to the Devonshire dock hall and carefully placed within the hull: an example of 'plug and play' construction that not only saves time but also minimises rework.

The structure of the sub is made up of a pressure hull – a perfect cylinder with rounded dome ends demonstrating that circularity is one of the keys to surviving deep ocean pressures. There are six sections between the end domes each containing different packages of equipment, and the hull sections are meticulously welded together in a process involving more than 2km of welding, all completed without a single defect and exhaustively examined for flaws using x-ray and ultra-sonic technology.

The reveal
Built at Europe's largest submarine dockyard, Astute first emerged to public gaze in 2007

FASTEST

1. HMS Astute
Nationality: British
Weight: 7,800 tons
Length: 97 metres
Speed: 29 knots

SLOWEST

2. USS Alabama
Nationality: American
Weight: 18,750 tons
Length: 170 metres
Speed: 20 knots

BIGGEST

3. Yuri Dolgoruki
Nationality: Russian
Weight: 24,000 tons
Length: 170 metres
Speed: 25 knots

DID YOU KNOW? The HMS Astute can circumnavigate the globe without surfacing

Astute

Galley
Five chefs provide a 24-hour service to the crew

Masts
Two masts carrying thermal imaging and low-light cameras replace the periscope. Breaking the surface for less than three seconds is enough for a 360-degree view of the surroundings. Six other masts service satellite, radar and navigation systems

Washing and sleeping
One bunk for each crew member and 11 extra bunks for passengers, most likely special forces soldiers. The 98 man crew share five showers, five toilets, two urinals and eight hand basins

How does a reactor power a submarine?

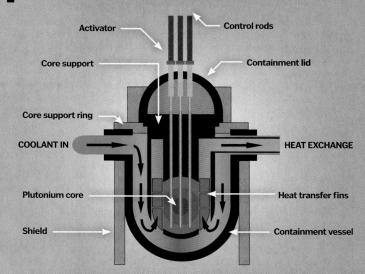

Astute's Rolls Royce PWR2 (Pressurised Water Reactor) contains enough nuclear fuel to power the submarine for its entire 25 year service. This energy is generated by nuclear fission that takes place inside a heavy shielded reactor compartment that protects the crew and environment from radiation. Water is pumped around a circuit where it is heated by the fission process, maintaining enough pressure to prevent the water from boiling. This heat is then used to generate steam, via steam generators, to drive the main turbine engines. A system of clutches and gearing drive a propulsor that transmits the power to propel the submarine. Steam is also used to drive the turbo-generators that supply the submarine with electricity.

MINI-GUIDE KEY
Each part of the submarine explained

1 Propeller
2 Upper rudder segment
3 Lower rudder segment
4 Starboard hydroplane
5 Aft anchor light
6 Rudder and hydroplane hydraulic actuators
7 No 4 main ballast tank
8 Propeller shaft
9 High pressure bottles
10 No 3 main ballast tank
11 Towed array cable drum and winch
12 Main ballast vent system
13 Aft pressure dome
14 Air treatment units
15 Naval stores
16 Propeller shaft thrust block and bearing
17 Circulating water transfer pipes
18 Lubricating oil tank
19 Starboard condenser
20 Main machinery mounting raft
21 Turbo generators, port and starboard
22 Combining gearbox

23 Main turbines
24 Steam delivery ducting
25 Engine room
26 Watertight bulkhead
27 Manoeuvring room
28 Manoeuvring room isolated deck mounting
29 Switchboard room
30 Diesel generator room
31 Static converters
32 Main steam valve
33 Reactor section
34 Part of pressure hull
35 Forward airlock
36 Air handling compartment
37 Waste management equipment
38 Conditioned air ducting
39 Galley
40 Forward section isolated deck mountings
41 Batteries
42 Junior ratings' mess
43 RESM office
44 Commanding officer's cabin

45 Port side communications office
46 Diesel exhaust mast
47 Snort induction mast
48 SHF/EHF (NEST) mast
49 CESM mast
50 AZL radar mast
51 Satcom mast
52 Integrated comms mast
53 Visual mast – starboard
54 Visual mast – port
55 Navigation mast
56 Bridge fin access
57 Junior ratings' bathroom
58 Senior ratings' bathroom
59 Battery switchroom
60 Control room consoles
61 Sonar operators' consoles
62 Senior ratings' bunks
63 Medical berth
64 Weapons stowage and handling compartment
65 Sonar array

66 Maintenance workshop
67 Sonar equipment room
68 Forward hydroplane
69 Hydroplane hydraulic actuator
70 Hydroplane hinge mounting
71 Ship's office
72 Junior ratings' berths
73 Torpedo tubes
74 Water transfer tank
75 Torpedo tube bow caps
76 Air turbine pump
77 No 2 main ballast tank
78 High pressure air bottles
79 Forward pressure dome
80 Weapons embarkation hatch
81 Gemini craft stowage
82 Hinged fairlead
83 Anchor windlass
84 No 1 main ballast tank
85 Anchor cable locker
86 Bow sonar

The sub that will rule the waves

Discover the awesome capabilities of the Royal Navy's latest supersub

When the first of the Astute-class subs finally enters full service it will not only be the Royal Navy's largest and most powerful nuclear attack submarines, but also the stealthiest.

Stealth is an important element of the submarine's operation because combined with advance sonar it enables the submarine to track, identify and neutralise an enemy before that vessel even knows the Astute is in the vicinity. Much of the equipment is shock mounted to prevent the transmission of sound and vibration into the surrounding ocean, and active vibration technology is also used with vibrating mounts tuned to a frequency effectively cancelling out the vibration of the equipment itself. There is also a multi-bladed propulsor housed at the rear and designed for near-silent running. The whole of the submarine casing is enveloped in a very dense rubber skin to reduce sound transmission into the ocean and also to diminish the submarine's own sonar profile. All this technology combines to make the submarine virtually invisible in the ocean.

In the cockpit itself, two Thales Optronics CM010 periscopes will ensure that Astute's commander never has to hunch over an optical periscope. Instead, the optronics masts are fitted with thermal imaging cameras, low light video and CCD TV sensors, replacing conventional line-of-sight systems to enable the Astute to first capture and then analyse any surface images. The masts are also non-hull penetrating, significantly reducing the risk of water leakage in the event of any damage the vessel may incur.

Astute is equipped with the Thales Sonar 2076, the world's most advanced sonar system, employing the processing power of 2,000 laptop computers to locate and identify other vessels that may be present across thousands of square miles of ocean. It is an integrated passive/active sonar that operates through hydrophones fitted to the bow, flanks and fin. However, details of Astute's counter measures are a closely guarded secret, in particular the exact thickness of the hull, which could be an indicator of dive performance. What we do know is that it is manufactured from special grade submarine steel and coated in over 39,000 rubberised acoustic tiles to mask its sonar signature. ✿

> "Despite weighing over 7,800 tons, Astute displays a sonar profile equivalent to a baby dolphin"

Plug and play
Some areas were manufactured as modules then carefully placed within the hull

The hull
Despite being the first part to emerge, Astute's hull is its most closely guarded secret

5 TOP FACTS
HMS ASTUTE

Slippery when wet
1 Despite weighing over 7,800 tons and measureing 97 metres in length, the Astute displays a sonar profile that is equivalent to a baby dolphin.

You are what you eat
2 On a ten-week patrol, the crew of Astute would get through an average of 18,000 sausages and 4,200 Weetabix for breakfast.

First in class
3 Since 1945 Barrow has built the 'first of class' for every Royal Navy submarine as well as every submarine currently in service with the Navy.

Too many cooks?
4 A team of five chefs (one petty officer caterer, one leading chef and three chefs) provide 24-hour service to the crew.

No easy task
5 One of the most challenging engineering projects in the UK, building Astute has been described as "more complex than the Space Shuttle."

DID YOU KNOW? If it was positioned in the English Channel the Astute could hit targets in North Africa

Weapons and missiles

When it comes to offensive capability, Astute marks a significant leap over the submarine classes it replaces. With a total of 38 Spearfish torpedoes and Tomahawk missiles – more than any previous RN submarine – and six 21-inch (533 mm) torpedo tubes, Astute has the capability to accurately engage targets over 1,000 miles away while remaining undetected.

Powered by a high-performance thermal engine, Spearfish has an analogue homing system and communicates with the launch submarine through a wire-guidance link.

Meanwhile the Tomahawk Block IV Land Attack Missile (LAM) is the latest version of McDonnell Douglas's medium-to-long range cruise missiles, designed to operate at low attitude and launch while the Astute is fully submerged. It is capable of delivering pin-point strikes 2,000km from the coast.

As far as defensive capabilities are concerned, Astute is armed with Boeing UGM-84 Harpoon anti-ship missiles. This short range turbo-fan propelled missile carries a single warhead and is designed for surface-to-surface strikes at a range of around 140km.

Spearfish torpedoes
Weighing nearly two tons, the Spearfish is a serious weapon

Tomahawk Block IV Land Attack Missile (LAM)
The UK is the only nation, other than the USA, to have the Tomahawk Block IV

Learn more

For additional information about HMS Astute, why not visit **www.naval-technology. com/projects/astute** where you can find more facts about this formidable addition to the Royal Navy fleet.

View from the bridge
An interview with Astute's commander

For Andy Coles, OBE, commanding Astute will mark the pinnacle of a 30-year Navy career that began as a radar operator. He told us what he's most looking forward to from the experience.

"HMS Astute is a keenly awaited and extremely capable submarine, which will prove to be a very potent weapon for the Royal Navy for the next 25 years. She represents a massive increase in capability over previous classes and I am really looking forward to putting the submarine through her paces during sea trials. Her offensive capability has been greatly enhanced. While she carries the same Spearfish torpedoes and Tomahawk Cruise missiles as previous classes, Astute's payload is significantly increased and a return to six torpedo tubes greatly enhances the flexibility. Astute is also the first submarine to have non hull-penetrating optronics masts, making it much easier for me to see what is happening on the surface as the picture is displayed on several large screens in the Control Room – the submarine's operations centre. One of the significant design changes is to enable the submarine to operate with Special Forces and I am looking forward to proving that part of the sea trials.

Of course, none of this technology would work if it wasn't for the people. Astute has been designed to reduce the manning at sea. I have a highly trained crew, from the officers, senior ratings and junior ratings who operate the submarine to marine engineers (propulsion, mechanical and electrical systems), weapon engineers to ensure the weapon and electrical systems are at maximum readiness and warfare specialists to operate them. Finally, I have a team of logisticians who look after everything from storing the submarine to providing three meals a day for over a hundred submariners."

> *"A skilled balloonist can manoeuvre horizontally by altering their altitude"*

Hot-air ballo

How do these gasbags get off the ground and return to Earth safely?

A hot-air balloon consists of three basic parts: an envelope big enough to displace a large amount of air, burners beneath the envelope to heat the air inside, and a basket in which to sit back and enjoy the ride. The scientific principle that enables this lift is convection, or heat transfer.

Heating the air inside the envelope causes it to expand, forcing some of the air out of the envelope. The weight of air inside then decreases, making the balloon lighter and giving it lift. Once the burner is shut off, however, the air inside cools and contracts, causing cold air to rush in from below, weighing the envelope down and causing the balloon to descend. If the burner is powered up intermittently, the balloon can maintain a pretty much constant altitude. Hot-air balloons have an upper limit because at very high altitudes the air is so thin that the lift is not actually strong enough to raise the balloon.

Because hot-air balloons have no real means of changing direction other than upwards and downwards, the vehicle will drift along with the wind. However, a skilled balloonist can manoeuvre horizontally by altering their altitude. You see, wind is known to blow in different directions at different heights and so the pilot can ascend or descend until they find the appropriate wind to send them in the direction they wish to travel. ✿

An alternative to queuing at the airport…

Envelope
Reinforced ripstop nylon fabric (also used for kites, sails and sleeping bags) is the principle material used for hot-air balloon envelopes. This lightweight fabric can also be coated with silicone to make it more hard-wearing.

What goes up...

The envelope is made from ripstop nylon

1. Inflation
A balloon crew inflate the envelope using a powerful fan to blow air in from the base of the envelope for several minutes.

2. Erection
To get the inflated envelope off the ground, the propane-fuelled burner beneath the envelope is placed at the entrance to the envelope and blasted.

4. Air expands and rises
Warm air expands and rises, causing about a quarter of the air to exit through the bottom of the envelope.

3. Burner on
The burner heats the air inside the envelope to a temperature of about 100°C. This causes the air particles to gain energy and move about faster and farther apart.

5. Ascent
The balloon ascends because the air inside the envelope is lighter and less dense than cold air outside.

5 TOP FACTS
HOT-AIR BALLOON FIRSTS

First across the Atlantic
1 In 1978 the Double Eagle II became the first balloon to cross the Atlantic. It took 137 hours for Ben Abruzzo, Maxie Anderson and Larry Newman to travel 3,120 miles.

Highest altitude
2 The highest manned trip in a hot-air balloon ever recorded was back in 2005 when Vijaypat Singhania (who was 67 at the time) took his balloon to 21,027m.

First across the Pacific
3 In 1991 entrepreneur Richard Branson and Per Lindstrand flew 7,671.91km from Japan to North Canada in just 47 hours on board the Virgin Pacific Flyer.

First round the globe
4 In 1999 the Breitling Orbiter 3 – piloted by Bertrand Piccard and Brian Jones – embarked on the first successful round the world trip in a hot-air balloon. It took them 19 days.

First solo round the globe
5 On his seventh attempt, Steve Fossett became the first successful solo balloonist to circumnavigate the globe. It took him 320 hours 33 minutes in 2002.

DID YOU KNOW? To lift a weight of 1,000lb you would need nearly 65,000 cubic feet of hot air

ons

Parachute vent
If the balloon needs to descend quickly, some colder air can enter via a parachute valve or vent in the top of the envelope controlled by a cord pulled by the pilot.

Turning up the heat gets you airborne...

Gores
To create the balloon shape from a flat piece of material, it must be cut into long panels (from the crown to the base) called gores. These gores are then stitched together to create the shape.

7. Air contracts
The cooler air contracts leaving space inside the envelope to suck in more cold air from below.

8. Descent
The increased weight of the cooler air inside the balloon exceeds the upthrust and so the balloon will start to sink.

6. Burner off
Shutting off the burner causes the air to cool down.

9. Landing
By gently controlling the burner and descent, the balloon will normally come in to land bouncing along the ground before stopping.

Propane tanks
Compressed liquid propane is stored in lightweight tanks in the basket.

Skirt
The flame-resistant material at the base of the envelope is called the skirt. This stops the rest of the envelope from catching fire.

10. Landing site
Given the relatively uncontrollable nature of directing a hot-air balloon, the landing site cannot always be predicted and so the pilot must select a large enough area free from pylons and bodies of water where they can lay out the envelope.

Burner
Liquid propane flows from the tanks through steel pipes coiled around the burner. When the balloonist triggers the burner, liquid propane flows out and is ignited by a pilot light. In the meantime this flame heats the metal pipes, turning the liquid propane into a gas that is more powerful and fuel-efficient than the liquid when it's cold.

Basket
Traditionally a hot-air balloon's basket is made of wicker because it's durable, flexible and lightweight. Today hot-air balloons can come with double-decker baskets that seat 50 people if necessary. Enclosed gondolas are also available for serious, long-distance ballooning.

219

Gearboxes

The gearbox is an essential part of a car's drivetrain, ensuring optimal acceleration and economy

Gear lever

Selectors

Synchromesh couplings

Constant mesh gears

You do it without thinking, but each time you change gear in a manual-transmission car, you fundamentally alter the relationship between the engine and the road wheels.

A gearbox is an essential component of a petrol- or diesel-engined vehicle because in order to develop enough power, the engine has to be spinning faster than the wheels are turning. For instance, let's say the engine needs to run at 4,000 revolutions per minute (rpm) to drive the car at 70mph, at which speed the wheels will, typically, only be turning at 1,000rpm. In other words, the output from the engine must be slowed down.

This is done with gears, which are basically toothed wheels that mesh with each other. If you have two gearwheels, one twice the diameter of the other, each time the small one makes one full rotation, the large one will make just half a turn – it will drive at half the speed. In addition, the torque produced will be doubled.

A car gearbox has an input shaft from the engine (via a clutch which allows the engine and gearbox to be separated) with a small gearwheel that drives a larger one on the layshaft, which has a number of different-sized gearwheels on. When the gearstick is moved, one of these gears will engage in one of a number of wheels on the output shaft that leads to the differential, which contains more gears to slow the output further, and then to the road wheels. Depending on which combination of gears are engaged, the engine will be rotating faster or slower in relation to the road wheels.

In first gear, the engine is turning relatively fast which ensures it has plenty of power to get the car moving. As the vehicle's speed increases, the driver works up through the gears, so that the engine doesn't rev too high. Using a high gear keeps the engine speed low, which saves fuel but does mean that there is less torque available to accelerate or get up a hill, so a lower gear then needs to be selected. ✿

The Jaws of Life

Metal-piercing, door-prising engineering – the Jaws of Life save many lives

Buckled and twisted car wrecks can trap victims in a metal cage impossible to pull open by hands alone. Under the impact of an accident, only certain tools can do the job of separating steel from steel. The Jaws of Life are a set of tools vital to a fireman's inventory. Where a person is trapped or crushed by a vehicle, fast access to powerful tools can save that person's life.

The name was coined by Hurst Performance Inc, and the Jaws of Life are split into three individual tools: cutters, rams and spreaders. Firemen or rescue workers use these life-saving devices to cut metal in two, prise open twisted doors, and shift and hold objects that would otherwise be too heavy to move. The cutters and spreaders can sometimes be seen as one tool, but are still treated separately.

Hydraulic power is the driving force behind these brilliant tools, proving to be a safe and reliable source. Operated by pistons and special heat and electrical resistant hydraulic fluid, the Jaws of Life can move in either direction by control of a valve.

The cutters of the Jaws of Life are heat-treated steel, and are the teeth of the machinery. They cut metal in half with a single bite and are ideal for detaching car roofs. Spreaders are used to open doors and to ease pressure off of trapped victims. They can open up a gap of 40 inches to create areas large enough for a person to wriggle free. Rams are driving rods that are used to prop up dashboards, or to move a collapsed steering column over a victim's legs. These are specially designed for pushing and pulling large weights and can reach distances of up to five feet.

They can save lives and give victims those vital minutes, which is why they are one of the most important engineering feats of the 21st Century. ✿

The rams open up gaps in crumpled cars

The hydraulic ram itself can extend up to five feet

© Daniel Schmen 2008

Ram facts
- 15,708 pounds opening force
- 5 feet extended length
- 3.1 inches in width

The cutters of the Jaws of Life slide through metal

These tubes carry hydraulic fluid

© Derek Elland 2006

Cutter facts
- 94,000 pounds cutting force
- 9 inches cutter opening
- 41 pounds in weight

The tips of a spreader open gaps of up to 40 inches

Spreaders can change their direction of power

© Malachite36 2006

Spreader facts
- 18,900 pounds spreading force
- 12,100 pounds pulling force
- 40 inches opening distance

Head to Head
REFUELLING EVOLUTION

1923

1. Basic
The first mid-air refuelling took place on 27 June 1923 between two US Army Air Service biplanes, allowing a DH-4B biplane to remain aloft for over 37 hours.

1963

2. Standard
The introduction of jet planes and supertankers meant aircraft needed to be – and more importantly could be – refuelled quicker and at higher speeds.

2008

3. Advanced
High-speed supersonic aircraft, such as this F-18A, are refuelled by colossal flying tankers using boom and drogue automated systems.

DID YOU KNOW? The world's first dedicated aerial fuel tanker was the Boeing KC-97 Stratotanker, built in 1950

Probe
The extended hose allows for an aircraft to be refuelled mid-flight, allowing for longer periods spent in the skies.

The probe-and-drogue system being used to refuel an S-3 Viking

Drogue
The shuttlecock-shaped drogue stabilises the hose and acts as a funnel when the probe is attempting to make a connection.

In-flight refuelling

Nozzle control
In a flying boom system, the boomer flies the nozzle into alignment with the receptacle by positioning the ruddervators with a control stick.

How It Works looks at the technology that is allowing military aircraft to stay in the air for extended periods of time

Aerial refuelling is the process of transferring fuel from one aircraft to another while in mid-flight in order to allow the receiving aircraft to continue operations for extended periods of time. This is a crucial factor for military aircraft while operating in war zones as it allows a round-the-clock instantaneous response time, meaning aircraft can support troops faster and more effectively. In-flight refuelling also allows aircraft to take-off with a greater armament payload to fuel reserve ratio, as it can receive more fuel while airborne.

Currently, there are two methods used in aerial refuelling procedures. The first option is a probe and drogue system, where fuel is transferred down a suspended, flexible hose to an aircraft's receptor probe. The other choice is a flying boom system where fuel is transferred down a static pipe extension and guided into the aircraft's fuel receptor by a human engineer. Hybrid systems, where both aforementioned systems are combined, also exist but they are rare, often being used to refuel helicopters instead of jet aircraft.

The boom and receptacle system – also called a 'flying boom' – allows for greater amounts of fuel to be transferred to the target aircraft faster than probe and drogue due to its rigid telescoping tube. The tube is stabilised when extended by twin wings, mounted on either side, which the operator – referred to as a 'boomer' – controls within the tanker-carrying aircraft to make adjustments to its positioning. The receiving aircraft's pilot then collaborates with the boomer – using radio communication and visual cues, such as flashing lights – to make a clean connection between boom and receptacle.

The probe and drogue system refuels aircraft differently, restricting the speed at which fuel can be transferred but allowing for greater flexibility and numbers of aircraft being refuelled at one time. The system employs a flexible hose (there can be multiple hoses) from the tanker aircraft that trails behind it, often from either of its wings. On the end of the hose lies the drogue, a shuttlecock shaped conical basket – this both stabilises the hose while trailed and also provides the receiving aircraft's probe a funnel aid when attempting to make a connection. Fuel flow is controlled from within the tanker aircraft, with a series of green and red lights indicating to the pilot of the receiving aircraft when fuel is flowing and when to disengage. ✿

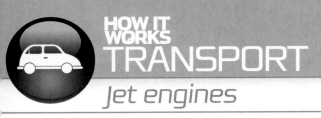

Jet engine

Despite its immense power and capabilities, in many ways a jet engine is less complex than the engine in your car

The very first aircraft used engine-driven propellers to drive them through the air and, of course, many planes still use propellers today. However, if you want to achieve serious speed in the air then you're going to need an awful lot of thrust, and for that you need a jet engine.

To demonstrate how a jet works, hold a high-pressure hosepipe up to the palm of your hand – the pressure of the water squirting out the end will try to push your hand back. In fact, the engine on a jet ski works by firing water out of a nozzle to drive the vessel forward.

The simplest form of jet is the firework rocket, which dates back to the 13th Century. An explosive is ignited and the resultant gases are propelled out of a nozzle which creates thrust to push the rocket forwards. Rocket engines in spacecraft work in the same way; they're simple but use a huge amount of fuel in a short time, and aren't practical for everyday use.

Most so-called jet planes have turbofan gas-turbine engines. Near the front of the engine is a compressor, which is essentially a larger number of vanes that suck air in, compress it, and then force it at high-pressure into a combustion chamber. At this point the air is moving at hundreds of miles an hour.

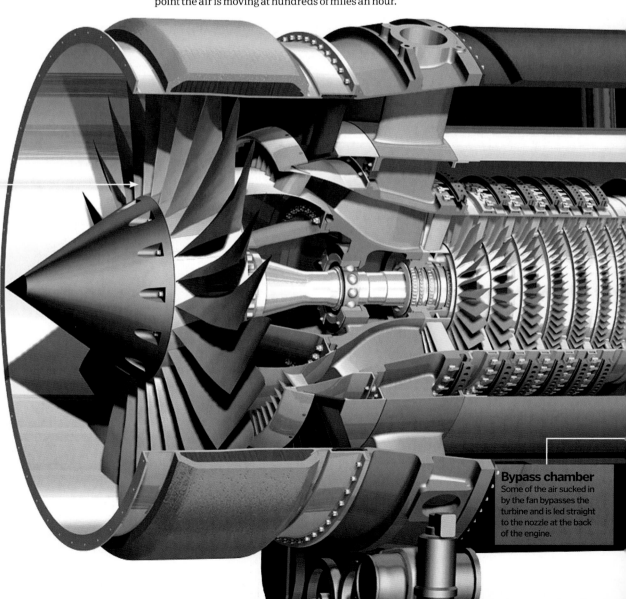

Fan
Works like a propeller to draw air into the engine, some of which is bypassed straight to the back.

Bypass chamber
Some of the air sucked in by the fan bypasses the turbine and is led straight to the nozzle at the back of the engine.

Head to Head
Jet engines

POWERFUL

1. Olympus 593 turbojet

Facts: Concorde's 593 turbojet engines had afterburners that developed 169.2kN of thrust.

MORE POWERFUL

2. GE90-115B

Facts: The GE90-115B was developed for the Boeing 777 and develops 568kN of thrust, making it the most powerful commercial jet engine.

MOST POWERFUL

3. Saturn V F-1

Facts: The F-1 that powered the Saturn V launch vehicle produced 7,740.5Kn of thrust. It's the most powerful single-chamber rocket engine.

DID YOU KNOW? *Jet engines react according to Newton's third law of motion: every action has an equal and opposite reaction*

Fuel is injected into the combustion chamber, where it mixes with the fast-moving compressed air and is ignited. The hot gases then pass back where they drive a turbine which, in turn, provides propulsion for the aforementioned compressor. The remaining energy is expelled from a nozzle at the back of the engine to create forward thrust.

At the very front of a turbofan engine is a large fan that also sucks air in. Some of this air is picked up by the compressor but the rest bypasses the main turbine and is led around to the back of the engine where it supplies additional thrust.

Because a turbofan relies on the rotating turbine to drive the compressor and fan, and the turbine can't turn without air from the compressor, it needs help to get started. This is done with compressed air that spins the compressor and fan at such a speed that, when the fuel is ignited, there is enough airflow to ensure the hot gases are thrust backwards and don't explode.

Compared to the internal combustion engines used in cars and propeller-driven aircraft, a turbofan is reassuringly free of complex parts and so is extremely reliable. Which in the case of an aeroplane is reassuringly good news. ⚙

Sir Frank Whittle

Sir Frank Whittle is credited with inventing the modern jet engine, along with German Hans von Ohain, who independently came up with a similar idea at the same time.

Born in Coventry in 1907, Whittle trained as an RAF officer and wrote a thesis on future aircraft which considered the idea of using a piston engine to create compressed air for thrust. He abandoned that plan but later thought of using a turbine in place of a conventional engine. He passed his idea to the Air Ministry but was told that it would never work.

Undeterred, Whittle raised finance to set up his own company, Power Jets Limited. He struggled to keep it going until, with the Second World War looming, the Air Ministry finally realised the project's potential and began to fund it. Finally, in 1939, the Air Ministry commissioned the Gloster Whittle – the first British jet plane, soon after the Germans trialled their Heinkel He 178 – the world's very first jet aircraft.

Whittle later moved to the United States, where he died in 1996 but is still remembered for changing the face of aviation forever.

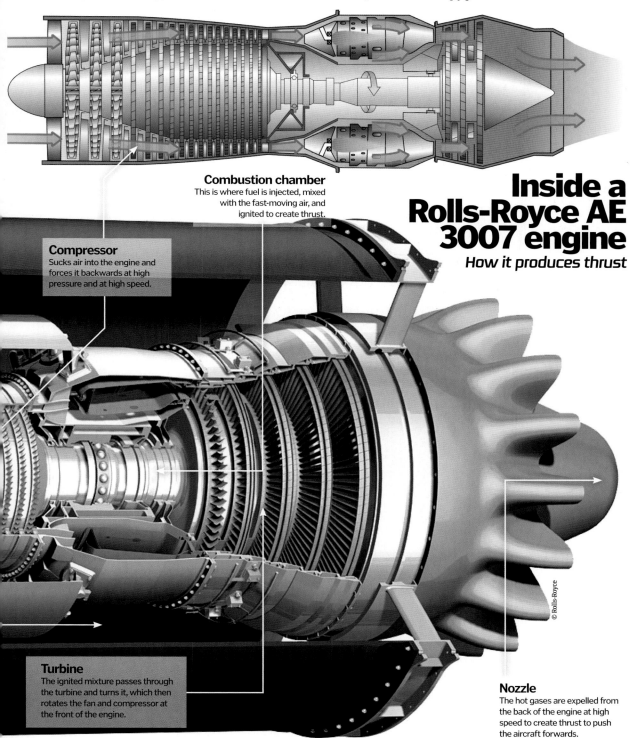

Compressor
Sucks air into the engine and forces it backwards at high pressure and at high speed.

Combustion chamber
This is where fuel is injected, mixed with the fast-moving air, and ignited to create thrust.

Inside a Rolls-Royce AE 3007 engine
How it produces thrust

© Rolls-Royce

Turbine
The ignited mixture passes through the turbine and turns it, which then rotates the fan and compressor at the front of the engine.

Nozzle
The hot gases are expelled from the back of the engine at high speed to create thrust to push the aircraft forwards.

"Once the driver starts the vehicle, the compressed hydrogen along with oxygen from the air will flow into the fuel cell"

Hydrogen-p

Discover how future hydrogen cars produce zero emissions have and less dependence upon foreign fossil fuels

There are two basic types of hydrogen car, including those that run on PEM (proton exchange membrane) fuel cells and those which burn hydrogen (H2) inside an internal combustion engine (ICE). All major car manufacturers have developed one or both of these types of vehicles.

The most popular of these two varieties are those that run on hydrogen fuel cells. This is because these are seen as zero-emission vehicles that will not contribute to greenhouse gases but will help towards breaking the dependence upon foreign fossil fuels.

The fuel cell car works as follows. Drivers at a refuelling station will pump compressed hydrogen gas into the vehicle's tank. Once the driver starts the engine, the compressed hydrogen along with oxygen from the air will flow into the fuel cell.

The positive and negative ions of hydrogen molecules will split around the fuel cell creating an electrical charge. On the backside of the fuel cell, the hydrogen ions join with the oxygen to form water vapour which flows out the tailpipe of the vehicle. The electrical current created by the fuel cell flows to an electric motor, which powers the wheels of the car.

The hydrogen ICE vehicle is a bit more simplistic in that it uses either compressed or liquid hydrogen and burns it inside the cylinders of the engine. Near zero tailpipe emissions are created when burning hydrogen in this fashion. ICE vehicles are currently cheaper to build or retrofit than fuel cell vehicles. ✿

3. Hydrogen fuel cell
The hydrogen PEM fuel cell takes in hydrogen gas from the tank along with ambient air from the atmosphere to create electricity for the electric motor.

5. Power drive unit (PDU)
The high-performance, compact PDU governs the electrical flow from the fuel cell to the high voltage electric motor.

4. Electric motor
The AC synchronous permanent-magnet electric motor, rated at 134hp and 100kw, provides front-wheel drive for the Clarity.

6. Hydrogen supply and humidifier systems
Compressed hydrogen gas flows from the tanks to the fuel cell and is humidified along the way, partly recycled from the waste steam from the reaction in the fuel cell.

Hydrogen cars Important moments in hydrogen car development

1807
Francois Isaac de Rivaz of Switzerland built the very first automobile to burn hydrogen inside an internal combustion engine.

1860
Etienne Lenoir of France built the Hippomobile, which was later fuelled by electrolysing water and using the hydrogen in a one-cylinder engine.

1941
During World War II, Boris Shelishch had converted a GAZ-AA truck to run off hydrogen after Nazi's had cut off Russian oil supplies.

CLEAN

1. Bio-fuel car
These vehicles use an internal combustion engine and may run on ethanol, biodiesel or other available non-fossil based fuels.

CLEANER

2. Plug-in hybrid
The plug-in hybrid (PHEV) combines the zero emissions of an electric car with a small engine as a mileage range extender.

CLEANEST

3. Electric car
EVs (electric vehicles) are zero emissions vehicles that the owner can recharge at home. These vehicles are mainly useful for making short trips.

DID YOU KNOW? The estimated cost of producing a Honda Clarity is $300,000 per car

owered cars

1. Hydrogen tank
Compressed hydrogen tank holds 3.92kg at 5,000psi and has passed all crash safety tests. It holds enough hydrogen to propel the vehicle 240 to 270 miles.

2. Lithium-ion battery
The lithium-ion battery makes the FCX Clarity a hybrid vehicle. It provides extra acceleration when needed and is recharged from regenerative braking.

The Statistics
Honda FCX Clarity

Manufacturer: Honda
Dimensions: Length: 190.3in, width: 72.7in, height: 57.8 inches
Driving range: 240-270 miles
Required fuel: Compressed hydrogen gas at 5,000psi
Estimated price: Leasing to select customers at $600/month
Carb emissions rating: Zero emission
Status: First production hydrogen fuel cell hybrid car available for lease to select customers in Japan and the US

Bringing down the cost of filling up

Hydrogen fuel cells

The hydrogen PEM fuel cell vehicle works by taking H2 from the compressed hydrogen tank and then running it along with oxygen from the air through a fuel cell. Hydrogen gas is channelled to the anode of the fuel cell while the oxygen is channelled to the cathode.

On the anode side, a catalyst (such as platinum) splits the hydrogen atom into protons (positively charged) and electrons (negatively charged). The PEM allows only the protons to pass through it to the cathode. The electrons must pass along an external circuit, which is how electricity is created.

1959
Harry Karl Ihrig created the first fuel cell vehicle (FCV), which is an Allis-Chalmers farm tractor which is now at the Smithsonian Institute.

1966
General Motors researchers created the Electrovan, which is the first hydrogen fuel cell car of record that resembles the FCVs of today.

1979
The BMW 520h prototype was built which had an internal combustion engine that could run on either hydrogen or gasoline.

1999
The Honda FCX-V1 prototype is created. It used a Ballard fuel cell for power and a 49kw electric motor.

History
FCX-V1, FCX-V2 (1999)

> "A mixture of hydrogen gas and ambient air is drawn into the engine where a spark ignites the H2"

H2ICE

Under the hood of a hydrogen internal combustion engine

Hydrogen internal combustion engines (H2ICE) work in a similar fashion to gasoline engines. Mazda uses a Wankel rotary engine and BMW, Ford and others use a piston engine, but the concept is the same. A mixture of hydrogen gas and ambient air is drawn into the engine where a spark ignites the H2. Hydrogen has a higher flame speed than gasoline, burning more quickly so timing adjustments need to be made. Also, since H2 is the smallest atom, it is prone to leaks, so couplings and fittings also need to be adjusted.

Specialist tanks are needed to transport the fuel

The Statistics
BMW Hydrogen 7

Manufacturer: BMW
Dimensions: Length: 205in, width: 74.9in, height: 58.4 inches
Driving range: Driving range is 125 miles on hydrogen and an additional 300 miles on gasoline
Required fuel: Hydrogen or gasoline
Estimated price: No price as it is being loaned to high-profile enthusiasts only
Carb emissions rating: Near zero emissions when using hydrogen
Status: Limited series production luxury vehicle

4. Heat exchanger
Here the liquid hydrogen is warmed into gaseous H2 to prevent sensors and valves failing and for use in the ICE.

2. Cryogenic tank
The cryogenic hydrogen tank contains liquid H2 at -423 degrees Fahrenheit and is super-insulated to prevent boil off.

3. Gasoline tank
The 16.3 gallon gasoline tank can propel the vehicle 300 miles and can be switched off or on to hydrogen at the touch of a button.

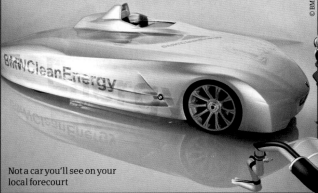

Not a car you'll see on your local forecourt

1. Hydrogen ICE
The BMW Hydrogen 7 runs on a dual-fuel hydrogen internal combustion engine using either hydrogen or gasoline for power.

Mix it up
Gaseous hydrogen (green arrow) is flowing from the pressure control valve and mixing with ambient air (blue arrows) as both are drawn into the engine's cylinders for combustion with gasoline for power.

5 TOP FACTS
USES OF HYDROGEN

Water
1 Hydrogen is the most abundant element in the universe and on planet Earth. Our oceans and drinking water are primarily hydrogen, so there's plenty of it available.

Refining gasoline
2 One of hydrogen's many practical uses includes using it to refine crude oil and remove sulphur to create the gasoline and diesel fuel we use in our cars.

Weather balloons
3 High-altitude weather balloons are typically filled with hydrogen due to low cost and the ascent rate, which can be easily controlled using the correct methods.

Making margarine
4 Hydrogen is used in the hydrogenation process to turn liquid corn oil or sunflower oil into margarine, perfect for spreading on your toast in the mornings.

Bleaching the body
5 Hydrogen peroxide has been used in current times to safely bleach a person's hair or teeth, and you can often spot when someone's had this done from a mile away.

DID YOU KNOW? *California aims to have 46 hydrogen stations in place by 2014*

Hydrogen refuelling stations

A vision of the petrol station forecourts of the future

Hydrogen refuelling stations may dispense compressed hydrogen gas, cryogenic liquid hydrogen or possibly even both. Those that dispense compressed H2 do so at two different pressures including 5,000psi (360 bar) or 10,000psi (700 bar).

The advantage of dispensing hydrogen at 10,000psi is that the hydrogen cars can travel approximately twice the distance than at the lower pressure. Most hydrogen produced today for refuelling stations is made by high temperature steam reforming of natural gas.

Hydrogen molecules from both the steam and natural gas are separated from the other molecules including CO_2. In recent years, more renewable hydrogen is being created using wind or solar energy to electrolyse water (H_2O), producing hydrogen (H_2) and oxygen (O). Another type of H2 refuelling station that is currently being developed is one for the home so that car owners can refuel in the privacy of their own garages.

Canadian hydrogen energy expert Air Liquide supplied fuel for the hydrogen fuel station that served a fleet of 20 zero-emission buses that carried visitors to and from the 2010 Winter Games.

The future of motoring?

We compare some of the hottest hydrogen cars from motoring's biggest names

The Statistics
X-8 Hydrogen RE

Manufacturer: Mazda
Dimensions: Length: 174.6in, width: 69.7in, height: 52.8 inches
Driving range: In hydrogen mode, 62 miles. In gasoline mode, 341 miles
Required fuel: Compressed hydrogen (dual fuel car)
Estimated price: Not for sale
Carb emissions rating: Hydrogen mode, near zero emissions
Status: Limited production using as a fleet vehicle in Japan

The Statistics
B-Class F-Cell

Manufacturer: Mercedes-Benz
Dimensions: Length: 168.2in, width: 70in, height: 63.1 inches
Driving range: 250 miles
Required fuel: Compressed hydrogen gas
Estimated price: Not for sale, but estimate price for a lease is $800/month
Carb emissions rating: Zero emissions
Status: Limited production as the plan is for 200 to be manufactured in 2010

The Statistics
Chevy Equinox Fuel Cell

Manufacturer: General Motors
Dimensions: Length: 188.8in, width: 71.4in, height: 69.3 inches
Driving range: 200-250 miles
Required fuel: Compressed hydrogen gas
Estimated price: Not for sale, only on loan to members of Project Driveway
Carb emissions rating: Zero emissions
Status: Limited production SUV

The Statistics
FCHV-adv

Manufacturer: Toyota
Dimensions: Length: 186.4in, width: 71.4in, height: 66.3 inches
Driving range: 450+ miles
Required fuel: Compressed hydrogen gas
Estimated price: Not for sale
Carb emissions rating: Zero emissions
Status: Currently a prototype, planned production in 2015

227

HOW IT WORKS

HISTORY
Discover How It Worked...

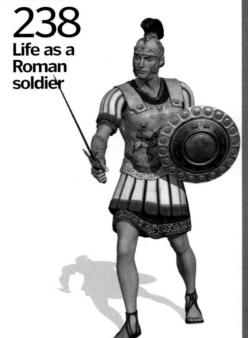

categories explained

Ancient world

Buildings & places

Industry

Inventions

Medieval times

People & places

Weapons & war

General

HOW IT WORKS
HISTORY

240
Mystery of the great pyramid

250
Dinosaurs: the prehistoric predators explained

239
How windmills worked

244
HMS Victory

"Medieval castles began to appear around 1066AD with the invasion of William the Conquerer"

The defensive duties of a castle

Inside a medieval castle

The inner wall
Up to four metres thick, with seven guard towers, the inner wall can only be reached by going through a dark passageway and the great square tower, making it difficult for intruders to find their way to the keep.

Master's lodgings
This room on the second floor of the keep is circular. Unlike many residential quarters in castles, it is elaborately and elegantly decorated.

Moat
This moat is at the south end between the outer and inner wall. Horses drank from it, and the water was used to fill baths.

Stone slope
Crusaders built this 24-metre thick stone slope to protect the castle's south side. Its smoothness made it difficult for invaders to scale.

Why did castles die out?
Gunpowder came into use in the 13th Century and spelled the end of castles as military strongholds. Thick, high stone walls could withstand the forces of catapults and trebuchets, but did not hold up as well against cannon fire. Some castles functioned solely as private residences for nobles and were built on aesthetic principles. Defensive castles evolved into castle-fortresses, with low-angled walls and rounded towers.

DID YOU KNOW?

The world's largest castle...
According to Guinness World Records, the world's largest castle is Prague Castle. Built around 880 CE by Prince BoDivoj, Prague Castle is actually a complex of towers, palaces and other buildings in various architectural styles. It covers nearly 70,000 square metres.

The stereotypical fairy tale castle design was actually the result of centuries of improvement upon existing structures

Medieval castles were an important part of feudal society. They began to appear around 1066 AD with the invasion of William the Conqueror. As he moved through England, Scotland and Wales, William had more than 30 castles built to help maintain power over his newly conquered lands. These castles served as bases for lords who held land from king and pledged loyalty and military service to him in return. These lords leased parts of their land to lesser lords and barons, who had knights that served under them.

These imposing structures had multiple functions. Castles were bases of offensive operations, defensive strongholds, seats of government and private residences for land-holding barons, knights and lords and their families. Most were built in stages over long periods of time and modified as greater defences were needed. Although their structures varied, they generally consisted of a tall building in the centre, which could function as a residence, prison or storage area, surrounded by one or more walls. Some castles were built on a mountain or hilltop, or on the edges of cliffs, to make invasion that little bit more difficult. ✿

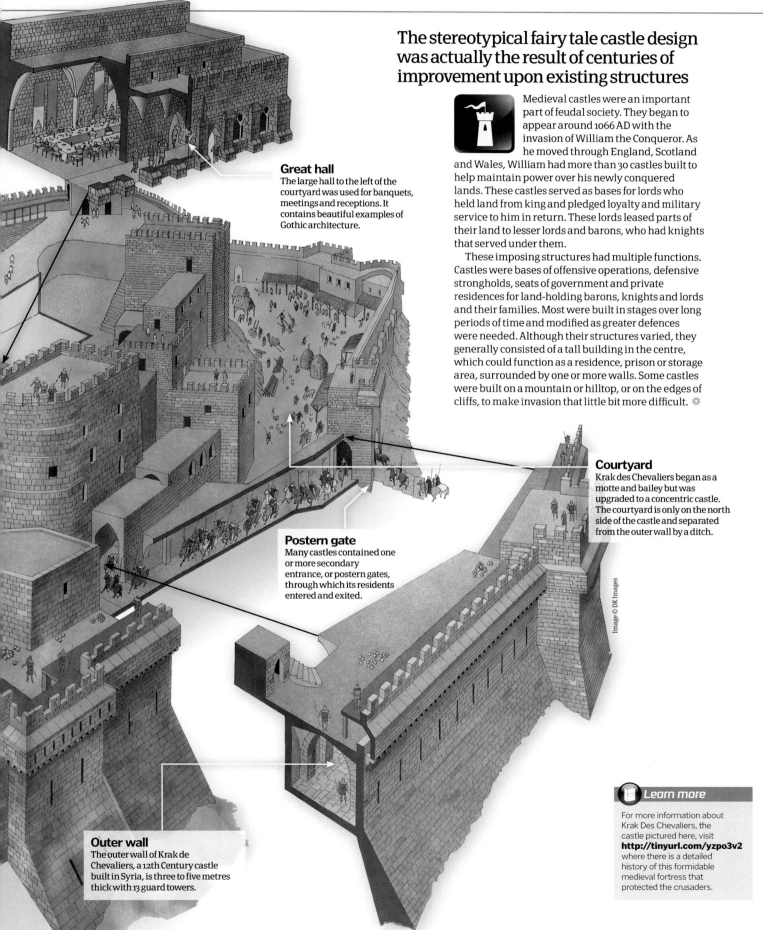

Great hall
The large hall to the left of the courtyard was used for banquets, meetings and receptions. It contains beautiful examples of Gothic architecture.

Courtyard
Krak des Chevaliers began as a motte and bailey but was upgraded to a concentric castle. The courtyard is only on the north side of the castle and separated from the outer wall by a ditch.

Postern gate
Many castles contained one or more secondary entrance, or postern gates, through which its residents entered and exited.

Outer wall
The outer wall of Krak de Chevaliers, a 12th Century castle built in Syria, is three to five metres thick with 13 guard towers.

Image © DK Images

Learn more
For more information about Krak Des Chevaliers, the castle pictured here, visit **http://tinyurl.com/yzpo3v2** where there is a detailed history of this formidable medieval fortress that protected the crusaders.

"Göring inherited a Luftwaffe of great numbers and experience"

Battle of Britain

70 years ago an epic conflict took place between allied and axis powers. It was one of the defining moments of World War II and changed the nature of armed conflict forever

The Battle of Britain was an exclusively aerial campaign between allied and axis forces which began in the summer of 1940 and culminated in May of 1941. The objective of the German-led aerial assault on Britain was to completely destroy the Royal Air Force (RAF) and render Fighter Command useless, so a planned land invasion of Britain could begin. The Luftwaffe (Germany's air force) was ordered by Hitler to drive the RAF from the skies in 'the shortest possible time'. Led by notable WWI veteran fighter pilot Hermann Wilhelm Göring, the then Reich Minister of Aviation, what was to follow was a costly – in both human and monetary terms – battle of attrition.

At the head of Britain's defence was Hugh Dowding, the then Air Chief Marshal of the RAF and Fighter Command, which had been set up in 1936 to oversee and manage Britain's emerging modern air force. Fighter Command led its RAF-based defence of Britain from Bentley Priory, London, communicating with airfields, radar stations, pilots and other communications headquarters over the south east (where the majority of the battle took place) and other regions of the country. At his disposal was a well-ordered yet numerically inferior air force to that of the Germans, with many pilots lacking valuable experience.

Contrary to Dowding, Göring inherited a Luftwaffe of great numbers and experience, with many of its pilots having gained valuable flight experience in WWI. This allowed Göring and his commanders to launch large raids on Britain – one of the most notable being a 500-strong assault on 15 September 1940 – causing large damage to a wide variety of areas and military buildings as well as, by the end of the war, 43,000 civilian deaths. Despite Göring's leadership, his other commanders held differences of opinion in how the RAF should be toppled – a factor that Dowding also had to deal with among Britain's commanders in how to defend the country.

Despite their experience and numbers, Germany failed to gain air superiority over Britain and by the end of the Battle they had lost 1,152 aircraft and 1,144 crew, compared to Britain's losses of 1,085 aircraft and 446 crew. Retrospectively, this result was caused by a single piece of state-of-the-art technology, as we find out over the page. ✿

A British air observer scans the skies for enemy bombers

Fighter Command
The men who led Britain's resistance

Name: Hugh Dowding
Rank: Air Chief Marshal
Description: An experienced officer, Dowding was set to retire shortly before WWII, only to be persuaded to stay on until the situation had stabilised. He is often credited as the mastermind behind Britain's success in the Battle of Britain.

Name: Keith Park
Rank: Air Vice Marshal
Description: In tactical command during the Battle of Britain, Park was in-charge of protecting London from attack. Flying a personalised Hurricane, Park held a reputation as a shrewd tactician.

Name: Trafford Leigh-Mallory
Rank: Air Officer Commanding
Description: The commander of 11 Group RAF had open disagreements with Park and Dowding over the tactics to counter the German threat. He was credited as creating the 'Big Wing' fighter formation to hunt German bombers.

Luftwaffe
The men who led the German attack

Name: Hermann Wilhelm Göring
Rank: Reich Minister of Aviation
Description: The last commander of legendary ace fighter pilot 'The Red Baron', Göring was responsible for German Luftwaffe. In his youth he had flown in the First World War and was respected by the Germans as a notable commander.

Name: Hugo Sperrle
Rank: General Field Marshal
Description: General Field Marshal of the Luftwaffe, Sperrle advised Hitler that the destruction of Britain's air force was key to winning the war. Air Fleet 3, which he commanded, played a major role in the battle but suffered heavy losses.

Name: Albert Kesselring
Rank: General Field Marshal
Description: Kesselring orchestrated combat in Poland, France and at the Battle of Britain. He is credited with the Coventry Blitz of November 1940 and won the respect of allied powers with his military accomplishments.

Head to Head
ICONIC PLANES

FAMOUS
1. Hawker Hurricane
The real hero, the Hurricane shot down more aircraft than either of its contemporaries and was the workhorse of the RAF.

MORE FAMOUS
2. Messerschmitt
Classed as heavy fighters, the Messerschmitt Bf 109E and Bf 110C were the Luftwaffe's main aerial threat and shot down many allied planes.

MOST FAMOUS
3. Spitfire
The most iconic fighter of World War II, the Spitfire was a formidable opponent, packing firepower, flexibility and unparalleled dynamism.

DID YOU KNOW? The RAF lost 1,085 planes during the Battle of Britain, while the Luftwaffe lost 1,152

Battle map

Charting the key military bases, RAF and Luftwaffe HQs, radar stations, and squadrons that took part in the Battle of Britain

Due to Germany's occupation of France, they could set up military bases at Calais and other coastal cities along the Channel. This put the German bombers in range of London and left the area to its south east (Kent) exposed to many attacks. Indeed, the majority of the Battle of Britain was fought over the south east of England and this led to the majority of Britain's air force bases being heavily used in the area. 11 Group RAF were responsible for protecting London and the south east, and they saw much action and suffered the bulk of the casualties during enemy attacks. As we see over the page, the careful and strategic use of the newly emerging technology of radar gave Britain valuable insight into the activities of approaching aircraft across the Channel, especially at night when countering German bombers in low-visibility situations.

Heinkel He 111's running aircraft bombing raids over Kent during the Battle of Britain

A Spitfire flies over the south east of England

Key:
- ○ Fighter command bases
- ⊕ Luftwaffe fighter bases
- + Luftwaffe bomber bases
- –·– RAF group boundaries
- –– Luftflotte boundaries
- — Range of Messerschmitt BF 109
- ‿ Range of low-level radar
- ⌒ Range of high-level radar

13 GROUP

12 GROUP

10 GROUP

11 GROUP

LUFTFLOTTE 2

LUFTFLOTTE 3

A selection of pilots from 303 Squadron walk away from their aircraft

© Hohum

233

"The main advantage that radar gave was
the ability to launch intercepting attack
aircraft at the right time"

How the battle was won

Thanks to the skilful implementation of the emerging technology of radar, allied forces were better equipped to counter German attacks

The importance of radar in the Battle of Britain was massive, something that its then leader Hugh Dowding knew all too well. Britain was facing larger numbers of enemy aircraft, pilots with more flight experience and frequent bombing runs in the dead of night – the favoured time for German attacks. Radar then was key, allowing enemy airborne movement to be tracked from across the Channel and, crucially, allowing Britain's smaller air force to be managed more acutely.

The main advantage that radar gave was the ability to launch intercepting attack aircraft at the right time. Not too early, forcing planes to reland for refuelling, leaving them vulnerable to attack and costing cash-strapped Britain in fuel bills. And equally not too late, giving the German planes a crucial height advantage in the proceeding dogfight and allowing them to reach inland areas of Britain. Dowding, operating his stringent Fabian Strategy, used this to great effect, having information on approaching aircraft sent from coastal stations to Bentley Priory (Fighter Command headquarters) with great haste so that finessed tactical plans could be quickly drawn up and relayed to air force bases.

The system did have drawbacks however. While radar was excellent and highly accurate in detecting aircraft movement, it was quite poor in expressing the numbers of aircraft and their formations, two factors crucial in decision-making if an effective

resistance was to be mounted. Because of this, Dowding's system also incorporated RDF-based detection – which allowed formations to be determined as they formed over France – and the pre-existing Observer Corps, groups of mainly volunteer civilians dotted throughout Britain, visually relaying information on approaching aircraft numbers and formations to Fighter Command. Indeed, many historians argue that without the Observer Corps, no matter how refined Britain's radar-based systems became, the Battle of Britain would've been lost – an opinion vocalised by Dowding when he said that "they constituted the whole means of tracking enemy raids once they had crossed the coastline. Their works throughout [the war] was quite invaluable."

Importantly, despite the benefits radar was providing Britain's air force, Göring and his commanders underestimated its ability and importance in what was going to be the deciding factor in the Battle of Britain. While initially the Luftwaffe were ordered to attack RAF radar stations (an activity they completed with little success, knocking out only one radar station on the Isle of Wight for under 24 hours), their attention was soon turned to the towns and cities of Britain, as their grip on the conflict slackened. It is generally agreed by historians that if Göring had persisted with his targeting of Britain's radar stations, Germany would have had considerably more success than they historically achieved.

Hawker Hurricanes fly in a single line formation above Britain

Members of the RAF Observer Corps count and identify incoming raids

RAF and WAAF staff plot bombing raids at RAF Uxbridge

303 Squadron

The Battle of Britain saw over a thousand enemy aircraft shot down by British RAF squadrons, and none more so than the famous Polish 303s. No. 303 Polish Fighter Squadron was one of 16 Polish squadrons in the Royal Air Force during the Second World War and won acclaim for their marksmanship and aerial ability during the conflict. Scoring higher than any other squadron, 303 competed with other RAF squadrons in a competition as to who could shoot down the most enemy aircraft. By the end of the Battle of Britain they had won unequivocally, recording an immense 808 hits. In fact, the top three places in this competition's leaderboard were taken by three of the 12 Polish squadrons, outgunning the best British squadron by far, who only racked up 150 hits.

A 303 captured Messerschmitt sporting anti-Hitler graffiti

5 TOP FACTS
BATTLE OF BRITAIN

Baron
1 Reich Minister of Aviation Hermann Göring was the last commander of the legendary World War I fighter ace Manfred von Richthofen, aka 'The Red Baron'.

Speech
2 The naming of the Battle of Britain originated from a speech by Winston Churchill, when he said: "The Battle of France is over. I expect the Battle of Britain is about to begin."

Axis
3 Joining the Luftwaffe in the attack on Britain during the battle was a small section of the Italian Air Corps, which saw much action in late 1940 but with limited success.

Eagle
4 The first main attack on Britain by Germany was code-named 'Eagle Attack', and it was designed to knock out numerous allied radar stations.

Celebration
5 The Battle of Britain is commemorated each year in the United Kingdom on 15 September, where it is referred to as Battle of Britain Day.

DID YOU KNOW? No. 303 Polish Fighter Squadron recorded 808 hits during the Battle of Britain

Hugh didn't think much of Fighter Command's new headquarters

Members of staff at the RAF museum, London, participating in a Battle of Britain re-enactment

The Battle of Britain memorial is located in Capel-le-Ferne, Kent

Interview
How It Works speaks to RAF historian David Keen about the Battle of Britain

How It Works: Was the Battle of Britain a turning point in World War II?

David Keen: The Battle of Britain was not a turning point in the war but was highly influential in the direction that it progressed. This was because in winning the Battle of Britain, Hugh Dowding, the then Air Chief Marshal of the RAF, prevented Fighter Command from being destroyed by the Germans and the Luftwaffe gaining complete air dominance. If this had been the case then Hitler could have rolled out his planned sea and land invasion of Britain (Operation Sea Lion) with very little resistance and the American forces would have had no base to launch their own attacks from.

HIW: In what state was Britain's air force in the run-up to the battle, how were the odds stacked?

DK: The German Luftwaffe found themselves in a strong position going into the Battle of Britain, with a solid infrastructure in place from World War I, vastly experienced pilots who had seen much combat experience during the Spanish Civil War and a total numerical superiority. The British, in contrast, had been very slow to start in its preparations for war (famously Lord Halifax had promoted and favoured a policy of appeasement with Germany until their invasion of Poland) and modernisation of their outdated air force. For example, Fighter Command was only set up in 1936 and without Dowding's good management and re-organisation would have struggled to combat the German threat. The RAF was also numerically inferior going into the battle and had less experienced pilots.

HIW: How important was Dowding and his integration of radar in the allied victory?

DK: The integrated use of radar was very important as it gave Fighter Command a far greater view over the Channel than it had ever had before, allowing approaching aircraft to be detected and identified far sooner and that information relayed back to Bentley Priory, Fighter Command's headquarters. By splitting the RAF into four main sectors – 10 for the south east, 11 for London, 12 for the Midlands and 13 for the north and Scotland, the radar garnered information could then be filtered quickly and effectively to the area of the country were action was necessary.

HIW: Aircraft had taken a massive step forward since they were last used in the First World War, what technology did the RAF and Luftwaffe have at their disposal?

DK: The RAF used two main fighters during the battle, the Hawker Hurricane and the Spitfire. Despite the Spitfire's lasting fame as the poster vehicle of the war, it was actually the Hurricane that was in greater use by the RAF and they shot down more enemy aircraft than the Spitfire throughout. The Hurricane was a solid fighter and was seen as the workhorse of the allied forces, providing good all-round performance and a solid gun platform. The Spitfire, for which there were fewer numbers, was technically the superior vehicle and in the hands of a fighter ace was a more formidable opponent though. In contrast, the Luftwaffe used mainly the Messerschmitt 109, which was classed as a heavy fighter and was famed for its stability and durability. Despite the aircrafts' differences, they were largely the same though and a skilled pilot in one would normally always get the better of another with an amateur at the helm.

HIW: Finally, in retrospect, what should Germany have done to win the Battle of Britain?

DK: Indecision and the spreading of forces was the real downfall for Germany at the time, something that stemmed right from the very top of the chain of command. Before their invasion of Poland, Hitler had promised Britain that if they left Germany alone during its military campaigns then he would leave it alone in payback, something that was favoured by many in Britain at the time. So when Germany suddenly found itself at war with Britain, no firm invasion plan had been secured and after Göring and his commanders failed to deliver the quick victory they predicted, many conflicting tactics entered the fray. With no land and sea invasion in place, the Luftwaffe were constantly ordered to change their bombing priorities, sometimes to go after Britain's radar stations, sometimes their cities (such as Coventry). Further, as Germany's progress on the Eastern front stagnated against the Russians, more and more aircraft were diverted to bolster their forces. In order to win the Battle of Britain Germany should have first concentrated on Britain's radar stations, then once they were destroyed shifted their total focus onto the airfields.

RAF museum

The RAF museum in London is currently celebrating the Battle of Britain's 70th anniversary with a host of events and its newly refurbished Battle of Britain exhibition hall. For more information about the Battle of Britain and what's on at the museum visit: www.rafmuseum.org.uk.

A great place for a school trip

Mammoths

Now extinct, mammoths used to roam the Earth with the frequency and variety of their modern relatives, elephants

Until their total extinction, mammoths were a highly successful and widespread species, found from central Africa, through Europe onto North America. Indeed, Mammuthus lived throughout the entire Pliocene and Pleistocene epochs – over 5 million years – and diversified into many species of various appearances and sizes. However, through myriad factors – including climate change, disease and human hunting – the majority of the last mammoths (which were woolly mammoths living in Siberia) were wiped out between 8,000 to 10,000 years ago. From the frozen remains of examples found during the 20th and 21st Centuries (specimens are preserved in mummified states in Siberian permafrost), mammoth DNA has been ratified by scientists to be almost identical to that of modern elephants, with their appearance being closely linked. ✿

The preserved carcass of a baby mammoth discovered in 1977

A mammoth excavation in Siberia

Fat
Mammoths tended to sport a fatty lump at the top of their spine that was used to store energy. This, as with the camels of today, allowed them to traverse many miles with no food or water.

Back
The hind legs of mammoths were shorter than those at the front, the consequence of which is a sloping back running from the shoulders to hips.

Legs
Due to their mighty weight (over eight tons) and colossal height (over five metres), the legs of mammoths were massive columns of flesh, muscle and bone.

Feet
Mammoths had four-toed feet, splayed outwards like those of a human to aid balance.

5m
4m
3m
2m
1m

Mammuthus Sungari was the largest variety of mammoth and stood at over five metres tall

MOST MASSIVE

1. Mammoth
So big and heavy that only large groups of predatory animals – such as humans or sabre-toothed tigers – could take it down, the mammoth was a colossus.

MOST DEADLY

2. Sabre-toothed tiger
A fierce hunter of the prehistoric period, it was named after the size and shape of its maxillary canines.

MOST USELESS

3. Dodo
A one-metre high flightless bird that is closely related to the pigeon, the dodo existed from 12,000 years ago up until the end of the 17th Century.

DID YOU KNOW? One variety of dwarf mammoth survived on Wrangel Island, Alaska, up until 4,500 years ago

Head
Mammoths had tall, dome-shaped heads and tough, thick skulls –handy when fighting and fending off attack.

Large body cavity

Tusks longer than modern elephants

Under the skin...
How mammoths could carry their massive frames

© DK Images

Sturdy leg bones

Four toed feet

Tusks
Mammoth tusks were considerably longer and more curved than those of elephants, curling inwards at the tip. They were used to scrape away snow and ice from the ground when feeding, as well as for protection and in dominance rituals.

Trunk
Akin to those of elephants today, mammoth trunks were used to drink and grab flora.

Hair
The woolly mammoth, a variety of mammuthus native to northern Europe and Russia, evolved so that it was completely covered in 90cm long hair. Mammoths in warmer climates, such as those of Africa, had less hair.

ON THE MAP

Where did mammoths roam?
1. M. africanavus – Africa
2. M. armeniacus – Armenia
3. M. columbi – Columbia
4. M. exilis – West America
5. M. imperator – North America
6. M. jeffersonii – Central America
7. M. trogontherii – Siberia
8. M. meridionalis – Central Europe
9. M. subplanifrons – South Africa
10. M. primigenius – Siberia / North America
11. M. lamarmorae – Sardinia
12. M. sungari – North China

Life as a Roman soldier

Despite the long hours, low pay and high mortality rate, soldiers were always the backbone of the Roman Empire

For nearly 500 years, one of the most sought after jobs in the world was that of a Roman soldier. Not because of the conditions, which were brutal, or the pay, which was infrequent, but because soldiers were Roman citizens, entitled to retire with a state pension or land, and a rare chance for foreigners to become part of the greatest empire on Earth.

Soldiers had to be at least 20 years old, serve for at least 25 years and were not allowed to marry. Although their training and formations changed, they were trained as infantry (either light known as Velites or heavy known as Hoplites) or cavalry and organised into legions of up to 5,000 infantry and 250 cavalry each.

When not on military exercises, soldiers spent their days training and patrolling, marching up to 30 kilometres a day in full armour before making or securing camp – digging and staking out the perimeter and protecting it with walls of wooden stakes, that also had to be carried when the unit decamped. Their diet consisted of unleavened bread, vegetables or porridge with wine where the location permitted, although this and fresh meat were usually reserved for centurions and generals.

However, it was in battle that the soldier earned his reputation, thanks to the years of training and discipline that inspired fear in all but the later Barbarian hordes that faced them. Armed with shields, swords, daggers, spears or javelins, soldiers typically fought in lines, forming a wall of shields against the enemy. They had to do precisely as they were told or face flogging, losing limbs, and, for the crime of desertion, beheading. ⚙

Helmet
The helmet was made from iron, brass or bronze and lined with leather to prevent bruising the skin.

A soldier's kit
When not in battle, Roman soldiers carried basic provisions with them. This included a dish, a cooking pan, and up to three days' rations. Sometimes, they carried extra clothing and an axe to help set up camp...

Sword
Soldiers usually carried a gladius – a short iron weapon designed for rapid stabbing movements.

Shield
Shields were usually made from wood and could be circular, oval or rectangular.

Breastplate
Breastplates and armour were made from metal strips held together with metal iron or leather ties. They were so heavy, soldiers had to help each other into them.

Tunic
Woollen tunics were worn to prevent chafing from the heavy metallic armour. They covered most of the torso.

Shoes
Sandals and leg-guards were made from leather. Required to survive battle as well as daily marching, sandals were often reinforced with metal studs to make them last longer.

© MatthiasKabel 2005

5 TOP FACTS
THE ROMAN SOLDIER

1 First among equals
According to historian Livy, Rome was originally defended by 1,000 men raised from the city's three founding tribes.

2 The Tortoise
Soldiers could adopt their trademark Tortoise formation by locking the edges of their shields together. It allowed them to advance while under fire from arrows, rocks and burning oil.

3 Punishment
In the early Empire, if an entire unit deserted during battle, one in ten of them would be put to death. Soldiers could also be beheaded, tortured, fined or deprived of citizenship.

4 Gladiators
Captured enemy soldiers of suitable age and physique were trained to be gladiators – effectively an extended death sentence played out for public entertainment.

5 Weaponry
Romans (and Greeks before them) used 'bullets' – usually made from lead, stone or clay and fired by a sling, not a gun.

Head to Head
THE WORLD's WINDMILLS

LARGEST

1. Enercon E-126
The largest turbine model built to date, with a hub height of 135m, rotor diameter of 126m and a total height of 198m.

OLDEST

2. Outwood post mill
Built in 1665 in Outwood Surrey, this is Britain's oldest working windmill. It was once one of a pair; the other collapsed in 1960.

MOST FAMOUS

3. Holland's windmills
The Netherlands are so closely associated with windmills that they have become part of their national identity. However, most of these windmills were used for drainage rather than for grinding corn.

DID YOU KNOW? Until Henry VIII dissolved the monasteries, villagers had to have their corn ground at their local lord's mill

Windmills

Before steam and electric power, windmills were used to grind grain

A windmill uses an array of sails to convert the energy of the wind. The horizontal motion of the shaft attached to the central hub of the sails is converted, through a gearing system, to turn the vertical shaft. The vertical shaft is attached to a runner grindstone. Beneath the rotating runner stone is the bed grindstone that is fixed in position. Grain is fed between the two stones and the grinding process produces flour. The fineness of the flour can be adjusted by using different grindstones or adjusting the distance between them.

The first designs used in Britain were basically post mills, which consisted of a wooden structure built around a vertical post. In 1745 Edmund Lee invented the fantail that was mounted on the cap opposite the sails, enabling the mill to automatically face the wind. Tower mills were made of brick and could reach a greater height and were not such a fire hazard, but were more expensive to build. They featured sails attached to a rotatable cap.

1. Sails
These sails have a lattice construction with windboards fitted on the inner half of the leading edge. This is known as a 'common' sail.

2. Cap
The sails are attached to the rotating cap of the mill. The horizontal shaft from the sails is called a windshaft.

3. Brakewheel
The brakewheel is mounted on the windshaft and turns with it. The cogs on its edge engage with the wallower wheel.

4. Wallower
This is mounted on the upright vertical shaft. The wallower engages with the brakewheel causing the upright shaft to turn.

5. Great spur wheel
The great spur wheel is mounted at the bottom end of the upright shaft and drives the stone nuts.

6. Stone nut
The stone nut engages with the great spur wheel. It turns a shaft that drives the runner stone.

7. Grindstones
The runner stone turns above the bed stone to grind grain. The flour from this process is dropped down chutes to grain sacks.

Catching the wind
The first windmills had vertical sails that were fixed to a vertical axis that turned a grinding stone.

The horizontal axis design proved more efficient and powerful. The optimum speed for a windmill grindstone is 150 revolutions a minute; any faster is dangerous, any slower is inefficient. To achieve this, sail cloths were attached to lattice-style sails to speed them up, or removed to slow them down. In the 18th Century sails featured adjustable shutters that could be used to control their speed.

© DK Images

> "Houdin believes that an external ramp was built to haul the rocks for the first 60 metres or so of the pyramid"

Mystery of the Great Pyramid

Jean-Pierre Houdin demonstrates his theory

The theories of French architect Jean-Pierre Houdin may hold the key to an ancient mystery

Although Egyptologists have been studying the Great Pyramid of Khufu for centuries, they haven't yet reached a consensus on how it was built. Specifically, how were the massive two-ton blocks placed 146 metres above the desert floor? French architect Jean-Pierre Houdin has formed a theory to explain the mystery. Houdin has devoted his time to studying the Great Pyramid and creating graphical models using 3D software.

Houdin believes that an external ramp was built to haul the rocks – pulled by ropes – for the first 60 metres or so of the pyramid. Then an internal ramp was built to continue hauling rocks up. It is a 1.6 kilometre-long narrow structure spiralling inside the pyramid much like the ramps in a parking garage. To allow for men to haul the stones, the ramp is at a seven per cent slope. Somehow it has remained hidden inside the pyramid since its completion 4,500 years ago.

However, how would men hauling the blocks up the ramp be able to make the turn at each corner of the ramp? They would need a place to stand in front of the blocks. Houdin believes that each corner was temporarily left open, with a notch of about three square metres. Wooden cranes were stationed in each of these open spaces to lift the blocks onto the next level of the ramp. Later the notches were filled in.

There is some evidence that an internal ramp exists. In 1986, a team of

Building a pyramid from the inside out

The Great Pyramid has both ascending and descending chambers

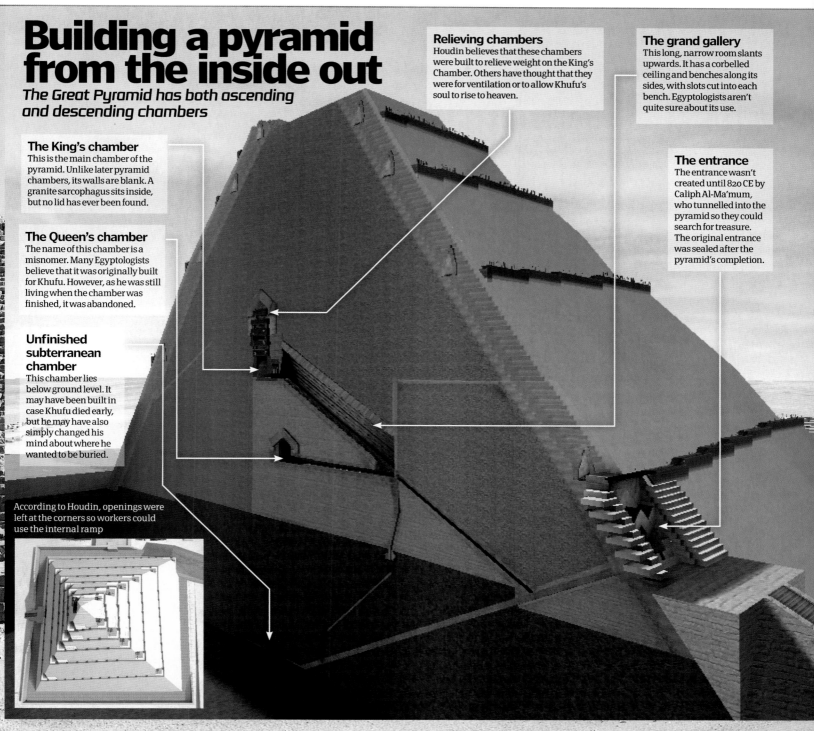

The King's chamber
This is the main chamber of the pyramid. Unlike later pyramid chambers, its walls are blank. A granite sarcophagus sits inside, but no lid has ever been found.

The Queen's chamber
The name of this chamber is a misnomer. Many Egyptologists believe that it was originally built for Khufu. However, as he was still living when the chamber was finished, it was abandoned.

Unfinished subterranean chamber
This chamber lies below ground level. It may have been built in case Khufu died early, but he may have also simply changed his mind about where he wanted to be buried.

Relieving chambers
Houdin believes that these chambers were built to relieve weight on the King's Chamber. Others have thought that they were for ventilation or to allow Khufu's soul to rise to heaven.

The grand gallery
This long, narrow room slants upwards. It has a corbelled ceiling and benches along its sides, with slots cut into each bench. Egyptologists aren't quite sure about its use.

The entrance
The entrance wasn't created until 820 CE by Caliph Al-Ma'mum, who tunnelled into the pyramid so they could search for treasure. The original entrance was sealed after the pyramid's completion.

According to Houdin, openings were left at the corners so workers could use the internal ramp

French scientists used microgravimetrics to survey the pyramid. They were looking for hidden chambers by checking for areas of low density, which would indicate open spaces. The team did find one new chamber that was filled with sand. However, one diagram puzzled them – there appeared to be a low density spiral inside the pyramid. In 2000, a member of the team met with Houdin and showed him this scan, which lends weight to his internal ramp theory.

During a 2007 visit to the Great Pyramid, Egyptologist Bob Brier pointed out two more features that could be evidence of the ramp. When the Sun hits the pyramid at a certain angle, you can see broad white lines at a seven per cent angle running around it. Brier climbed the pyramid to examine what appeared to be a notch. Although it had irregular measurements, there was a small chamber that he had never heard about before. It could be the remains of the open notch leading to a ramp. In addition, Brier has pointed out that the Sun Temple, built 100 years after the Great Pyramid and now partially in ruins, contains an internal ramp. This shows that the Egyptians were building these types of ramps.

Working with the former director of the German Archaeological Institute, Houdin's petitioned the Egyptian Supreme Council of Antiquities to survey the pyramid in a non-destructive way. If he gets the go-ahead, he may be able to prove his theory after all.

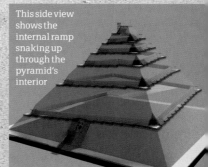

This side view shows the internal ramp snaking up through the pyramid's interior

"To maintain the correct seven per cent slope all the way to the top, the ramp had to be a kilometre from the pyramid"

The old theories debunked

Houdin's theory is very different from the traditional theories

Plateau
The pyramid is built on a plateau. Its north side has a very steep drop-off, making it unsuitable for the placement of an external ramp.

Cemeteries
The pyramid has cemeteries to its east and west, which were built at the same time. This means that an external ramp could not have been placed there.

External ramp
Many Egyptologists believe that an external ramp was used to build the pyramid. This ramp would've been massive and required nearly as many stones as the pyramid itself to build.

One common theory states that an external ramp was used to haul the blocks all the way to the top. The problem is that there isn't anywhere around the pyramid to place a ramp of this size. The pyramid is built on a plateau, with a steep drop to the north. Cemeteries were built at the same time as the pyramid to its east and west. In order to maintain the correct seven per cent slope all the way to the top, a ramp built to the south had to be over a kilometre from the pyramid. This huge undertaking of labour and use of materials seems impractical.

Another theory maintains that there was a spiral ramp coiling around the outside of the pyramid. However, this type of ramp wouldn't allow the pyramid's architect, Hemiunu, to maintain the sight lines necessary to ensure that the pyramid's faces met correctly at its top.

Forget the gym, build a pyramid instead...

Building a pyramid STEP-BY-STEP

Houdin's theory posits that the pyramid was built with two ramps

PHASE 1

PHASE 2

1. The pyramid base
According to Houdin, the pyramid's base was built using an external ramp until the base reached a height of about 60 metres. Workers then slowly broke down the external ramp and used its blocks to build the rest of the pyramid.

2. Starting the internal ramp
As workers continued building the rest of the pyramid, they also built and used an internal ramp to haul the heavy blocks. This allowed them to build the pyramid from the inside out.

Massive workforce...

It is estimated that during the 80 years it took to build the pyramids at Giza, between 20,000 and 30,000 workers had a helping hand in their construction.

A search for truth

Dr David Jeffreys, an Egyptologist at University College London, has suggested that Houdin's theory is "far-fetched and horribly complicated." Houdin has countered this by saying that his theory is actually no more complicated than the idea of building a 1.6-kilometre-long ramp leading up to the top of the pyramid.

Dr Zahi Hawass, Secretary General of the Egyptian Supreme Council of Antiquities (SCA), seemed to initially consider Houdin's theory as a possibility. However, in a 2009 interview, Dr Hawass stated that Houdin's theory is "completely wrong" and "the theory of other theorists." Houdin has invited Dr Hawass to lead the survey of the pyramid.

However they did it, the feat of constructing the pyramids is breathtaking

Head to Head PYRAMIDS

BIGGEST

1. Great Pyramid of Cholula
Location: Cholula, Puebla, Mexico
Height: 66 metres
Estimated age: 1,000 years
Facts: This pyramid was built in four stages and has a volume of about 4.45 million square metres.

OLDEST

2. Pyramid of Djoser
Location: Northwest of Memphis, Egypt
Height: 62 metres
Estimated age: 4,600 years
Facts: Built for the Pharaoh Djoser, this pyramid comprises six steps built in stages.

TALLEST

3. Transamerica Pyramid
Location: San Francisco, California, United States
Height: 260 metres
Estimated age: 37 years
Facts: Although not an ancient pyramid, this office building is currently the tallest pyramid in the world.

PHASE 3

PHASE 4

3. Completing the pyramid
After the core of the pyramid was completed, workers filled in the corners that had previously held cranes. Egyptologist Bob Brier found one area on the pyramid's exterior that may be evidence of one of these corners.

4. A smooth surface
Originally the exterior of the pyramid was also covered with casing stones, which gave it a smooth appearance. Today only the core inner structure is visible.

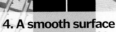

> "Victory was an oceanic behemoth, fitted with three massive gundecks and 104 multiple-ton cannons"

HMS Victory

One of the most famous ships of all time, HMS Victory was instrumental in ensuring British naval supremacy during the late-18th and early-19th Centuries

The only surviving warship to have fought in the American War of Independence, the French Revolutionary War and the Napoleonic wars, the HMS Victory is one of the most famous ships ever built. An imposing first rate ship of the line – line warfare is characterised by two lines of opposing vessels attempting to outmanoeuvre each other in order to bring their broadside cannons into best range and angle – the Victory was an oceanic behemoth, fitted with three massive gundecks, 104 multiple-ton cannons, a cavernous magazine and a crew of more than 800 men. It was a vessel capable of blowing even the largest enemy vessels out of the water with magnificent ferocity and range, while also outrunning and outmanoeuvring other aggressors.

Historically, it also became Vice-Admiral Horatio Lord Nelson's flagship during the epic naval battle off the Cape of Trafalgar, where it participated in the last great line-based conflict of the age, one in which it helped to grant Nelson a decisive victory over the French and Spanish but at the cost of his own life.

The Statistics
HMS Victory

Class: First rate ship of the line
Displacement: 3,500 tons
Length: 69 metres
Beam: 16 metres
Draught: 9 metres
Propulsion: Sails – 5,440m²
Speed: 9 knots (17kmph)
Armament: 104 guns
Complement: 800

Turner's famous painting of the Battle of Trafalgar in which the HMS Victory is shown in the midst of battle

Sails
The HMS Victory is a fully rigged ship, with three sets of square sails covering 5,440m². The breadth of the Victory's sails allowed it to sport a maximum top speed of nine knots when operational, which was for the time very impressive considering its size and weight. During the 18th and 19th Centuries a fully rigged ship necessitated three or more masts each of which with square rigging. At full flight the Victory could spread a maximum of 37 sails at one time and could carry 23 spares.

Crew
There were over 800 people on board the HMS Victory, including gunners, marines, warrant officers and powder monkeys among many others. Life on board was hard for the sailors, who were paid very little for their services and received poor food and little water. Disease was rife too, and punishments for drunkenness, fighting, desertion and mutiny ranged from flogging to hanging.

5 TOP FACTS
HMS VICTORY

Back-up
1 Upon completion, the HMS Victory was not put directly into use, but was moored in the River Medway for 13 years until France joined the American War of Independence.

Wood
2 Building the HMS Victory required over 6,000 trees to be cut down, 90 per cent of which were oak. The other ten per cent consisted of elm, pine, fir and lignum vitae.

Mirabilis
3 Victory was commissioned to celebrate the Annus Mirabilis (year of miracles) of 1759, where the British achieved great military success against French-led opponents.

Trafalgar
4 Victory was Nelson's flagship during the famous Battle of Trafalgar in 1805, which, despite Nelson's mortal wounds, saw the British Navy win a decisive victory.

Rest
5 The HMS Victory was docked down in No 2 Dock Portsmouth – the oldest dry-dock in the world – in 1922 due to deterioration of its bodywork.

DID YOU KNOW? HMS Victory cost £63,176 when finished in 1765, the equivalent of roughly £7 million today

Masts
The HMS Victory sported a bowsprit (the pole extending beyond the ship's head), fore mast, main mast, mizzen mast and main yard. A total of 41.9 kilometres of cordage and 768 elm and ash blocks were used to rig the ship.

Decks
The HMS Victory had seven main decks, including the hold, orlop, lower gundeck, middle gundeck, upper gundeck, quarterdeck and poop deck.

© Alex Pang

(A) The hull
The hull was the largest storage area on the ship where up to six months' worth of food and drink could be stored, as well as any excess supplies.

(B) The orlop
The only other deck below the waterline, the orlop was another storage area and also habitation deck for certain crew members such as the purser.

(C) The gundecks
The gundecks housed most of the Victory's cannons, with a tiered arrangement from top to bottom (largest cannons on the bottom, smallest on the top). These decks also housed the majority of the crew and Royal Marines, sleeping in hammocks suspended from battens fixed to overhead beams. The lower gundeck also acted as mess deck, the space where the crew would live and eat.

(D) The quarterdeck
The nerve centre of the ship, where its commander dictated its manoeuvres and actions often under heavy gunfire from rival vessels.

(E) The poop deck
Located at the stern, this short deck takes its name from the Latin word puppis, which literally means 'after deck' or 'rear deck'. This deck was mainly used for signalling, but also gave some protection to the man helming the ship's wheel.

Cannons
As a first rate ship of the line, the Victory was a three-gundeck warship with over 100 guns. In fact, the Victory was fitted with 104 cannons: 30 x 2.75 ton long pattern 32-pounders on the gundeck, 28 x 2.5 ton long 12-pounders on the middle gundeck, 30 x 1.7 ton short 12-pounders on the upper gundeck, 12 x 1.7 ton short 12-pounders on the quarterdeck, and 2 x medium 12-pounders and 2 x 68-pounder carronades on the forecastle.

© Alex Pang

© Alex Pang

"With his contraption, Galileo achieved groundbreaking astronomical discoveries"

The invention of the telescope changed the way people thought

Galileo's Telescope

How the ancient astronomer explored the skies

A name now associated with the most advanced modern space discoveries, Galileo Galilei was an Italian astronomer and philosopher born in Pisa in 1564. By far his most celebrated invention was his telescope. Modelled on others of the time, by November 1609 Galileo had invented the world's first telescope with x20 magnification.

With his contraption Galileo achieved groundbreaking astronomical discoveries with the potential to change the way 17th Century man perceived the cosmos. 400 years ago he was the first to realise that the Moon was not completely spherical but in fact had cavities and imperfections. He also discovered the first four moons of Jupiter, which became known as the Galilean moons.

In 1610, upon observing the lighting variations across the surface of Venus, or the 'phases of Venus', Galileo came to the assumption that Venus moved around the Sun – a theory that wrenched the Earth from the centre of the universe. ✿

How the telescope worked

Galileo's telescope employed the same mechanics as modern-day refractor telescopes. It consisted of a tube containing a simple arrangement of a convex objective lens (which changes the path of incoming light waves) and a concave eyepiece lens. Light passing through the objective lens is bent to a focus near the eyepiece, magnifying the image. The main downside to the telescope was its narrow field of view, which diminished with magnification, so only a portion of the moon can be viewed at one time.

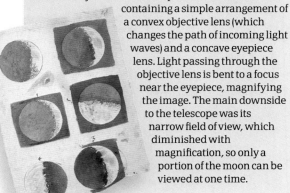

Big Ben

The untold saga of Britain's most famous bell

Though synonymous with the clock tower, 'Big Ben' is the nickname of the 13-ton bell at the heart of the building. Big Ben was cast by Warners of Norton near Stockton-on-Tees in August 1856 and taken to London by rail and sea, before a carriage pulled by 16 white horses took it across Westminster Bridge.

Before being winched up the tower, it was tested daily until, in October 1857, a huge crack appeared. Warners blamed the clockmaker for upping the hammer's weight from 355kg to 660kg and demanded a fortune to start over. So it was decided the new bell would be cast by George Mears at the Whitechapel Bell Foundry. This bell was 2.5 tons lighter but had to ascend the tower on its side – a task that took 30 hours. Then, in September 1859 the new bell also cracked and didn't ring for four years until the Astronomer Royal, Sir George Airy, suggested cutting a square into the metal to halt the crack, and using a lighter hammer. This is the bell we hear today. ✿

© DS Pugh, 2001

Big Ben was the largest bell ever cast at the time, and since Sir George Airy solved the cracking conundrum it's continued to strike more or less without a hitch

Hadrian's Wall

Was this ancient man-made border really built to exclude the Scots?

An enduring sight on the rural landscape of northern England, Hadrian's Wall stands as a symbol of Roman engineering. Commissioned by Emperor Hadrian in 122AD, for around six years three legions of the Roman army worked on its construction. At 117 kilometres the fortification is northern Europe's largest ancient monument, extending across the north of England from Bowness-on-Solway in the west to Wallsend near Newcastle-upon-Tyne in the east.

72 kilometres of the eastern portion was constructed from local stone with an inner core of rubble. The area to the west, meanwhile, consisted of a turf barrier made with a cobbled base. Hadrian's Wall was mistakenly thought to have been built to keep the Scots out, but historians believe it was likely built as a form of border control to monitor population flow between England and Scotland. ✿

At intervals of one Roman mile were small defensive fortlets called milecastles for sheltering the troops patrolling that section of the wall

Head to Head
DESTROYING THE STATUE OF LIBERTY

FROZEN

1. The Day After Tomorrow (2004)
When New York is devastated by global warming, the Statue of Liberty is frozen. Here she becomes a symbol of the end of civilisation.

OVERTURNED

2. Independence Day (1996)
The statue is toppled by an incoming force of extraterrestrials and lands in the Hudson River. Will Smith ensured humanity had the last laugh...

BURIED

3. Planet Of The Apes (1968)
The statue is used to symbolise an apocalyptic revelation. She appears during the finale of the film – half buried in sand.

DID YOU KNOW? The Statue of Liberty has been the site of bungee jumps, suicides and even a birth

The Statue of Liberty

The Statue of Liberty was officially titled 'Liberty Enlightening the World'. It was built as a monument commemorating the centenary of the Declaration of Independence

Constructed by the French, the Statue of Liberty was designed as a colossal copper statue. Gustave Eiffel, the designer of the Eiffel Tower, was asked to build a massive iron pylon and a skeletal framework to act as the support for the sculpture. While remaining fixed to its steel frame, the structure was able to move in the wind – subsequently, wind speeds of 80 kilometres per hour have been recorded, and the statue has been known to sway up to eight centimetres under pressure.

The pedestal, crafted from Scottish sandstone, was built in the USA. Once this was erected, it was time to assemble the statue proper. Parts of the statue were shipped from France, arriving in 350 pieces packed into 214 crates. It took four months to assemble the statue and secure it on the pedestal. The pedestal is supported by two sets of iron girders which are connected by iron tie beams – these extend upwards into the framework of the statue creating a strong link from the ground. The Statue of Liberty was originally designed as a lighthouse and functioned as such from 1886 to 1902. It housed an electric light that could be seen several kilometres out to sea. ✿

The construction process began by creating a wooden frame and mould

The Statistics
Statue of Liberty

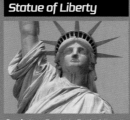

Sculptor: Frederic Batholdi
Year built: 1879-1884
Purpose: The statue was a commemorative gift given by the French to their fellow republicans in the USA.
Location: Liberty Island, NYC
Height: 46 metres
Steps: 354
Weight: 204.1 metric tons

Torch
In 1986, the old torch was replaced. It is now displayed in the lobby. The current torch is illuminated by large spotlights that cast a magnificent reflection on its gold plating.

Ladders to the right arm
This area has been closed for many years. The ladders are used by the maintenance team when repairs are necessary.

Staircases
There are two spiral staircases that wind around a central column. One staircase is ascending while the other is used for the descent.

Observation platform
The observation platform is situated at the top of the statue. There is space here for 30 people. The platform affords a magnificent view through 25 windows in the crown.

Tablet of the Law
The Tablet of the Law is situated in the left hand of the statue which represents the Goddess of liberty. It bears the Roman letters for the date 4 July 1776, American Independence Day.

Girders and staircases
Here we see the original skeletal frame of the Statue of Liberty. Around it we see the staircases that lead to the viewing platform.

Foot of the statue
Six storeys above the base, this landing takes the visitor to the fourth level, which is situated at the foot of the statue. From here the visitors can access the spiral staircase that leads to the viewing platform 12 storeys above.

Pedestal
Once the visitor enters through doors at the base of the pedestal, they find a stairway that leads up to the second level.

Pavement
The pavement is situated between the walls and the lawns. It allows the visitors to take in a vertical view of the statue and leads them to the door of the monument.

> "It housed important official offices and acted as a storage centre and a treasury"

Greek templ

Inside these multi-use architectural marvels

The temple acted as a cosmic generator. It was regarded as a dwelling designed for the gods and was also seen as a reception area for prayer, magical petition and divination. It also became a political symbol that emphasised the might and power of the state through ancient architectural achievement. The temple, now the most famous symbol of ancient Greece, was also functional – it housed important official offices and acted as a storage centre and a treasury. ✿

The Doric temple of Segesta

The Statistics
The Parthenon

Location:
Athenian Acropolis, Greece
Length of construction:
447 BC – 438 BC
Designer: Phidias
Type of building/purpose:
Temple and treasury
Type of architecture:
Classical – Doric
Cost of construction:
In modern terms, it is estimated that the Parthenon cost over £3 million
Architects:
Ictinos and Callicrates
Area coverage: 69.5m x 30.9m

 **Learn more**

For a fantastic video on the building, history and secrets of the Parthenon, visit our website and click on the history section **www.howitworksdaily.com**.

Metopes and triglyphs
Metopes are individual sections of sculpted stone that show figures of war. Triglyphs may represent the wooden beam of a primitive hut.

Column flutes
The number of flutes on each column changed with each architectural style.

Columns
Valued for their beautiful architectural features, columns were also seen as pillars of the sky.

Stereobate or foundation blocks
Foundation blocks were placed at the base of the temple. Doric columns were directly built upon the stereobate.

The ramp
A ceremonial causeway. It leads the individual from the earthly plain and guides him or her to the divine.

Portico
The portico led to an entrance route through which the individual would approach the sacred cult statue.

OLD

1. Temple of Hephaestus
Athens, Greece, 447 BC
This elaborate temple, which was built on the tip of the Agoraios Kolonos Hill, was used (until 1834) as a Greek Orthodox church.
© Scott Ware 07

OLDER

2. Temple of Poseidon
Paestum, Italy, 470-460 BC
This temple dedicated to the Goddess Hera was described as "oppressive" by the philosopher Goethe.
© Heinz-Josef Lücking 08

OLDEST

3. Temple of Delians
Delos, Greece, 478 BC
Temple of Delians was founded on the island of Delos – the birthplace of Apollo. The temple, which is thus dedicated to Apollo and Artemis, was never actually completed.

DID YOU KNOW? The Parthenon has been used as an early Christian church and the site of a Turkish mosque

Cult statue
The cult statue was situated in a prime position – it was venerated as the temple deity.

Cornice
The cornice was an ornamental structure protruding notably from the roof.

Doric designs followed the rules of harmony

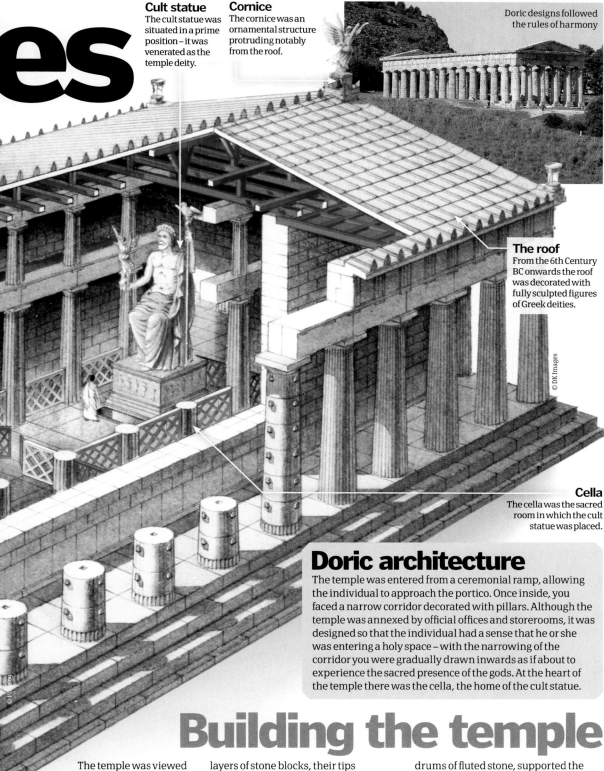

© DK Images

© PD

The roof
From the 6th Century BC onwards the roof was decorated with fully sculpted figures of Greek deities.

Cella
The cella was the sacred room in which the cult statue was placed.

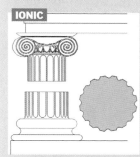

Doric architecture

The temple was entered from a ceremonial ramp, allowing the individual to approach the portico. Once inside, you faced a narrow corridor decorated with pillars. Although the temple was annexed by official offices and storerooms, it was designed so that the individual had a sense that he or she was entering a holy space – with the narrowing of the corridor you were gradually drawn inwards as if about to experience the sacred presence of the gods. At the heart of the temple there was the cella, the home of the cult statue.

Building the temple

The temple was viewed not only as an edifice of marble, wood and stone, but also a magical structure designed on astronomical principles. With this in mind, early construction of the temple began with the foundation ceremony, creating a base that is known as a stereobate. This consisted of several layers of stone blocks, their tips protruding above ground.

The workers employed simple tools of bronze and copper. During construction they also used mallets, chisels and ropes to create a further foundation block called a crepidoma, which acted as a base for the columns and walls. The columns, which were made of several drums of fluted stone, supported the entablature, which consisted of the architrave and the frieze which lay below the cornice. Temple construction could take over a decade, the building often covered 115m x 55m of land and boasted columns that reached 15m to 20m in height. On completion, the temple was decorated by craftsmen.

Prehistoric predators

Until they were wiped out 65 million years ago dinosaurs ruled the Earth. Among them, monstrous beasts stamped their authority over the menagerie, devouring all who stood in their way. These were the dinosaur kings, the largest carnivores the world has ever seen

Evolving from archosaurs (large lizards) in the latter part of the middle Triassic period, dinosaurs quickly gained a strong and prolific foothold all over Pangaea, the super continent of which all our continents were once part. Indeed, as the dominant terrestrial vertebrates through the Jurassic and Cretaceous periods, thousands of species of dinosaur have been unearthed as fossils by palaeontologists all over the world, with new discoveries being presented every year. Among them, huge behemoths with skeletons over 16 metres long and six metres tall, with skulls the size of bath tubs have surfaced and delivered a scary and disturbing glimpse into the creatures that once prowled the countries we inhabit today.

Among the largest of these giants, a group of massive carnivorous theropods (bipedal dinosaurs) emerged throughout the Jurassic and Cretaceous periods, casting a shadow over the rest of the dinosaur population. The most famous of these is the Tyrannosaurus Rex, as made popular by the *Jurassic Park* films. However, this type of theropod was but one of a host of killers and, amazingly, not the largest! Historically, of course, the reign of these carnivorous kings was cut short in the mass-extinction of the dinosaur population at the close of the Cretaceous period, when a 110-mile radius asteroid crashed into the Yucatán Peninsula, setting off a chain-reaction of events – tsunamis, dust clouds, temperature variation, food-chain collapse – that eventually led to their extermination.

Here, though, we explore the giddy heights of the pinnacle of dinosaur evolution, the time when nothing living on Earth could match these beasts in size and strength. Better run for cover; things are about to get prehistoric... ✿

"Among them, huge behemoths with skeletons over 16 metres long and six metres tall, with skulls the size of bath tubs have surfaced"

5 TOP FACTS
DINOSAURS

Long neck
1 The tallest of all the dinosaurs was the giant Brachiosaurus. This was mainly thanks to its giraffe-like neck, which stood tall at a rather impressive height of 15 metres.

The shortest
2 In contrast, one of the smallest dinosaurs to roam the Earth was the Compsognathus, standing at a measly 0.4 metres tall and four feet long.

The fastest
3 Two of the quickest of all dinosaurs were the Ornithomimus and Gallimimus, which are estimated to have been able to reach speeds of 110 kmph.

Feathered
4 Contrary to their portrayal in films, many dinosaurs were actually feathered like birds, with the Sinosauropteryx the first to be un-earthed by palaeontologists.

Velociraptor
5 The Velociraptor, made famous by the *Jurassic Park* films, was not actually as big as it was portrayed, standing at 2 metres long and only 0.5 metres high.

Why the long face?
At some 1.75m long, Spinosaurus had one of the longest skulls of any carnivore.

Snout and about
The long, crocodile-like snout suggests it plunged its jaw into water to catch fish.

© Bugboy52.4

Sail of the century
The sail of Spinosaurus was formed of very tall neural spines growing on the back vertebrae.

Image used with kind permission of Jerry Lofaro

CARNIVORE 1

Spinosaurus

Step aside, T-Rex. This was the ultimate theropod...

Bigger and arguably meaner than the Tyrannosaurus Rex, the Spinosaurus is thought to be the largest theropod dinosaur to ever roam the planet. Over 16 metres long, six metres high and weighing a monumental 12 tons, the Spinosaurus was a relatively common animal in the late-Cretaceous period. Palaeontologists have found fossilised remains of the Spinosaurus in Morocco, Libya and Egypt, including a well-preserved but now destroyed (blown-up in a World War II bombing run) specimen that included the lower jaw and vertebrae with complete spines. Spinosaurus was typical for a large theropod but differed in its skull and vertebrae construction. The snout of the 1.75-metre skull was long like a crocodile, with the nostril openings placed well back from the tip. Its teeth were also conical, rounded in a cross section and did not contain any serrations – these features suggest that the Spinosaurus plunged its jaw into water in order to catch fish. However, considering its size, jaw strength, and number of teeth, it equally had no trouble in hunting small, medium and other large dinosaurs on land.

The Statistics
Spinosaurus

Height: 6 metres
Length: 16 metres
Weight: 12 tons
Head size: 1.75 metres
Interesting fact: The spines on the Spinosaurus grew up to two metres tall
Fear factor: 9/10

Not a dinosaur you'd want to meet down a dark alley...

CARNIVORE 2

Giganotosaurus

The dinosaur with a big name to live up to, but was it as colossal as it sounds?

Meaning 'giant southern lizard', the Giganotosaurus was roughly the same size as the largest Tyrannosaurus Rexs, measuring over 12 metres long, five metres tall and weighing over eight tons. The skull of the Giganotosaurus was adorned with shelf-like bony ridges, notably above the eye sockets and had low horn-like projections, while the neck was considerably thicker than that of the Spinosaurus, with a stout and powerful head supported by it. Giganotosaurus remains have been found in Argentina and it has been postulated by palaeontologists that it dined mainly on medium-sized dinosaurs such as Andesaurus.

The Statistics
Giganotosaurus

Height: 4.5 metres
Length: 12 metres
Weight: 8 tons
Head size: 1.80 metres
Interesting fact: The Giganotosaurus had a brain half the size of the Tyrannosaurus
Fear factor: 7/10

© Arthur_Weasley

Ridge too far
Giganotosaurus had bony ridges above the eye sockets.

Size comparison
Who was the real king of the dinosaurs...

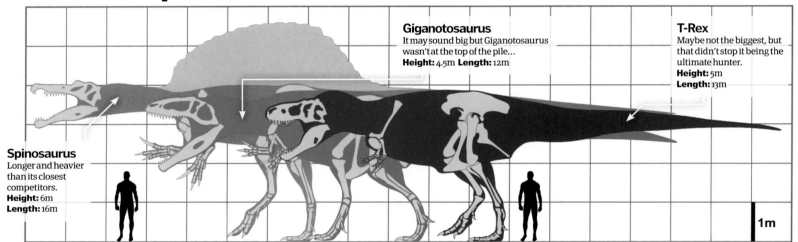

Giganotosaurus
It may sound big but Giganotosaurus wasn't at the top of the pile...
Height: 4.5m **Length:** 12m

T-Rex
Maybe not the biggest, but that didn't stop it being the ultimate hunter.
Height: 5m
Length: 13m

Spinosaurus
Longer and heavier than its closest competitors.
Height: 6m
Length: 16m

1m

CARNIVORE 3

The Statistics
Carcharodontosaurus

Height: 4 metres
Length: 11 metres
Weight: 6 tons
Head size: 1.60 metres
Interesting fact: The Carcharodontosaurus could run over 20mph
Fear factor: 8/10

Carcharodontosaurus

Not the world's easiest name to pronounce...

Named in 1931, the African Carcharodontosaurus was a huge theropod with serrated teeth similar to the great white shark. The skull of the Carcharodontosaurus was very narrow although it reached up to 1.6 metres in length, while its body was taller at the back than at the front, giving it a low, streamlined physicality. The thigh muscles of the Carcharodontosaurus were some of the largest of any dinosaur and this, in partnership with its narrow streamlined frame and ferocious sharp teeth, made chasing down and devouring prey elementary. Arguably the quickest of the carnivorous theropods, the Carcharodontosaurus was a fearsome predator. Fossilised remains have been found in Morocco, Tunisia and Egypt

This incredible beast was named after its deadly serrated teeth

© Didier Descovens 2010

Shark-like teeth
The serrations in the teeth are very similar to a shark's

© F.Fonseca

© Arthur_Weasley

The biggest bite
The strength of the Tyrannosaurus Rex's bite is estimated by palaeontologists to be greater than that of any other animal ever to have lived on the Earth.

© Arthur_Weasley

CARNIVORE 4

Mapusaurus

The dinosaur that proved teamwork can be the best way to get a good meal

The Statistics
Mapusaurus

Height: 4 metres
Length: 12 metres
Weight: 4 tons
Head size: 1 metre
Interesting fact: Unlike other large theropod dinosaurs, Mapusauruses would often hunt in groups
Fear factor: 6/10

Dating from the late-Cretaceous period and stalking the area that is now Argentina, the Mapusaurus was a close relative of the Giganotosaurus. Despite being one of the smaller giant carnivores, with a length of 12 metres, height of four metres and weight of four tons, it was still a fearsome predator. Interestingly, palaeontologists believe that the Mapusaurus would engage in group hunting activity, allowing packs of them to take down larger foes than they would be able to achieve on their own. The remains of the Mapusaurus were first excavated between 1997 and 2001 and now complete the majority of a full skeleton. Due to its connection to the Giganotosaurus, it shares many of the same characteristics.

Leg up
Researchers believe that the structure of the femur suggests a close relationship to Giganotosaurus

CARNIVORE 5

Tyrannosaurus Rex
The most famous dinosaur of them all and the ultimate predator

The T-Rex was one of the largest terrestrial carnivores in the world, with the estimated strength of its bite greater than that of any other animal that has ever existed on Earth. Standing at a height of five metres, measuring over 13 metres in length and weighing over nine tons, the T-Rex is considered to be one of the most fearsome hunters ever.

The body of the T-Rex was perfectly balanced, with a horizontal backbone positioned above the hips giving completely equal weight distribution. The head was also colossal, measuring 1.6 metres long and far bulkier than any other theropod, containing 58 serrated teeth and large forward-facing eye sockets giving it acute binocular vision. From fossilised remains of Tyrannosaurus faeces, palaeontologists have discovered that the T-Rex crushed bones of the prey it consumed. The T-Rex was prolific over the entire western North America.

Good eyes
The T-Rex had binocular, colour vision.

A nice bit of colour... in case you didn't spot it running at you!

Matter of balance
The massive skull of the T-Rex was balanced by a thick, heavy tail.

Quite a bite
The T-Rex had 58 serrated, banana-shaped teeth.

The Statistics
Tyrannosaurus Rex

Height: 5 metres
Length: 13 metres
Weight: 9 tons
Head size: 1.6 metres
Interesting fact: The Tyrannosaurus Rex could consume 230kg of meat in a single bite
Fear factor: 10/10

Head to Head
WORST DINOSAUR MOVIES

BAD

1. The Lost World
Year: 1960
Due to massive late-in-production funding cuts, *The Lost World* was forced to abandon stop-motion photography to bring its dinosaurs to life, opting instead to film lizards with badly glued-on horns and gills.

BADDER

2. Planet Of The Dinosaurs
Year: 1978
Following a group of space adventurers who get stranded on a planet inhabited by dinosaurs, the movie features such tragic lines as, "We can't risk lives trying to tame dinosaurs."

BADDEST

3. Carnosaur
Year: 1993
With the poster tagline stating, 'Driven to extinction. Back for revenge', *Carnosaur* begs the question, revenge against whom? The infamous giant meteor that wiped them out over 65 million years ago?

Advanced Photoshop Premium Collection vol 5

256 pages of expert Photoshop tutorials, in-depth interviews and technical info on using Photoshop's tools.

SRP: £14.99

iPhone App Directory vol 4

The latest collection of iPhone, iPad and iPod touch apps are reviewed here including the very best for iPhone 3GS, with every App Store category featured inside.

SRP: £9.99

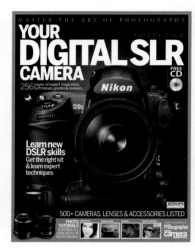

Mac for Beginners vol 2

Starting with the basics, this essential guide will teach you how to master all aspects of switching to Mac including OS X, Snow Leopard, Mail and Safari.

SRP: £12.99

Your Digital SLR Camera vol 4

256 pages of DSLR advice. Master your SLR, learn shooting skills, fix your photos and expert advice on the best camera kit.

SRP: £12.99

The world's best cr
to collect and keep

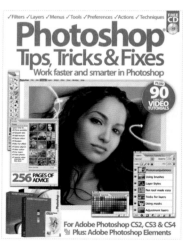

Photoshop Tips, Tricks & Fixes vol 1

The ultimate guide to Photoshop cheats! This fun guide will show you how to get the results you want from Photoshop fast!

SRP: £14.99

The iPad Book

This is the ultimate guide to the iPad. It takes you through all the basics you need and will also show you how to get the very most from the worlds coolest gadget.

SRP: £9.99

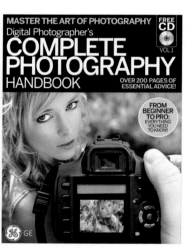

Complete Photography Handbook vol 1

Shooting ideas to practical tips, become a professional shooter, this tome is the only resource for digital photographers

SRP: £12.99

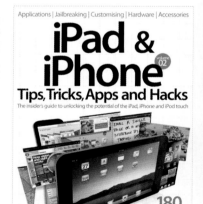

iPad & iPhone Tips, Tricks, Apps and Hacks vol 2

Get the most out of your iPad and iPhone with this fantastic bookazine detailing all you need to know. Slick, accessible – a must for all.

SRP: £9.99

Prices may vary, stocks are limited and shipping prices vary

Order online www

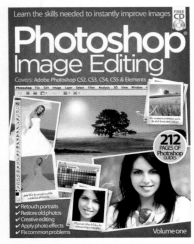
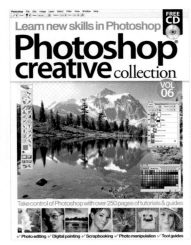

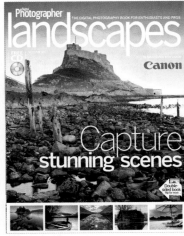

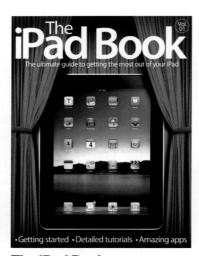